Voices for Evolution

Voices for Evolution

Third edition edited by Carrie Sager

The National Center for Science Education, Inc.
Berkeley, CA

Library of Congress 2007943779

Voices for evolution

ISBN 978-0-6152-0461-1
© 2008 The National Center for Science Education, Inc.

Cover design by Debra Turner.
Cover photographs:
American Toad, Red-legged Seriema, Sumatran Tiger, and Maned Wolf photos by
Jon McRay, nikographer.blogspot.com.
Red Deer, Asian Short Clawed Otter and Indian Peacock photos by
Stuart Reynolds, stuartyreynolds@hotmail.com.
Asian Elephant and California Sea Lion photos by suneko,
flickr.com/photos/suneko/. Licensed under Creative Commons Attribution 2.0 Generic.
Howler Monkey photo by dpfunsun, flickr.com/photos/dpfunsun/.

Published by The National Center for Science Education, Inc.
P.O. Box 9477, Berkeley, California 94709.
Printed and bound in the United States.

TABLE OF CONTENTS

Foreword v
Acknowledgments vii

PART ONE: LEGAL BACKGROUND

10 Significant Court Decisions Regarding Evolution/Creationism 2
McLean v. Arkansas (1982) 4
State of Tennessee, Office of the Attorney General (1988) 5
Webster v. New Lenox School District (1990) 7
Peloza v. Capistrano Unified School District (1994) 8
Kitzmiller v. Dover Area School District (2005) 9

PART TWO: SCIENTIFIC ORGANIZATIONS

Brief of Amici Curiae by 56 Scientific Organizations in Selman v. Cobb County 12
Alabama Academy of Science (1981) 16
Alabama Academy of Science (1994) 16
American Anthropological Association (1980) 16
American Anthropological Association (2000) 17
American Association for the Advancement of Science (1923)................................. 20
American Association for the Advancement of Science (1972)................................. 20
American Association for the Advancement of Science (1982)................................. 21
American Association for the Advancement of Science (2002)................................. 22
American Association for the Advancement of Science Commission on Science Education ... 23
American Association of Physical Anthropologists 23
American Astronomical Society (1982) 24
American Astronomical Society (2000) 25
American Astronomical Society (2005) 25
American Chemical Society (1981) 26
American Chemical Society (2005) 27
American Geological Institute 27
American Geophysical Union 28
American Institute of Biological Sciences 28
American Physical Society 29
American Psychological Association (1982) 30
American Psychological Association (2007) 30
American Society of Biological Chemists 32
American Society for Microbiology 32
American Society of Parasitologists 33
American Sociological Association 35
Association of Southeastern Biologists 36
Association for Women Geoscientists 37
Australian Academy of Science 37
Biophysical Society 38
Botanical Society of America 39
California Academy of Sciences 42
Committee for the Anthropology of Science, Technology, and Computing 43
Committee for Scientific Investigation of Claims of the Paranormal 44
Ecological Society of America 44
Federation of American Societies for Experimental Biology 45

Genetics Society of America 46
Geological Society of America (1983) 47
Geological Society of America (2001) 48
Geological Society of Australia 49
Georgia Academy of Science (1980) 50
Georgia Academy of Science (1982) 51
Georgia Academy of Science (2003) 51
History of Science Society 52
Idaho Scientists for Quality Science Education 53
InterAcademy Panel 54
Iowa Academy of Science (1986)... 56
Iowa Academy of Science (2000)... 57
Kansas Academy of Science 58
Kentucky Academy of Science 62
Kentucky Paleontological Society 64
Louisiana Academy of Sciences 65
National Academy of Sciences (1972) 65
National Academy of Sciences (1984) 66
National Academy of Sciences (1999) 71
New Mexico Academy of Science 72
New Orleans Geological Society 73
New York Academy of Sciences 75
North American Benthological Society 76
North Carolina Academy of Science... 76
Ohio Academy of Science 77
Ohio Math and Science Coalition.. 78
The Paleontological Society 79
Pennsylvania Academy of Science 79
Pennsylvania Council of Professional Geologists 80
Philosophy of Science Association 81
Research!America 82
Royal Astronomical Society of Canada - Ottawa Centre 82
Royal Society 83
Royal Society of Canada 84
Royal Society of Canada, Academy of Science 85
Sigma Xi, Louisiana State University Chapter 86
Society for Amateur Scientists 86
Society for Integrative and Comparative Biology 87
Society for Neuroscience 88
Society of Physics Students 89
Society for the Study of Evolution 89
Society of Systematic Biologists 90
Society of Vertebrate Paleontology (1986) 91
Society of Vertebrate Paleontology (1994) 91
Southern Anthropological Society 92
Tallahassee Scientific Society 93
Tennessee Darwin Coalition.. 94
Virginia Academy of Science.. 95
West Virginia Academy of Science 95

PART THREE: RELIGIOUS ORGANIZATIONS

African Americans for Humanism.. 98
American Humanist Association 98
American Jewish Committee 99
American Jewish Congress 100
American Scientific Affiliation 101
Center for Theology and the Natural Sciences 102
Central Conference of American Rabbis... 102
Clergy Letter Project 103
Council for Democratic and Secular Humanism....................................... 103
Episcopal Bishop of Atlanta, Pastoral Letter...................................... 104
Episcopal Church, General Convention (1982) 106
Episcopal Church, General Convention (2006) 106
Humanist Association of Canada 107
Lexington Alliance of Religious Leaders 108
The Lutheran World Federation 109
National Council of Jewish Women 111
Presbyterian Church (USA), General Assembly 111
Rabbinical Council of America... 112
Roman Catholic Church (1981) 113
Roman Catholic Church (1996) 113
Unitarian Universalist Association (1977) 116
Unitarian Universalist Association (1982) 116
United Church Board for Homeland Ministries 117
United Methodist Church 120
United Presbyterian Church in the U.S.A. (1982) 121
United Presbyterian Church in the U.S.A. (1983) 122

PART FOUR: EDUCATIONAL ORGANIZATIONS

American Association of Physics Teachers 128
American Association of University Professors 128
American Association of University Women 129
Arkansas Science Teachers Association 129
Association of College and University Biology Educators 130
Association of Pennsylvania State College and University Biologists 130
Auburn University Faculty Senate (1981) 131
Auburn University Faculty Senate (1983) 132
Authors of Biology Textbooks 133
Biological Sciences Curriculum Study (1971)....................................... 134
Biological Sciences Curriculum Study (1995)....................................... 136
California Science Teachers Association 137
Empire State Association of Two Year College Biologists (1998) 137
Georgia Citizens' Educational Coalition 138
Idaho Science Teachers Association.. 139
Illinois Community College Faculty Association Delegate Assembly 141
Inter-University Council of Ohio 141
Iowa Council of Science Supervisors 143
Iowa Department of Public Instruction 144
Maryland Association of Science Teachers 147
Michigan Science Teachers Association (1981) 148
Michigan Science Teachers Association (2003) 149
Michigan Science Teachers Association (2005) 150
Michigan Science Teachers Association (2007) 151
Michigan State Board of Education 152
National Association of Biology Teachers (1980) 153
National Association of Biology Teachers (1995) 154

National Association of Biology Teachers (2000) 154
National Council for the Social Studies (1981) 158
National Council for the Social Studies (2007) 159
National Education Association 161
National Science Education Leadership Association 161
National Science Teachers Association (1973, 1982) 162
National Science Teachers Association (1985) 162
National Science Teachers Association (2003) 163
New Mexico Coalition for Excellence in Science and Math Education 167
New York State Education Department 168
New York State Science Supervisors Association 169
North Carolina Science Teachers Association 170
Oklahoma Science Teachers Association 170
Oklahoma State University Department of Zoology 171
Science Museum of Minnesota.. 172
Science Teachers Association of New York State... 173
Society for College Science Teachers 174
Syracuse Parent-Teacher Association 175
University of Alabama at Huntsville Faculty Senate 176
University of California Academic Senate 176
University of New Mexico History Department... 177
University of Oklahoma Department of Zoology 178
University of Queensland (Australia) Board of the Faculty of Science 179
University System of Georgia Biology Academic Advisory Committee......................... 180
Utah Science Teachers Association 181
Utah State Board of Education 182
Wisconsin Department of Public Instruction 183

PART FIVE: CIVIL LIBERTIES ORGANIZATIONS

American Civil Liberties Union 188
American Civil Liberties Union of Ohio 189
American Civil Liberties Union of Utah 190
Americans for Religious Liberty 192
Americans United for Separation of Church and State (1994) 192
Americans United for Separation of Church and State (2006) 193
Council of Europe 196
Freedom from Religion Foundation.. 198
Institute for First Amendment Studies.. 199
National Committee for Public Education and Religious Liberty 199
People for the American Way Foundation 203

FOREWORD

Stephen Jay Gould once wrote, "Evolution is not a peripheral subject but the central organizing principle of all biological science. No one who has not read the Bible or the Bard can be considered educated in Western traditions; so no one ignorant of evolution can understand science." Yet the teaching of evolution in the public schools of the United States is under constant attack. *Voices for Evolution* is a vital part of the defense.

The first edition of *Voices for Evolution* was published just two years after the Supreme Court's decision in *Edwards v. Aguillard* (1987), ruling that teaching creationism in the public schools violates the Establishment Clause of the First Amendment to the Constitution of the United States. Even though the *Edwards* decision was a serious blow, creationism continued to evolve as creationists regrouped in a number of ways.

Abandoning any hope of imposing creationism in the public schools, the flagship organization of young-earth creationism, the Institute for Creation Research, concentrated on the development of a creationist counterestablishment, complete with conferences, journals, and even a graduate school. In the same vein, the young-earth creationist ministry Answers in Genesis opened the doors of its twenty-seven-million-dollar Creation Museum in the summer of 2007.

Meanwhile, a group of creationists not so closely allied with young-earth creationism sought to repackage creationism in a way that would survive constitutional scrutiny. The result was dubbed "intelligent design" and introduced in *Of Pandas and People* (1989; second edition 1993). *Kitzmiller v. Dover* (2005), however, revealed that *Pandas* began as a creationist textbook; "creation" and its cognates had been hastily replaced with "design" and its cognates in the wake of the *Edwards* decision.

Realizing that attempts to require or allow the teaching of creationism—whether as "creation science" or "intelligent design"—are likely to be ruled unconstitutional, creationists also proposed various ways to attack evolution without mentioning any creationist alternative. To their creationist advocates, such strategies offer the promise of encouraging students to acquire or retain a belief in creationism while not running afoul of the Establishment Clause.

Such fallback creationist strategies include requiring disclaimers, oral or written, about evolution (as in Alabama in 1996); taking steps to undermine the treatment of evolution in science textbooks (as in Texas in 2003) and in state science standards (as in Kansas in 1999 and 2005); and calling for "objectivity" or "balance" or "critical analysis" in the teaching of evolution (as in Ohio in 2002)—all of which in practice are intended to instill scientifically unwarranted doubts about evolution.

Moreover, not all creationist resistance to the teaching of education is explicit. In a recent informal survey among members of the National Science Teachers Association (2005), a staggering 30% of respondents indicated that they experienced pressure to omit or downplay evolution and related topics in their science curriculum, while 31% indicated that they felt pressure to include nonscientific alternatives to evolution in their science classrooms.

Amid the dizzying panoply of creationist activity, what is gratifyingly constant is the thoughtful, balanced, and authoritative opposition from the scientific, educational, and civil liberties communities, as well as from a considerable portion of the faith community. Organizations small and large, local, national, and international, have expressed their unflinching support for evolution education. Their statements are collected here, in *Voices for Evolution*.

When creationists claim that evolution is a theory in crisis, tottering on the verge of extinction, ready for the dustbin of history, the scientific community—including the most prestigious scientific organizations in the country, the National Academy of Sciences and the American Association for the Advancement of Science—is always there to tell the truth. "The contemporary theory of biological evolution is one of the most robust products of scientific inquiry," the AAAS observes.

When creationists claim that evolution is intrinsically antireligious, a deadly threat to faith and morals, a goodly portion of the faith community—Catholic, Protestant, Jewish, and humanist—is always there to demonstrate that there are people of faith who regard their acceptance of evolution as compatible with, or even enriching, their religious faith, and who reject any creationist attempts to portray a rejection of evolution as essential to their faith.

And when creationists claim that it is unfair not to teach creationism along with evolution, or not to teach that evolution is in a precarious state, the rebuttal is twofold. The science education community—including the National Association of Biology Teachers and the National Science Teachers Association—is always there to explain that compromising the integrity of science education in order to cater to creationist ideology is not fair to students or teachers.

For its part, the civil liberties community—including the American Civil Liberties Union, People for the American Way, and Americans United for Separation of Church and State—is always there to insist that for the government to promote creationism or compromise the teaching of evolution to placate a creationist minority is not fair to the citizens of a republic in which a basic constitutional principle is the government's religious neutrality.

Just as gratifying as the constancy of the opposition to the creationist assault is the increase in the number of organizations offering it: The first edition of *Voices for Evolution* contained 68 statements; the second edition, a round 100; the third edition, which you are reading now, 176. The National Center for Science Education is grateful to the organizations represented in *Voices for Evolution* for taking a stand in defense of the teaching of evolution in the public schools.

NCSE is immensely grateful also to those intrepid people, across the country and around the world, who have used these statements during controversies over the teaching of evolution in their own communities. With the powerful support of the statements contained in *Voices of Evolution*, they have tirelessly fought, and largely prevailed, in the battle to defend the teaching of evolution in the public schools. May this new edition of *Voices for Evolution* help you to do likewise.

Glenn Branch
National Center for Science Education

ACKNOWLEDGMENTS

You hold in your hands the third edition of *Voices for Evolution*, a book which took twenty years and the work of many people to complete. For the origin of the *Voices* project one must go back to 1984, when NCSE treasurer Ken Saladin took on the task of assembling a comprehensive collection of position statements on the creation/evolution issue for NCSE. The late Betty McCollister of the Iowa Committee of Correspondence edited these position statements into the first edition of *Voices*, diligently gathering permissions for reprinting statements.

The second edition, published in 1995, was edited by former NCSE Network Project Director Molleen Matsumura, who expanded *Voices* not just with additional statements but with the addition of the sections for civil liberties organizations and legal background. In addition to its practical use as support for the teaching of evolution, the second edition has been widely cited by scholars studying this long-term controversy.

In this third edition, special thanks go to Deputy Director Glenn Branch, whose preternatural ability to find new statements ensured constant updates to our website as well as giving us much of the new content in this edition.

The National Center for Science Education is funded by memberships, donations, and grants from a number of private foundations, so we are also grateful to all of our members and supporting foundations for making the important work of NCSE possible.

Carrie Sager
National Center for Science Education

PART ONE

LEGAL BACKGROUND

Voices for Evolution

1. In 1968, in *Epperson v. Arkansas*, the United States Supreme Court invalidated an Arkansas statute that prohibited the teaching of evolution. The Court held the statute unconstitutional on the grounds that the First Amendment to the U.S. Constitution does not permit a state to require that teaching and learning must be tailored to the principles or prohibitions of any particular religious sect or doctrine (*Epperson v. Arkansas* (1968) 393 U.S. 97, 37 U.S. Law Week 4017, 89 S. Ct. 266, 21 L. Ed 228).

2. In 1981, in *Segraves v. State of California*, the court found that the California State Board of Education's Science Framework, as written and as qualified by its anti-dogmatism policy, gave sufficient accommodation to the views of Segraves, contrary to his contention that class discussion of evolution prohibited his and his children's free exercise of religion. The anti-dogmatism policy provided that class discussions of origins should emphasize that scientific explanations focus on "how", not "ultimate cause", and that any speculative statements concerning origins, both in texts and in classes, should be presented conditionally, not dogmatically. The court's ruling also directed the Board of Education to disseminate the policy, which in 1989 was expanded to cover all areas of science, not just those concerning evolution. (*Segraves v. California* (1981) Sacramento Superior Court #278978).

3. In 1982, in *McLean v. Arkansas Board of Education*, a federal court held that a "balanced treatment" statute violated the Establishment Clause of the U.S. Constitution. The Arkansas statute required public schools to give balanced treatment to "creation-science" and "evolution-science". In a decision that gave a detailed definition of the term "science", the court declared that "creation science" is not in fact a science. The court also found that the statute did not have a secular purpose, noting that the statute used language peculiar to creationist literature. The theory of evolution does not presuppose either the absence or the presence of a creator (*McLean v. Arkansas Board of Education* (1982) 529 F. Supp. 1255, 50 U.S. Law Week 2412).

4. In 1987, in *Edwards v. Aguillard*, the U.S. Supreme Court held unconstitutional Louisiana's "Creationism Act". This statute prohibited the teaching of evolution in public schools, except when it was accompanied by instruction in "creation science". The Court found that, by advancing the religious belief that a supernatural being created humankind, which is embraced by the term creation science, the act impermissibly endorses religion. In addition, the Court found that the provision of a comprehensive science education is undermined when it is forbidden to teach evolution except when creation science is also taught (*Edwards v. Aguillard* (1987) 482 U.S. 578).

5. In 1990, in *Webster v. New Lenox School District*, the Seventh Circuit Court of Appeals found that a school district may prohibit a teacher from teaching creation science in fulfilling its responsibility to ensure that the First Amendment's establishment clause is not violated and that religious beliefs are not injected into the public school curriculum. The court upheld a district court finding that the school district had not violated Webster's free speech rights when it prohibited him from teaching "creation science", since it is a form of religious advocacy (*Webster v. New Lenox School District* #122, 917 F. 2d 1004).

6. In 1994, in *Peloza v. Capistrano School District*, the Ninth Circuit Court of Appeals upheld a district court finding that a teacher's First Amendment right to free exercise of religion is not violated by a school district's requirement that evolution be taught in biology classes. Rejecting plaintiff Peloza's definition of a "religion" of "evolutionism", the Court found that the district had simply and appropriately required a science teacher to teach a scientific theory in biology class (*John E. Peloza v. Capistrano Unified School District*, (1994) 37 F. 3rd 517).

7. In 1997, in *Freiler v. Tangipahoa Parish Board of Education*, the United States District Court for the Eastern District of Louisiana rejected a policy requiring teachers to read aloud a disclaimer whenever they taught about evolution, ostensibly to promote "critical thinking". Noting that the policy singled out the theory of evolution for attention, that the only "concept" from which students were not to be "dissuaded" was "the Biblical concept of Creation", and that students were already encouraged to engage in critical thinking, the Court wrote that, "In mandating this disclaimer, the School Board is endorsing religion by disclaiming the teaching of evolution in such a manner as to convey the message that evolution is a religious viewpoint that runs counter to ... other religious views". Besides addressing disclaimer policies, the decision is noteworthy for recognizing that curriculum proposals for "intelligent design" are equivalent to proposals for teaching "creation science" (*Freiler v Tangipahoa Board of Education*, No. 94-3577 (E.D. La. Aug. 8, 1997). On August 13, 1999, the Fifth Circuit Court of Appeals affirmed the decision; on June 19, 2000, the Supreme Court declined to hear the School Board's appeal, thus letting the lower court's decision stand.

8. In 2000, Minnesota State District Court Judge Bernard E. Borene dismissed the case of *Rodney LeVake v. Independent School District 656, et al.* (Order Granting Defendants' Motion for Summary Judgment and Memorandum, Court File Nr. CX-99-793, District Court for the Third Judicial District of the State of Minnesota [2000]). High school biology teacher LeVake had argued for his right to teach "evidence both for and against the theory" of evolution. The school district considered the content of what he was teaching and concluded that it did not match the curriculum, which required the teaching of evolution. Given the large amount of case law requiring a teacher to teach the employing district's curriculum, the judge declared that LeVake did not have a free speech right to override the curriculum, nor was the district guilty of religious discrimination.

9. In January 2005, in *Selman et al. v. Cobb County School District et al.*, U.S. District Judge Clarence Cooper ruled that an evolution warning label required in Cobb County textbooks violated the Establishment Clause of the First Amendment (*Selman et al. v. Cobb County School District and Cobb County Board of Education* 390 F. Supp. 2d 1286, 1313 [N.D. Ga. 2005]). The disclaimer stickers stated, *"This textbook contains material on evolution. Evolution is a theory, not a fact, regarding the origin of living things. This material should be approached with an open mind, studied carefully, and critically considered."* After the district court's decision, the stickers were removed from Cobb's textbooks. The school district, however, appealed to the 11th Circuit Court of Appeals and in May 2006 the Appeals Court remanded the case to the district court for clarification of the evidentiary record. On December 19, 2006, the lawsuit reached a settlement; the Cobb County School District agreed not to disclaim or denigrate evolution either orally or in written form.

10. On December 20, 2005, in *Kitzmiller et al. v. Dover*, U.S. District Court Judge John E. Jones III ordered the Dover Area School Board to refrain from maintaining an Intelligent Design Policy in any school within the Dover Area School District. The ID policy included a statement in the science curriculum that "students will be made aware of gaps/problems in Darwin's Theory and other theories of evolution including, but not limited to, intelligent design." Teachers were also required to announce to their biology classes that "Intelligent Design is an explanation of the origin of life that differs from Darwin's view. The reference book *Of Pandas and People* is available for students to see if they would like to explore this view in an effort to gain an understanding of what Intelligent Design actually involves. As is true with any theory, students are encouraged to keep an open mind". In his 139-page ruling, Judge Jones wrote it was "abundantly clear that the Board's ID Policy violates the Establishment Clause". Furthermore, Judge Jones ruled that "ID cannot uncouple itself from its creationist, and thus religious, antecedents". In reference to whether Intelligent Design is science Judge Jones wrote ID "is not science and cannot be adjudged a valid, accepted scientific theory as it has failed to publish in peer-reviewed journals, engage in research and testing, and gain acceptance in the scientific community". This was the first challenge to the constitutionality of teaching "intelligent design" in the public school science classroom. (*Tammy Kitzmiller, et al. v. Dover Area School District, et al.*, Case No. 04cv2688)

McLean v. Arkansas (1982)

...The approach to teaching "creation science" and "evolution science" found in Act 590 is identical to the two-model approach espoused by the Institute for Creation Research and is taken almost verbatim from ICR writings. It is an extension of Fundamentalists' view that one must either accept the literal interpretation of Genesis or else believe in the godless system of evolution....

In addition to the fallacious pedagogy of the two model approach, Section 4(2) lacks legitimate educational value because "creation science" as defined in that section is simply not science. Several witnesses suggested definitions of science. A descriptive definition was said to be that science is what is "accepted by the scientific community" and is "what scientists do." The obvious implication of this description is that, in a free society, knowledge does not require the imprimatur of legislation in order to become science.

More precisely, the essential characteristics of science are:

1. It is guided by natural law;
2. It has to be explanatory by reference to natural law;
3. It is testable against the empirical world;
4. Its conclusions are tentative, i.e., are not necessarily the final word; and
5. It is falsifiable. (Ruse and other science witnesses).

Creation science as described in Section 4(a) fails to meet these essential characteristics....

Creation science, as defined in Section 4(a), not only fails to follow the canons defining scientific theory, it also fails to fit the more general descriptions of "what scientists think" and "what scientists do." The scientific community consists of individuals and groups, nationally and internationally, who work independently in such varied fields as biology, paleontology, geology and astronomy. Their work is published and subject to review and testing by their peers. The journals for publication are both numerous and varied. There is, however, not one recognized scientific journal which has published an article espousing the creation science theory described in Section 4(a). Some of the State's witnesses suggested that the scientific community was "close-minded" on the subject of creationism and that explained the lack of acceptance of the creation science arguments. Yet no witness produced a scientific article for which publication had been refused. Perhaps some members of the scientific community are resistant to new ideas. It is, however, inconceivable that such a loose knit group of independent thinkers in all the varied fields of science could, or would, so effectively censor new scientific thought.

... The methodology employed by creationists is another factor which is indicative that their work is not science. A scientific theory must be tentative and always subject to revision or abandonment in light of facts that are inconsistent with, or falsify, the theory. A theory that is by its own terms dogmatic, absolutist and never subject to revision is not a scientific theory.

The creationists' methods do not take data, weigh it against the opposing scientific data, and thereafter reach the conclusions stated in Section 4(a). Instead, they take the literal wording of the Book of Genesis and attempt to find scientific support for it....

The Court would never criticize or discredit any person's testimony based on his or her religious beliefs. While anybody is free to approach a scientific inquiry in any fashion they choose, they cannot properly describe the methodology used as scientific, if they start with a conclusion and refuse to change it regardless of the evidence developed during the course of the investigation.

Excerpts from McLean v.Arkansas Board of Education, 529 F.Supp. 1255

State of Tennessee, Office of the Attorney General (1988)

Public Schools – Theories of Origins of Life – Creation Science – Establishment Clause

Question:

Whether a teacher in a public school in Tennessee can teach all theories of the origin of life for the purpose of enhancing the effectiveness of science instruction?

Opinion:

It is the opinion of this office that a public school teacher can teach any scientific theory of the origin of life, such as evolution. However, no theory of the origin of life which is religiously based can be taught in the public schools as part of the science curriculum, because its teaching would violate the establishment clause of the First Amendment of the United States Constitution.

Analysis:

The establishment clause of the First Amendment of the United States Constitution provides that "Congress shall make no law respecting an establishment of religion...." Through the Fourteenth Amendment, the United States Supreme Court has applied the establishment clause to the states. See *Cantwell v. Connecticut,* 310 U.S. 296 (1940). In determining whether there is a violation of the establishment clause in a particular situation, the Supreme Court, in the case of *Lemon v. Kurtzman,* 403 U.S. 602, 612-613 (1971) announced the following three-prong test:

First, the legislature must have adopted the law with a secular purpose. Second, the statute's principal or primary effect must be one that neither advances nor inhibits religion. Third, the statute must not result in an excessive entanglement of government with religion.

It should also be noted that the establishment clause applies not only to statutes, but to all actions by public employees and officials which would result in a prohibited promotion of religion. See *Breen v. Runkel*, 614 F. Supp. 355 (W.D. Mich. 1985) (when acting in capacity as classroom instructors, teachers are "state actors" for purpose of determining whether their praying in classrooms, reading from the Bible, and telling stories that have a biblical basis violates the establishment clause.); *Collins v. Chandler Unified School District*, 644 F.2d 759, cert. denied, 454 U.S. 863 (1980) (where a high school principal, with the concurrence of their superintendent, granted permission for a student council to recite prayers and Bible verses of their choosing during school hours, there was a violation of the establishment clause).

With regard to your question, a recent decision by the United States Supreme Court held a Louisiana statute that required the teaching of "creation science" in public schools if evolution was taught to be violative of the establishment clause. *Edwards v. Aguillard*, 107 S. Ct. 2573 (1987). In concluding that the statute was unconstitutional, Justice William Brennan, writing for the majority, stated the following with regard to "creation science" as a scientific theory of the origin of life:

> The preeminent purpose of the Louisiana legislature was clearly to advance the religious viewpoint that a supernatural being created human kind. The term 'creation science' was defined as embracing this particular religious doctrine by those responsible for the passage of the Creationism Act. Senator Keith's leading expert on creation science, Edward Boudreaux, testified at the legislative hearings that the theory of creation science included belief in the existence of a supernatural creator.... The legislative history therefore reveals that the term 'creation science' as contemplated by the legislature that adopted this act, embodies the religious belief that a supernatural creator was responsible for the creation of human kind.

Id. at 2581-82. Thus, according to Justice Brennan, "creation science", as understood to include the concept of a supernatural creator, is religiously based and cannot be taught in the public schools as part of the science curriculum without violating the establishment clause.

Justice Brennan's opinion was based upon the record of the legislative debates of the Louisiana statute. No such record exists in this situation. However, the fact that a statute has not been passed in Tennessee requiring the teaching of "creation science" or prohibiting the teaching of evolution unless "creation science" is taught, would not render the actions of a teacher who taught "creation science" as part of the science curriculum to be constitutional. Rather, the teaching of "creation science", if it is intended to include the belief that a supernatural creator was responsible for the creation of life, is an attempt to advance a particular religious view and is violative of the establishment clause of the First Amendment of the United States Constitution.

On the other hand, there would appear to be no constitutional problem with presenting the Biblical account of creation as part of a comparative religion course. See *Abington School District v. Schempp*, 374 U.S. 203, 225 (1963) (Bible may constitutionally be used in an appropriate study of history, civilization, ethics, or comparative religion); Stone v. Graham, 449 U.S. 39 (1980) (Ten Commandments cannot be posted on classroom walls but could be discussed in course on ethics).

Opinion no. 88-149
August 18, 1988

Voices for Evolution

Webster v. New Lenox School District (1990)

I. Background*

A. Facts

Ray Webster teaches social studies at the Oster-Oakview Junior High School in New Lenox, Illinois. In the Spring of 1987, a student in Mr. Webster's social studies class complained that Mr. Webster's teaching methods violated principles of separation between church and state. In addition to the student, both the American Civil Liberties Union and the Americans United for the Separation of Church and State objected to Mr. Webster's teaching practices. Mr. Webster denied the allegations. On July 31, 1987, the New Lenox school board (school board) through its superintendent, advised Mr. Webster by letter that he should restrict his classroom instruction to the curriculum and refrain from advocating a particular religious viewpoint.

Believing the superintendent's letter vague, Mr. Webster asked for further clarification in a letter dated September 4, 1987. In this letter, Mr. Webster also set forth his teaching methods and philosophy. Mr. Webster stated that the discussion of religious issues in his class was only for the purpose of developing an open mind in his students. For example, Mr. Webster explained that he taught nonevolutionary theories of creation to rebut a statement in the social studies textbook indicating that the world is over four billion years old. Therefore, his teaching methods in no way violated the doctrine of separation between church and state. Mr. Webster contended that, at most, he encouraged students to explore alternative viewpoints.

The superintendent responded to Mr. Webster's letter on October 13, 1987. The superintendent reiterated that advocacy of a Christian viewpoint was prohibited, although Mr. Webster could discuss objectively the historical relationship between church and state when such discussions were an appropriate part of the curriculum. Mr. Webster was specifically instructed not to teach creation science, because the teaching of this theory had been held by the federal courts to be religious advocacy.**

Mr. Webster brought suit, principally arguing that the school board's prohibitions constituted censorship in violation of the first and fourteenth amendments. In particular, Mr. Webster argued that the school board should permit him to teach a nonevolutionary theory of creation in his social studies class.

B. The District Court

The district court concluded that Mr. Webster did not have a first amendment right to teach creation science in a public school. The district court began by noting that, in deciding whether to grant the school district's motion to dismiss, the court was entitled to consider the letters between the superintendent and Mr. Webster because Mr. Webster had attached these letters to his complaint as exhibits. In particular, the district court determined that the October 13, 1987 letter was critical; this letter clearly indicated exactly what conduct the school district sought to proscribe. Specifically, the October 18 letter directed that Mr. Webster was prohibited from teaching creation science and was admonished not to engage in religious advocacy. Furthermore, the superintendent's letter explicitly stated that Mr. Webster could discuss objectively the historical relationship between church and state.

The district court noted that a school board generally has wide latitude in setting the curriculum, provided the school board remains within the boundaries established by the constitution. Because the establishment clause prohibits the enactment of any law "respecting an establishment of religion," the school board could not enact a curriculum that would inject religion into the public schools. U.S. Const. amend. I. Moreover, the district court determined that the school board had the responsibility to ensure that the establishment clause was not violated.

The district court then framed the issue as whether Mr. Webster had the right to teach creation science. Relying on *Edwards v. Aguillard*, 482 U.S. 578 (1987), the district court determined that teaching creation science would constitute religious advocacy in violation of the first amendment and that the school board correctly prohibited Mr. Webster from teaching such material. The court further noted:

Webster has not been prohibited from teaching any nonevolutionary theories or from teaching anything regarding the historical relationship between church and state. Martino's [the superintendent] letter of October 13, 1987 makes it clear that the religious advocacy of Webster's teaching is prohibited and nothing else. Since no other constraints were placed on Webster's teaching, he has no basis for his complaint and it must fail.

Webster v. New Lenox School Dist., Mem. op. at 4-5 (N.D., Ill. May 25, 1989). Accordingly, the district court dismissed the complaint....***

Conclusion

For the foregoing reasons, the judgment of the district court is affirmed.

Webster v. New Lenox School District #122, 917 F. 2d 1004

*Introductory material in Background section, preceding the summary of "Facts," is omitted here.

**Footnote in original refers to definition of "creation science" in Edwards v. Aguillard, 482 U.S. 578, 592 (1987)

***Footnote in original omitted here

Peloza v. Capistrano Unified School District (1994)

...Charitably read, Peloza's complaint at most makes this claim: the school district's actions establish a state-supported religion of evolutionism, or more generally of "secular humanism." See complaint at 2-4, 20. According to Peloza's complaint, all persons must adhere to one of two religious belief systems concerning "the origins of life and of the universe": evolutionism, or creationism. Id. at 2. Thus, the school district, in teaching evolutionism, is establishing a state-supported "religion."

We reject this claim because neither the Supreme Court, nor this circuit, has ever held that evolutionism or secular humanism are "religions" for Establishment Clause purposes. Indeed, both the dictionary definition of religion and the clear weight of the caselaw are to the contrary. The Supreme Court has held unequivocally that while the belief in a divine creator of the universe is a religious belief, the scientific theory that higher forms of life evolved from lower forms is not. Edwards v. Aguillard, 482 U.S. 578, 96 L. Ed. 2d 510, 107 S. Ct. 2573 (1987) (holding unconstitutional, under Establishment Clause, Louisiana's "Balanced Treatment for Creation-Science and Evolution-Science in Public School Instruction Act").

Peloza would have us accept his definition of "evolution" and "evolutionism" and impose his definition on the school district as its own, a definition that cannot be found in the dictionary, in the Supreme Court cases, or anywhere in the common understanding of the words. Only if we define "evolution" and "evolutionism" as does Peloza as a concept that embraces the belief that the universe came into existence without a Creator might he make out a claim. This we need not do. To say red is green or black is white does not make it so. Nor need we for the purposes of a 12(b)(6) motion accept a made-up definition of "evolution." Nowhere does Peloza point to anything that conceivably suggests that the school district accepts

Voices for Evolution

anything other than the common definition of "evolution" and "evolutionism." It simply required him as a biology teacher in the public schools of California to teach "evolution." Peloza nowhere says it required more.

The district court dismissed his claim, stating:

Since the evolutionist theory is not a religion, to require an instructor to teach this theory is not a violation of the Establishment Clause.... Evolution is a scientific theory based on the gathering and studying of data, and modification of new data. It is an established scientific theory which is used as the basis for many areas of science. As scientific methods advance and become more accurate, the scientific community will revise the accepted theory to a more accurate explanation of life's origins. Plaintiff's assertions that the teaching of evolution would be a violation of the Establishment Clause is [sic] unfounded.

Id. at 12-13. We agree....

John E. Peloza v. Capistrano Unified School District, 37 F. 3d 517.
Footnotes in original are omitted here

Kitzmiller v. Dover Area School District (2005)

ID [Intelligent Design] is not science. We find that ID fails on three different levels, any one of which is sufficient to preclude a determination that ID is science. They are: (1) ID violates the centuries-old ground rules of science by invoking and permitting supernatural causation; (2) the argument of irreducible complexity, central to ID, employs the same flawed and illogical contrived dualism that doomed creation science in the 1980's; and (3) ID's negative attacks on evolution have been refuted by the scientific community. ... [I]t is additionally important to note that ID has failed to gain acceptance in the scientific community, it has not generated peer-reviewed publications, nor has it been the subject of testing and research. ...

Notably, every major scientific association that has taken a position on the issue of whether ID is science has concluded that ID is not, and cannot be considered as such. ... Not a single expert witness over the course of the six week trial identified one major scientific association, society or organization that endorsed ID as science. What is more, defense experts concede that ID is not a theory as that term is defined by the [National Academy of Sciences] and admit that ID is at best "fringe science" which has achieved no acceptance in the scientific community. ...

ID is at bottom premised upon a false dichotomy, namely, that to the extent evolutionary theory is discredited, ID is confirmed. This argument is not brought to this Court anew, and in fact, the same argument, termed "contrived dualism" in McLean, was employed by creationists in the 1980's to support "creation science." ... We do not find this false dichotomy any more availing to justify ID today than it was to justify creation science two decades ago.

ID proponents primarily argue for design through negative arguments against evolution, as illustrated by Professor Behe's argument that "irreducibly complex" systems cannot be produced through Darwinian, or any natural, mechanisms. However, we believe that arguments against evolution are not arguments for design. Expert testimony revealed that just because scientists cannot explain today how biological systems evolved does not mean that they cannot, and will not, be able to explain them tomorrow. ...

Despite the scientific community's overwhelming support for evolution, Defendants and ID proponents insist that evolution is unsupported by empirical evidence. Plaintiffs' science experts, Drs. Miller and Padian, clearly explained how ID proponents generally and *Pandas* specifically, distort and misrepresent scientific knowledge in making their anti-evolution argument. ...

The disclaimer's plain language, the legislative history, and the historical context in which the ID Policy arose, all inevitably lead to the conclusion that Defendants consciously chose to change Dover's biology curriculum to advance religion. We have been presented with a wealth of evidence which reveals that the District's purpose was to advance creationism, an inherently religious view, both by introducing it directly under the label ID and by disparaging the scientific theory of evolution, so that creationism would gain credence by default as the only apparent alternative to evolution. ... Any asserted secular purposes by the Board are a sham and are merely secondary to a religious objective. Defendants' previously referenced flagrant and insulting falsehoods to the Court provide sufficient and compelling evidence for us to deduce that any allegedly secular purposes that have been offered in support of the ID Policy are equally insincere.

[W]e first note that since ID is not science, the conclusion is inescapable that the only real effect of the ID Policy is the advancement of religion. .... Second, the disclaimer read to students "has the effect of implicitly bolstering alternative religious theories of origin by suggesting that evolution is a problematic theory even in the field of science." Third, reading the disclaimer not only disavows endorsement of educational materials but also "juxtaposes that disavowal with an urging to contemplate alternative religious concepts implies School Board approval of religious principles."

The effect of Defendants' actions in adopting the curriculum change was to impose a religious view of biological origins into the biology course, in violation of the Establishment Clause. ...

The proper application of both the endorsement and Lemon tests to the facts of this case makes it abundantly clear that the Board's ID Policy violates the Establishment Clause. In making this determination, we have addressed the seminal question of whether ID is science. We have concluded that it is not, and moreover that ID cannot uncouple itself from its creationist, and thus religious, antecedents. ...

The breathtaking inanity of the Board's decision is evident when considered against the factual backdrop which has now been fully revealed through this trial. The students, parents, and teachers of the Dover Area School District deserved better than to be dragged into this legal maelstrom, with its resulting utter waste of monetary and personal resources.

Excerpts from Kitzmiller et al v. Dover Area School District et al, *Case No. 04cv2688, John E. Jones, III, presiding. Footnotes in original are omitted here.*

PART TWO

SCIENTIFIC ORGANIZATIONS

Voices for Evolution

Brief of Amici Curiae
by 56 Professional Scientific Organizations
in Selman v. Cobb County

Statement of Interest of the Professional Scientific Organizations

The *amici* are scientific organizations whose members are current and retired professional scientists. They are seriously concerned about the low level of science literacy in the United States and recognize that public school science education is a major way through which the public gains basic knowledge of science.

When the nature and content of science are erroneously presented in the public schools, the position of science in society is negatively affected, which directly affects the interests of scientists. The technological innovations that drive our economy and provide for our national security are dependent on sound scientific research. So too are the breakthroughs that will provide for the improved health of our population, for a dependable food supply, and for increasingly needed new energy sources. At no point in our nation's history has American leadership in science, technology, and medicine been more important. As professional scientists, the *amici* have a direct stake in sound science education.

Statement of the Issue

Whether there is any pedagogical or scientific merit to the Cobb County School District's requirement that biology textbooks carry a disclaimer that singles out evolution as a theory.

Argument

Amici professional scientific organizations submit this brief for the limited purpose of expressing the view of the scientific community regarding the status of evolution as well-established science. The scientific community does not qualify evolution, or any other scientific theory, as "theory not fact"; it is, therefore, unnecessary and misleading to do so in the public schools.

I. The Disclaimer Misuses the Scientific Terms "Theory" and "Fact"
In 2002, the Cobb County Board of Education required a sticker (hereafter, "the disclaimer") to be placed in biology textbooks that read:

> This textbook contains material on evolution. Evolution is a theory, not a fact, regarding the origin of living things. This material should be approached with an open mind, studied carefully and critically considered.

In the view of the scientific community, which the *amici* represent, the disclaimer employs the terms "theory" and "fact" in a manner both incorrect and misleading.

First, the phrasing of the disclaimer implies that a theory is a speculative or unsubstantiated proposition. This is fundamentally incorrect. In codified bodies of scientific knowledge such as textbooks, the word "theory" is reserved for our most well-substantiated and comprehensive explanations. The National Academy of Sciences, an organization of leading scientists in every field which advises the administration and Congress on scientific affairs, defines the synonym for theory as "explanation":

> In science, a well-substantiated explanation of some aspect of the natural world that can incorporate facts, laws, inferences, and tested hypotheses. Nat'l Acad. of Sciences., *Science and Creationism: A View from the National Academy of Sciences*, 2 (2d ed. 1999).

This definition also makes it clear that scientific theories "out-rank" facts by sub-suming facts and laws within them. Well-known scientific theories include the atomic theory, the general theory of relativity, the theory of gravitation, the germ theory of disease, and the gene theory of heredity.

Even well-established scientific theories may be, and usually are, incomplete. Atom-ic theory, for example, expresses the general understanding that matter is composed of atoms. It does not mean that physicists fully understand everything about atoms; there are "gaps" in our knowledge of atomic theory. Nonetheless, no reputable scien-tist doubts the basic proposition that matter is made of atoms or that atomic theory is a powerful framework for understanding natural phenomena.

Not only does the disclaimer use "theory" incorrectly, it also employs the word "fact" in a misleading way. In a non-scientific context, the word "fact" implies certainty, finality, and immutability; facts are permanent and unproblematic. In science, however, everything – including what we take to be facts - is in principle revisable in the light of more accurate instrumentation, further evidence, or changes in theory that cause us to look differently at phenomena.[1] By speciously opposing "theory" and "fact," the disclaimer misleads its reader about the scientific use of those terms, and does so in such a way as to deprecate evolution.

Scientists do not doubt the basic proposition that living things share common an-cestry. By using the terms "fact" and "theory" wrongly and misleadingly, the disclaimer serves to propagate an incorrect view of science and of evolution. Certainly, there is no valid pedagogical or scientific reason for using scientific terms incorrectly and thereby thwarting the purpose of science education.

II. The Disclaimer Incorrectly Defines Evolution

In its broadest sense, evolution is the idea that the universe has had a history, that as-tronomical, geological, biological and anthropological phenomena have changed through time, although different sciences may invoke different underlying mecha-nisms in their explanations. Biological evolution is a subset of this larger idea: it holds that living things have descended with modification from common ancestors. Bio-logical evolution incorporates the idea that species are genealogically related: com-mon ancestry is the key to understanding biological evolution.[2]

Evidence for common ancestry comes from many different scientific disciplines, including comparative anatomy, developmental biology, genetics, biogeography, bio-chemistry, and paleontology. Evolutionary biology includes the study of the patterns of evolution - how the tree of life has branched through time - and the various pro-cesses that affect or bring about evolution.

Thus, the Cobb County disclaimer does not use the term "evolution" correctly when it defines evolution as "regarding the origin of living things." That definition is either too narrow or simply mistaken. Evolution in the broad sense is a complex topic studied by a number of disparate scientific disciplines and is not limited to "the origin of living things." If the disclaimer means to refer only to biological evolution, as seems likely by its presence only in biology textbooks, it makes another error - by using the phrase "origin of living things," the disclaimer conflates the question of the evolution of living things with the very different question of the origin of life.

III. The Disclaimer Erroneously Implies that Biological Evolution is Not Well-Established Science

Because it selects only evolution as a subject to be "critically considered," the disclaimer implies that evolution is in special need of critical consideration. This is incorrect. Evolution is a well-established scientific theory with empirical validation and explanatory force. Not only is biological evolution the only scientific explanation for the presence and diversity of living things, the evidence for it is overwhelming. The National Academy of Sciences has written:

> The concept of biological evolution is one of the most important ideas ever generated by the application of scientific methods to the natural world. The evolution of all the organisms that live on Earth today from ancestors that lived in the past is at the core of genetics, biochemistry, neurobiology, physiology, ecology, and other biological disciplines. It helps to explain the emergence of new infectious diseases, the development of antibiotic resistance in bacteria, the agricultural relationships among wild and domestic plants and animals, the composition of Earth's atmosphere, the molecular machinery of the cell, the similarities between human beings and other primates, and countless other features of the biological and physical world. Nat'l Acad. of Sciences, *supra*, at viii.

Because of its importance in science, evolution is taught matter-of-factly, without qualification or compromise, in secular universities and in prestigious religiously-affiliated universities such as Brigham Young, Baylor, and Notre Dame. The view of the scientific community is that evolution should not be singled out for special qualification and should be taught matter-of-factly at the secondary level, without qualification.

Opponents of evolution typically claim that evolution is weak or poorly-supported science, citing debates over the detailed pattern of life's history and the role and interactions of various mechanisms of evolution. In reality, scientific debates about the details of the patterns and processes of evolution confirm the overwhelming consensus among scientists that living things have, indeed, evolved.[3]

By emphasizing that evolution – but no other scientific theory – is "a theory, not a fact," the Cobb County school district disclaimer draws a distinction that the scientific community does not make. The implication of the disclaimer is that evolution, among all other scientific principles, is particularly weak, controversial, or unsubstantiated. This is simply wrong.[4]

Conclusion:
Disclaiming Evolution Serves No Valid Scientific or Pedagogical Purpose

The Cobb County disclaimer displays a serious lack of understanding of the nature of science and of biological evolution. By using the terms "fact", "theory," and "evolution" wrongly and misleadingly, the disclaimer serves to propagate an incorrect view of the status of scientific theories in general and of evolution in particular. No scientific or educational purpose is served by treating evolution differently from other theories. Rather, the disclaimer gives scientifically unwarranted support to religious opponents of evolution.

Given the great importance of evolution as a fundamental, unifying, explanatory theory and its well-established place in science education, there can be no valid pedagogical or scientific reason to disclaim or qualify its validity in public school science textbooks. For all of the above reasons, the *amici* professional scientific organizations urge the court to uphold the District Court's decision.

Dated: June 9, 2005
Amicus Curiae filed in Selman v. Cobb County
by the following professional scientific associations:
Academy of Science of St. Louis
American Anthropological Association
American Association for the Advancement of Science
American Association of Anatomists
American Association of Physics Teachers
American Association of Physical Anthropologists
American Astronomical Society
American Crystallographic Association
American Geological Institute
American Geological Union
American Institute of Biological Sciences
American Institute of Chemists
American Institute of Physics
American Physical Society
American Physiological Society
American Society for Biochemistry and Molecular Biology
American Society for Bone and Mineral Research
American Society for Investigative Pathology
American Society of Agronomy
American Society of Human Genetics
American Society of Ichthyologists and Herpetologists
American Society of Plant Biologists
American Society of Plant Taxonomists
Association of American Geographers
Association of Anatomy, Cell Biology and Neurobiology Chairs
Association of College & University Biology Educators
Association of Southeastern Biologists
Association for Women in Science
The Biophysical Society
Botanical Society of America
Clay Minerals Society
Crop Science Society of America
Federation of American Societies for Experimental Biology
Foundation for Neuroscience and Society
Geological Society of America
Georgia Academy of Science
Indiana Academy of Science
Iowa Academy of Science
The Kentucky Academy of Science
National Academy of Sciences
Nebraska Academy of Sciences
New Mexico Academy of Science
New York Academy of Sciences
Ohio Academy of Science
Paleontological Society
Phi Sigma: The Biological Honors Society
Phycological Society of America
Sigma Xi – The Scientific Research Society
Society of Economic Geologists
Society for Industrial and Applied Mathematics
Society for Developmental Biology
Society for Integrative and Comparative Biology
Society for Sedimentary Geology
Society for the Study of Evolution
Society for Systematic Biologists
Soil Science Society of America

[1] "Fact: In science, an observation that has been repeatedly confirmed and for all practical purposes is accepted as 'true'. Truth in science, however, is never final, and what is accepted as a fact today may be modified or even discarded tomorrow." Nat'l Acad. Of Sciences., supra, at 2.

[2] "Biological evolution concerns changes in living things during the history of life on Earth. It explains that living things share common ancestors. Over time, biological processes such as natural selection give rise to new species. Darwin called this process 'descent with modification,' which remains a good definition of biological evolution today." Nat'l Acad. of Sciences, supra, at 27.

[3] The Brief of Amici Curiae Biologists from the Discovery Institute incorrectly claims that a valid scientific debate is "raging" over whether evolution occurred. On the contrary, debate occurs over the details of evolution, not over whether evolution occurs. (D.I. Br. at 9). Typical is a statement from the American Institute of Biological Sciences: "As a community, biologists agree that evolution occurred and that the forces driving the evolutionary process are still active today. This consensus is based on more than a century of scientific data gathering and analysis." Voices for Evolution, 33 (M. Matsumura, Nat'l Ctr. for Sci. Educ., ed., rev. ed. 2004).

[4] See e.g., Voices for Evolution, supra (reporting statements of scientific organizations, such as the Association of Southeastern Biologists: "[We strongly oppose attempts to undermine or compromise the teaching of evolution, whether by eliminating the word 'evolution' from state science standards, requiring textbook disclaimers that misleadingly describe evolution as 'merely' a theory, or by encouraging scientifically unwarranted criticism of evolution under the guise of 'analysis,' 'objectivity,' 'balance,' or 'teaching the controversy.' Such tactics are clearly intended to leave the false impression that evolution is scientifically precarious and will thus deprive students of a sound scientific education.").

Alabama Academy of Science (1981)

The Executive Committee of the Alabama Academy of Science hereby records its opposition to legislation to introduce "scientific creationism" into the Alabama classroom. Furthermore, the Executive Committee of the Alabama Academy of Science believes that the introduction of classroom subject content through the political process not only violates the academic freedom of the subject specialist to determine relevant and scientifically sound concepts, but also represents an inappropriate and potentially dangerous precedent for American education.

Adopted by a vote of 24 in favor to 7 opposed; copy hand-dated 1981.

Alabama Academy of Science, Inc. (1994)

The Executive Committee of the Alabama Academy of Science strongly deplores efforts to insert into the Course of Study for Science for the public schools of this state theories and hypotheses which do not meet the cardinal criteria of the hypotheses, theories and laws of science: that they be based on facts and that they be capable of being proven false. To be scientific, hypotheses, theories and laws must be in accord with the results of repeatable controlled experiments or be formulated as the result of consistent and verifiable observations.

Adopted by the Executive Committee October 29, 1994

American Anthropological Association (1980)

Whereas evolutionary theory is the indispensable foundation for the understanding of physical anthropology and biology;

Whereas evolution is a basic component of many aspects of archeology, cultural anthropology, and linguistics;

Whereas evolution is a basic component of allied disciplines such as the earth sciences and a cornerstone of 20th century science in general;

Whereas a century of scientific research has confirmed the reality of evolution as a historical process, and the concept of evolution, in all its diversity, has explained the scientifically known evidence and successfully predicted fruitful paths of further research; and

Whereas local and national campaigns by so-called scientific Creationists and other antievolutionists nevertheless challenge the right of public schools to teach

Voices for Evolution

evolutionary theory without giving scientific credence or equal time to Creationist and other antievolutionist explanations of the origin and development of life;

Be it moved that the American Anthropological Association affirms the necessity of teaching evolution as the best scientific explanation of human and nonhuman biology and the key to understanding the origin and development of life, because the principles of evolution have been tested repeatedly and found to be valid according to scientific criteria;

The Association respects the right of people to hold diverse religious beliefs, including those which reject evolution, as matters of theology or faith but not as tenets of secular science;

Efforts to require teaching Creationism in science classes, whether exclusively, as a component of science curricula, or in equal-time counterpoint to evolution, are not based on science but rather are attempts to promote unscientific viewpoints in the name of science without basis in the record of scientific research by generations of anthropologists and other scholars;

The subject of life origins is addressed in tremendous diversity among the world's religions, and efforts to promote particular Judeo-Christian creation accounts in public schools are ethnocentric as well as unscientific.

Be it further moved that the Association shall communicate this motion upon passage to the public news media, to commissioners of education or equivalent officials in each of the 50 states, and to other officials and organizations deemed appropriate by the Executive Board or Executive Director.

Be it further moved that members of the Association are encouraged to promote these points of professional concern in their home communities among educators, parents, and students and in appropriate public forums beyond the boundaries of traditional, professional, and academic disciplines.

Passed at 1980 annual meeting in Washington, DC.

American Anthropological Association (2000)

Statement on Evolution and Creationism
Affirmation

The Executive Board of the American Anthropological Association affirms that:

Evolution is a basic component of many aspects of anthropology (including physical anthropology, archeology, cultural anthropology, and linguistics) and is a cornerstone of modern science, being central to biology, geology, and astronomy;

The principles of evolution have been tested repeatedly and found to be valid according to scientific criteria. Evolution should be part of the pre-college curriculum; it is the best scientific explanation of human and nonhuman biology and the key to understanding the origin and development of life;

Religious views are an important part of human cultures, and deserve a place in the pre-college curriculum, provided that they are not presented dogmatically or in a proselytizing context. A comparative, anthropological study of religion would not violate the Constitutional requirement of religious neutrality in the classroom. An anthropological understanding of religion would be helpful in resolving some of the perceived conflict between creationism and evolution;

The Association respects the right of people to hold diverse religious beliefs, including those who reject evolution as matters of theology or faith. Such beliefs should not be presented as science, however;

Teachers, administrators, school board members and others involved in pre-college education are under pressure to teach creationism as science and/or eliminate or downgrade evolution, to the detriment of public scientific literacy. Many succumb to this pressure, for lack of expressed support from scientists and other community members;

Therefore anthropologists are encouraged to use their knowledge both of evolution and of human social and cultural systems to assist communities in which evolution and creationism have become contentious. Anthropologists should help the public and public officials understand that good science education requires that evolution be presented in the same manner as other well-supported scientific theories, without special qualifications or disclaimers, and that an understanding of religion and other cultural systems should be part of the education of each child.

Background Information

Anthropologists study human beings both at the present time and as they were in the past, therefore the creationism and evolution dispute is of particular interest to members of the American Anthropological Association. We are sensitive to social, cultural, religious, and political differences among citizens, and we also appreciate (and contribute to the understanding of) the long evolutionary history of our species. Anthropology's cultural, biological, linguistic, and archaeological perspectives are especially relevant for helping to understand this controversy.

Anthropologists are aware of diversity within cultures, including our own. It is empirically incorrect to describe creation and evolution controversies as simplistic dramas of fundamentalism versus atheism. Evolution is not equivalent to atheism; studies demonstrate that those who accept evolution hold a variety of religious beliefs. Similarly, Christian creationist thought spans a range of positions, from biblical literalism to progressive creationism–and many non-Christian forms of creationism exist among the world's peoples.

In contrast to this diversity of religious views, the single general idea of biological evolution is that species share common ancestors from which they have diverged. There is much debate over the details, but descent with modification itself is no longer debated by scholars. As the National Academy of Sciences has said,

> The scientific consensus around evolution is overwhelming. Those opposed to the teaching of evolution sometimes use quotations from prominent scientists out of context to claim that scientists do not support evolution. However, examination of the quotations reveals that the scientists are actually disputing some aspect of how evolution occurs, not whether evolution occurred.[1]

Such debates about the mechanisms and details of evolution are a normal part of the scientific process, and gradually have led to a consensus about the history of life on Earth. The ability to alter explanations when new evidence or theory is encountered is one of the strengths of a scientific way of knowing. Religious or philosophical interpretations should be distinguished from scientific knowledge per se, to the extent that it is possible to delineate such distinctions. Science describes and explains the natural world: it does not prove or disprove beliefs about the supernatural.

The study of the evolution of humans is a scientific enterprise. Good scientific knowledge possesses these features:

1. it explains natural phenomena in terms of natural laws and processes, without reference to overt or covert supernatural causation;

Voices for Evolution

2. it is empirically grounded in evidence from observations and experiments; and

3. it is subject to change as new empirical evidence arises.

Because humans are part of nature, the study of human evolution can be conducted within these parameters.

With these thoughts in mind, the following summarizes a consensus of anthropological judgments regarding human evolution:

1. The ancestors of humans extend back in time for several million years. This consensus of anthropological judgment is derived from reliable scientific methods that are well accepted in geology, paleontology and archaeology, including (a) a series of absolute dating methods based on radiometric techniques that independently affirm the dates of hominid fossils, plus (b) the stratigraphy-based principles of relative chronology, including superposition, association, and cross-dating. Together these methods constitute our best indicators of the ages of past events.

2. Human anatomy has changed over time in response to natural selection and other evolutionary processes. This consensus of anthropological judgment is derived from anatomy, paleoanthropology, paleoecology, taphonomy, paleoethnobotany, and related fields.

3. Human evolution is an on-going process. Our species remains subject to evolutionary mechanisms, including natural selection and non-Darwinian evolution. This consensus is derived from functional anatomical studies as well as discoveries in medicine and medical anthropology.

4. Humans are more closely related to primates than to other mammals, and within the primates, are more closely related to the African great apes. Our species shares some common ancestors with other primates and mammals. This consensus is derived from primatology, the fossil record, comparative anatomy, and genetics.

5. Evolutionary assumptions and methods provide persuasive explanations for the great variety of Earth's living things, including human beings. Evolutionary concepts tie together such natural phenomena as genetic diversity, environmental change, adaptation, differential reproductive success, and speciation, thereby making evolution the central organizing principle of the life sciences. This consensus of scientific opinion is derived from biology, geology, paleontology, primatology, and archaeology. As is the case with other scholars, our goals in teaching evolution are to instruct, not to indoctrinate. Anthropologists seek to inculcate a critical understanding of how scientists and other scholars think and work, so that our students will be able to employ anthropological reasoning and methods in their own thinking and research. All students, regardless of religious belief, as a matter of scientific literacy should understand basic principles of anthropology and other sciences relevant to evolution.

Submitted April 29, 2000, by the Ad-Hoc Committee on Evolution:
Francis Harrold, harrold@uta.edu
Eugenie C. Scott, scott@NCSEweb.org
Chris Toumey, toumey@pop.uky.edu
Linda Wolfe, WOLFEL@MAIL.ECU.EDU

Adopted by the AAA Executive Board, April, 2000

[1] 1999 Science and Creationism. National Academy Press, "Frequently Asked Questions"

American Association for the Advancement of Science (1923)

A Statement on the Present Scientific Status of the Theory of Evolution

Inasmuch as the attempt has been made in several states to prohibit in tax-supported institutions the teaching of evolution as applied to man, and

Since it has been asserted that there is not a fact in the universe in support of this theory, that it is a "mere guess" which leading scientists are now abandoning, and that even the American Association for the Advancement of Science at its last meeting in Toronto, Canada, approved this revolt against evolution, and

Inasmuch as such statements have been given wide publicity through the press and are misleading public opinion on this subject,

Therefore, the council of the American Association for the Advancement of Science has thought it advisable to take formal action upon this matter, in order that there may be no ground for misunderstanding of the attitude of the association, which is one of the largest scientific bodies in the world, with a membership of more than 11,000 persons, including the American authorities in all branches of science. The following statements represent the position of the council with regard to the theory of evolution.

1) The council of the association affirms that, so far as the scientific evidences of the evolution of plants and animals and man are concerned, there is no ground whatever for the assertion that these evidences constitute a "mere guess." No scientific generalization is more strongly supported by thoroughly tested evidences than is that of organic evolution.

2) The council of the association affirms that the evidences in favor of the evolution of man are sufficient to convince every scientist of note in the world, and that these evidences are increasing in number and importance every year.

3) The council of the association also affirms that the theory of evolution is one of the most potent of the great influences for good that have thus far entered into human experience; it has promoted the progress of knowledge, it has fostered unprejudiced inquiry, and it has served as an invaluable aid in humanity's search for truth in many fields.

4) The council of the association is convinced that any legislation attempting to limit the teaching of any scientific doctrine so well established and so widely accepted by specialists as is the doctrine of evolution would be a profound mistake, which could not fail to injure and retard the advancement of knowledge and of human welfare by denying the freedom of teaching and inquiry which is essential to all progress.

Resolution adopted 1923

American Association for the Advancement of Science (1972)

Whereas the new Science Framework for California Public Schools prepared by the California State Advisory Committee on Science Education has been revised by the California State Board of Education to include the theory of creation as an alternative to evolutionary theory in discussions of the origins of life, and

Whereas the theory of creation is neither scientifically grounded nor capable of performing the roles required of scientific theories, and

Whereas the requirement that it be included in textbooks as an alternative to evolutionary theory represents a constraint upon the freedom of the science teacher in the classroom, and

Whereas its inclusion also represents dictation by a lay body of what shall be considered within the corpus of a science,

Therefore we, the members of the Board of Directors of the American Association for the Advancement of Science, present at the quarterly meeting of October 1972, strongly urge that the California State Board of Education not include reference to the theory of creation in the new Science Framework for California Public Schools and that it adopt the original version prepared by the California State Advisory Committee on Science Education.

22 October 1972

American Association for the Advancement of Science (1982)

Forced Teaching of Creationist Beliefs in Public School Science Education

Whereas it is the responsibility of the American Association for the Advancement of Science to preserve the integrity of science, and

Whereas science is a systematic method of investigation based on continuous experimentation, observation, and measurement leading to evolving explanations of natural phenomena, explanations which are continuously open to further testing, and

Whereas evolution fully satisfies these criteria, irrespective of remaining debates concerning its detailed mechanisms, and

Whereas the Association respects the right of people to hold diverse beliefs about creation that do not come within the definitions of science, and

Whereas Creationist groups are imposing beliefs disguised as science upon teachers and students to the detriment and distortion of public education in the United States

Therefore be it resolved that because "Creationist Science" has no scientific validity it should not be taught as science, and further, that the AAAS views legislation requiring "Creationist Science" to be taught in public schools as a real and present threat to the integrity of education and the teaching of science, and

Be it further resolved that the AAAS urges citizens, educational authorities, and legislators to oppose the compulsory inclusion in science education curricula of beliefs that are not amenable to the process of scrutiny, testing, and revision that is indispensable to science.

> *The above resolution was passed by the AAAS Board of Directors on 4 January 1982 and submitted to the Council as a proposed joint resolution of the Board and Council. It was passed by Council on 7 January, and published in Science 215:1072 on 26 February.*

AAAS Board Resolution on Intelligent Design Theory

The contemporary theory of biological evolution is one of the most robust products of scientific inquiry. It is the foundation for research in many areas of biology as well as an essential element of science education. To become informed and responsible citizens in our contemporary technological world, students need to study the theories and empirical evidence central to current scientific understanding.

Over the past several years proponents of so-called "intelligent design theory," also known as ID, have challenged the accepted scientific theory of biological evolution. As part of this effort they have sought to introduce the teaching of "intelligent design theory" into the science curricula of the public schools. The movement presents "intelligent design theory" to the public as a theoretical innovation, supported by scientific evidence, that offers a more adequate explanation for the origin of the diversity of living organisms than the current scientifically accepted theory of evolution. In response to this effort, individual scientists and philosophers of science have provided substantive critiques of "intelligent design," demonstrating significant conceptual flaws in its formulation, a lack of credible scientific evidence, and misrepresentations of scientific facts.

Recognizing that the "intelligent design theory" represents a challenge to the quality of science education, the Board of Directors of the AAAS unanimously adopts the following resolution:

Whereas, ID proponents claim that contemporary evolutionary theory is incapable of explaining the origin of the diversity of living organisms;

Whereas, to date, the ID movement has failed to offer credible scientific evidence to support their claim that ID undermines the current scientifically accepted theory of evolution;

Whereas, the ID movement has not proposed a scientific means of testing its claims;

Therefore Be It Resolved, that the lack of scientific warrant for so-called "intelligent design theory" makes it improper to include as a part of science education;

Therefore Be Further It Resolved, that AAAS urges citizens across the nation to oppose the establishment of policies that would permit the teaching of "intelligent design theory" as a part of the science curricula of the public schools;

Therefore Be It Further Resolved, that AAAS calls upon its members to assist those engaged in overseeing science education policy to understand the nature of science, the content of contemporary evolutionary theory and the inappropriateness of "intelligent design theory" as subject matter for science education;

Therefore Be Further It Resolved, that AAAS encourages its affiliated societies to endorse this resolution and to communicate their support to appropriate parties at the federal, state and local levels of the government.

Approved by the AAAS Board of Directors on 10/18/02

American Association for the Advancement of Science Commission on Science Education

The Commission on Science Education of the American Association for the Advancement of Science is vigorously opposed to attempts by some boards of education and other groups to require that religious accounts of creation be taught in science classes.

During the past century and a half, the earth's crust and the fossils preserved in it have been intensively studied by geologists and paleontologists. Biologists have intensively studied the origin, structure, physiology, and genetics of living organisms. The conclusion of these studies is that the living species of animals and plants have evolved from different species that lived in the past. The scientists involved in these studies have built up the body of knowledge known as the biological theory of the origin and evolution of life. There is no currently acceptable alternative scientific theory to explain the phenomena.

The various accounts of creation that are part of the religious heritage of many people are not scientific statements or theories. They are statements that one may choose to believe, but if he does, this is a matter of faith, because such statements are not subject to study or verification by the procedures of science. A scientific statement must be capable of test by observation and experiment. It is acceptable only if, after repeated testing, it is found to account satisfactorily for the phenomena to which it is applied.

Thus the statements about creation that are part of many religions have no place in the domain of science and should not be regarded as reasonable alternatives to scientific explanations for the origin and evolution of life.

Adopted by the Commission on Science Education of the AAAS at its meeting on 13 October 1972 in Washington, DC.

American Association of Physical Anthropologists

1. *Be it resolved* that the American Association of Physical Anthropologists strongly endorses the recent resolution of the American Association for the Advancement of Science condemning the concepts of and teaching of, at public expense, so-called scientific creationism.

2. *Whereas* the American Association of Physical Anthropologists recognizes the advantages to any society which accrue when its members accept some moral code of behavior, and

Whereas the Association supports the Constitutional provision separating church and state,

Therefore be it resolved that the Association condemns any effort by the state to dictate specific religious instruction to the people, and

Be it further resolved that the Association condemns any effort by the state or any group within the state to restrict the right of all individuals to freedom of religious expression by advancing one religious viewpoint.

3. *Whereas* the American Association of Physical Anthropologists recognizes that our modern society is based on a high degree of technological and scientific sophistication, and

Whereas the Association realizes that such technology and science can only be sustained if there is continuous advancement in our knowledge of and control over natural phenomena, and

Whereas such continuous advancement can only be sustained if instruction in the current state of knowledge be available to all our citizens, and

Whereas public understanding of our technological society, which will promote the individual's ability to cope and serve, can only be achieved if instruction in the sciences reflects the current content of scientific research,

Be it resolved that the American Association of Physical Anthropologists charges the state with the duty of providing, through the public education system, the people with instruction in the current state of objective knowledge concerning our natural universe.

4. *Be it resolved* that the Secretary is directed to communicate these three resolutions to as many individuals or organizations as possible who may be concerned with these issues.

1982

American Astronomical Society (1982)

Resolution on Creationism

During the past year, religious fundamentalists have intensified their effort to force public school science classes to include instruction in "creationism." As defined in publications of the Institute for Creation Research and in laws passed or under consideration by several state legislatures, this doctrine includes the statement that the entire universe was created relatively recently, i.e. less than 10,000 years ago. This statement contradicts results of astronomical research during the past two centuries indicating that some stars now visible to us were in existence millions or billions of years ago, as well as the results of radiometric dating indicating that the age of the earth is about 4.5 billion years.

The American Astronomical Society does not regard any scientific theory as capable of rigorous proof or immune to possible revision in the light of new evidence. Such evidence should be presented for critical review and confirmation in the appropriate scientific journals. In this case, no such evidence for recent creation of the earth and universe has survived critical scrutiny by the scientific community. It would therefore be most inappropriate to demand that any science teacher present it as a credible hypothesis.

We agree with the findings of Judge William Overton that the Arkansas creationism law represents an unconstitutional intrusion of religious doctrine into the public schools, that "creation science" is not science, and that its advocates have followed the unscientific procedure of starting from a dogmatically held conclusion and looking only for evidence to support that conclusion.

The American Astronomical Society deplores the attempt to force creationism into public schools and urges Congress, all state legislatures, local school boards and textbook publishers to resist such attempts.

Adopted unanimously on 10 January 1982

American Astronomical Society (2000)

Statement on the Teaching of the History of the Universe

The American Astronomical Society (AAS) is the largest organization of professional astronomers in the United States. Its 6,000 members are men and women of all convictions and a variety of religious faiths. They work in ALL fields of astronomy, including the study of planets, of stars and of the Universe as a whole. Research in each of these areas, and in many other areas of astronomy, has produced clear, compelling and widely accepted evidence that astronomical objects and systems evolve. That is, their properties change with time, often over very long time scales.

Specifically, the scientific evidence clearly indicates that the Universe is 10 to 15 billion years old, and began in a hot, dense state we call the Big Bang.

Given the ample evidence that change over time is a crucial property of planets, including our own, of stars, of galaxies and of the Universe as a whole, it is important for the nation's school children to learn about the great age of, and changes in, astronomical systems, as well as their present properties.

More generally we believe that it is important to teach students the nature of the scientific method. Scientific inquiry involves the development and testing of hypotheses based on a systematic collection and analysis of data acquired through observations, experiments, and computer simulations. Science is not a collection of facts but an ongoing process, with continual revisions and refinements of concepts necessary in order to arrive at the best current views of the Universe. Science is unified; it is not possible to make use of scientific laws in one context, and then deny them in another. The same laws of science that govern – or empower – our advanced technology also underlie changes in time of astronomical systems. Science is not based on faith, nor does it preclude faith. Whatever personal beliefs teachers, students, parents or administrators may hold, the teaching of important scientific concepts, such as the formation and aging of planets, stars, galaxies and the Universe, should not be altered or constrained in response to demands external to the scientific disciplines.

The astronomical discoveries of the past century, many made by American scientists, are among the great triumphs of the human intellect, and we deeply regret any attempt to ignore them or deny them.

Children whose education is denied the benefits of this expansion of our understanding of the world around us are being deprived of part of their intellectual heritage. They may also be at a competitive disadvantage in a world where scientific and technological literacy is becoming more and more important economically and culturally.

Adopted 11 January 2000, Atlanta, GA
Copyright 2000 AAS

American Astronomical Society (2005)

Statement on the Teaching of Evolution

The American Astronomical Society supports teaching evolution in our nation's K-12 science classes. Evolution is a valid scientific theory for the origin of species that has been repeatedly tested and verified through observation, formulation of testable statements to explain those observations, and controlled experiments or additional observations to find out whether these ideas are right or wrong. A scientific theory is not speculation or a guess – scientific theories are unifying concepts that explain the physical universe.

Astronomical observations show that the Universe is many billions of years old (see the AAS publication, *An Ancient Universe*), that nuclear reactions in stars have produced the chemical elements over time, and recent observations show that gravity has led to the formation of many planets in our Galaxy. The early history of the solar system is being explored by astronomical observation and by direct visits to solar system objects. Fossils, radiological measurements, and changes in DNA trace the growth of the tree of life on Earth. The theory of evolution, like the theories of gravity, plate tectonics, and Big Bang cosmology, explains, unifies, and predicts natural phenomena. Scientific theories provide a proven framework for improving our understanding of the world.

In recent years, advocates of "Intelligent Design," have proposed teaching "Intelligent Design" as a valid alternative theory for the history of life. Although scientists have vigorous discussions on interpretations for some aspects of evolution, there is widespread agreement on the power of natural selection to shape the emergence of new species. Even if there were no such agreement, "Intelligent Design" fails to meet the basic definition of a scientific idea: its proponents do not present *testable* hypotheses and do not provide evidence for their views that can be verified or duplicated by subsequent researchers.

Since "Intelligent Design" is not science, it does not belong in the science curriculum of the nation's primary and secondary schools.

The AAS supports the positions taken by the National Academy of Sciences, the American Association for the Advancement of Science, the National Science Teachers' Association, the American Geophysical Union, the American Chemical Society, and the American Association of Physics Teachers on the teaching of evolution. The AAS also supports the National Science Education Standards: they emphasize the importance of scientific methods as well as articulating well-established scientific theories.

Adopted 20 September 2005

American Chemical Society (1981)

Addendum to Report of Committee on Professional and Member Relations

There is increased pressure on boards of education to mandate the teaching of biblical creationism in the nation's public school science classes. As recent examples of this pressure, the state legislatures of Arkansas and Louisiana have passed measures requiring that such creationism be taught whenever biological (Darwinian) evolution is taught.

The Board of Directors of the American Chemical Society reaffirms its statement of December 2, 1972 that creationism theories, often mistermed "scientific creationism," should not be taught as science in the nation's science classes. These theories were not derived from scientific data and are not amenable to scientific test. Any implication that such theories are within the framework of science would confuse students about the nature of both religion and science.

Endorsed by the ACS Board of Directors on 6 December 1981.

American Chemical Society (2005)

Statement on Teaching of Evolutionary Theory

The American Chemical Society (ACS) strongly supports the inclusion of evolution in K-12 science curricula, at an age-appropriate level, because evolution is central to our modern understanding of science. Evolutionary theory is not a hypothesis, but is the scientifically accepted explanation for the origin of species, and explains significant observations in chemistry, biology, geology, and other disciplines. Because of the overwhelming evidence supporting evolution, it has been recognized and endorsed as a key component of science education by all major scientific societies including the National Academy of Sciences (NAS), the American Association for the Advancement of Science (AAAS), and the National Science Teachers Association (NSTA). The ACS joins these prestigious organizations in recognizing the critical importance of the scientific principles embodied in evolutionary theory.

Science is a human activity that uses the observation of natural phenomena and systems, and the study of modifications to these systems, to develop models that explain the order and function of the universe. The theory of biological evolution is based on hundreds of years of scientific observation and experimentation and tens of thousands of scientific publications. It provides students with a unifying concept that explains the incredibly rich diversity of living things and their capacity to change and evolve over time to adapt to changing environments. It is a central component of modern biology and biotechnology. Evolution is an active field of research in which new discoveries continue to increase our knowledge and understanding of the specific processes and paths that biological evolution has followed over the millions of years that life has existed on earth.

Evolution cannot be dismissed or diminished by characterizing it as mere conjecture or speculation. Scientific explanations of the natural world have been reached through observation and experimentation, are testable through observation and manipulation of natural systems, and can be modified as a result of new information. The inclusion of non-scientific explanations in science curricula misrepresents the nature and processes of science and compromises a central purpose of public education – the preparation of a scientifically literate workforce.

The American Chemical Society urges

- State and local education authorities to support high-quality science standards and curricula that affirm evolution as the only scientifically accepted explanation for the origin and diversity of species.

- Administrators and curriculum supervisors to ensure that evolution is taught in their classrooms, accurately represented in their science textbooks, and assessed on local and state science tests.

This article first appeared on June 20, 2005.

American Geological Institute

Scientific evidence indicates beyond any doubt that life has existed on Earth for billions of years. This life has evolved through time producing vast numbers of species of plants and animals, most of which are extinct. Although scientists debate the mechanism that produced this change, the evidence for the change is undeniable. Therefore, in the teaching of science we oppose any position that ignores this scientific reality, or that gives equal time to interpretations based on religious beliefs only.

Unanimously approved by the governing board on 5 November 1981.

American Geophysical Union

Earth History and the Evolution of Life Must Be Taught: Creationism Is Not Science

The American Geophysical Union affirms the central importance of scientific theories of Earth history and organic evolution in science education. An educated citizenry must understand these theories in order to comprehend the dynamic world in which we live and nature's complex balance that sustains us.

Science employs a logical and empirical methodology to understand the natural world. Scientific research entails observation of natural phenomena, formulation of hypotheses as tentative, testable statements to explain these phenomena, and experiments or observations to test these hypotheses. Scientific theories, like evolution and relativity and plate tectonics, are hypotheses that have survived extensive testing and repeated verification. Scientific theories are therefore the best-substantiated statements that scientists can make to explain the organization and operation of the natural world. Thus, a scientific theory is not equal to a belief, a hunch, or an untested hypothesis. Our understanding of Earth's development over its 4.5 billion-year history and of life's gradual evolution has achieved the status of scientific theory.

"Creation science" is based on faith and is not supported by scientific observations of the natural world. Creationism is not science and does not have a legitimate place in any science curriculum.

AGU opposes all efforts to require or promote teaching creationism or any other religious tenets as science. AGU supports the National Science Education Standards, which incorporate well-established scientific theories including the origin of the universe, the age of Earth, and the evolution of life.

Adopted by Council December 1981
Reaffirmed May 1990, May 1994;
expanded and reaffirmed December 1999
reaffirmed December 2003

American Institute of Biological Science

The AIBS Executive Committee passed a resolution in 1972 deploring efforts by Biblical literalists to interject creationism and religion into science courses. It is very troubling that more than 20 years later, there is an urgent need to reaffirm AIBS's earlier position. Despite rulings by the Supreme Court declaring it unconstitutional to promote a religious perspective in public school education, such attempts by creationists continue in a variety of guises.

The theory of evolution is the only scientifically defensible explanation for the origin of life and development of species. A theory in science, such as the atomic theory in chemistry and the Newtonian and relativity theories in physics, is not a speculative hypothesis, but a coherent body of explanatory statements supported by evidence. The theory of evolution has this status. The body of knowledge that supports the

Voices for Evolution

theory of evolution is ever growing: fossils continue to be discovered that fill gaps in the evolutionary tree and recent DNA sequence data provide evidence that all living organisms are related to each other and to extinct species. These data, consistent with evolution, imply a common chemical and biological heritage for all living organisms and allow scientists to map branch points in the evolutionary tree.

Biologists may disagree about the details of the history and mechanisms of evolution. Such debate is a normal, healthy, and necessary part of scientific discourse and in no way negates the theory of evolution. As a community, biologists agree that evolution occurred and that the forces driving the evolutionary process are still active today. This consensus is based on more than a century of scientific data gathering and analysis.

Because creationism is based almost solely on religious dogma stemming from faith rather than demonstrable facts, it does not lend itself to the scientific process. As a result, creationism should not be taught in any science classroom.

Therefore, AIBS reaffirms its 1972 resolution that explanations for the origin of life and the development of species that are not supportable on scientific grounds should not be taught as science.

Board Resolution 1994

American Physical Society

The Council of the American Physical Society opposes proposals to require "equal time" for presentation in public school science classes of the biblical story of creation and the scientific theory of evolution. The issues raised by such proposals, while mainly focused on evolution, have important implications for the entire spectrum of scientific inquiry, including geology, physics, and astronomy.

In contrast to "Creationism," the systematic application of scientific principles has led to a current picture of life, of the nature of our planet, and of the universe which, while incomplete, is constantly being tested and refined by observation and analysis. This ability to construct critical experiments, whose results can require rejection of a theory, is fundamental to the scientific method.

While our society must constantly guard against oversimplified or dogmatic descriptions of science in the education process, we must also resist attempts to interfere with the presentation of properly developed scientific principles in establishing guidelines for classroom instruction or in the development of scientific textbooks.

We therefore strongly oppose any requirement for parallel treatment of scientific and nonscientific discussions in science classes. Scientific inquiry and religious beliefs are two distinct elements of the human experience. Attempts to present them in the same context can only lead to misunderstandings of both.

Published as a news release dated 15 December 1981 on letterhead of the American Institute of Physics. The APS describes itself in this release as "the largest professional society of physicists in America, with more than 32,000 members."

An identical statement was passed in 1982 by the American Association of Physics Teachers.

American Psychological Association (1982)

Principles of evolution are an essential part of the knowledge base of psychology. Any attempt to limit or exclude the teaching of evolution from the science curriculum would deprive psychology students of a significant part of their education.

Currently, groups identifying themselves as "creationists" are proposing legislation to require teaching of "creation science" as part of the science curriculum of public schools. The American Psychological Association, without questioning the right of any individual to hold "creationist" beliefs, views "creationism" as a set of religious doctrines that do not conform to criteria of science. Scientific views are empirically testable, continually open to the process of scrutiny and experimentation that are the essence of science.

The American Psychological Association believes that "creationism" does not meet the criteria of science and should not be taught as part of the public school science curriculum. Further, the American Psychological Association is opposed to any attempts to require by statue or other means the inclusion of "creationism" within the science curriculum of the public schools.

Passed by a vote of 100 in favor to 1 opposed at the APA annual meeting, 1982.

American Psychological Association (2007)

APA Council of Representatives Resolution Rejecting Intelligent Design as Scientific and Reaffirming Support for Evolutionary Theory

The science, practice, and application of psychology depend on science education and the culture of evidence and critical thought to which it contributes. Evolutionary theory is one of the most powerful elements of contemporary science. With due diligence in repudiating misappropriations of evolution to justify social injustices, scholars informed by evolutionary theory can unify scientific knowledge and serve public interests in invaluable ways. Proponents of Intelligent Design (ID) present ID theory as a viable alternative scientific explanation for the origins and diversity of life. However, ID has not withstood the scrutiny of scientific peer review of its empirical, conceptual, or epistemological bases and thus is not properly regarded as a scientific theory.

Whereas: Intelligent Design Theory poses a threat to the quality of science education in the United States, and recognizing the urgency pressed upon it by the endorsement of teaching ID alongside evolutionary theory by some political leaders (Baker & Slevin, 2005; Santorum, 2005)

Whereas: Evolutionary theory is a major unifying force in contemporary science; (Gould, 1994; National Science Teachers Association, 2003; Wilson, 1998)

Whereas: The bases of continuity and variation that follow from evolutionary theory inform, explicitly or implicitly, the work of many psychologists with humans and other animals; (Caporael, 2001; Crawford, 1989; Gray, 1996)

Whereas: ID proponents dismiss contemporary evolutionary theory as scientifically invalid; (Discovery Institute, n.d., Wells, 2000/2001)

Whereas: ID proponents promulgate their theory as science in the absence of empirical evidence or, indeed, a means of testing it that passes scientific muster; (Young & Edis, 2004) and

*Whereas:*The teaching of ID as science would seriously undermine both the vitality of psychological science and the science literacy so essential to an informed, responsible citizenry (Gray 1996; Lombrozo, Shtulman & Weisberg, 2006; National Science Teacher's Association, 2003)

Therefore Be It Resolved, that APA applauds the consistent repudiation by federal courts of Creationism, Creation Science, and now ID as a part of science education; *(Edwards v. Aguillard*, 1987; *Kitzmiller et al v. Dover Area School District*, 2005; *McLean v. Arkansas Board of Education*, 1982; *Peloza v. Capstriano Unified School District*, 1994; *Webster v. New Lennox School District*, 1990)

Therefore Be It Further Resolved, that the APA reaffirms earlier relevant resolutions (APA, 1982 & 1990) and joins other leading scholarly organizations including American Association for the Advancement of Science (2002), American Astronomical Society (2005), American Society of Agronomy (2005), Federation of American Societies of Experimental Biology (2005), and National Association of Biology Teachers (2005) in opposing the teaching of Intelligent Design as a scientific theory.

References

American Association for the Advancement of Science (2002) Resolution on intelligent design theory. Retrieved May 9, 2006 from http://www.aaas.org/news/releases/2002/1106id2.shtml

American Astronomical Society (2005) Statement on the teaching of evolution. Retrieved May 9, 2006 from http://www.aas.org/governance/ council/resolutions.html

American Psychological Association. (1982). APA Council of Representatives resolution on creationism. Retrieved May 9, 2006 from http://www.apa.org/about/division/cpmscientific.html

American Psychological Association. (1990). APA Council of Representatives endorsement of American Association for the Advancement of Science resolution on the use of animals in research, testing, and education. Retrieved May 9, 2006 from http://www.apa.org/about/division/cpmscientific.html

American Society of Agronomy (2005). Position statement in support of teaching of evolution (2005) Retrieved May 9, 2006 from http://www.asa-csssa-sssa.org/pdf/intdesign_05815.pdf

Baker, P. & Slevin P. (2005, August 3). Bush remarks on "Intelligent design" theory fuels debate. *The Washington Post*. Retrieved May 10, 2006, from http://www.washingtonpost.com/wp-dyn/content/article/2005/08/02/AR2005080201686_pf.html

Caporael, L. R. (2001). Evolutionary psychology: Toward a unifying theory and a hybrid science. *Annual Reviews of Psychology*, 52, 607-628.

Crawford, C. B. (1989). The theory of evolution: Of what value to psychology? *Journal of Comparative Psychology*, 103(1), 4-22.

Discovery Institute (n.d.) A scientific dissent from Darwinism. Retrieved May 4, 2006 from http://www.dissentfromdarwin.org/

Edwards v. Aguillard, 482 U.S. 578 (1987).

Gray, P. (1996). Incorporating evolutionary theory into the teaching of psychology. *Teaching of Psychology*, 23, 207-214.

Gould, S. (1994). The evolution of life on earth. *Scientific American*, 271, 85-91.

Lombrozo, T., Shtulman, A., Weisberg, M. (2006). The Intelligent Design controversy: Lessons from psychology and education. *Trends in Cognitive Sciences*, 10(2), 56-57.

Kitzmiller et al. v. Dover Area School District. 400 F. Supp. 2d 707 (MD Pa. 2005).

McLean v. Arkansas Board of Education, 529 F. Supp. 1255 (ED Ark. 1982).

National Association of Biology Teachers (2000). Statement on teaching evolution. Retrieved May 9, 2006 from http://www.nabt.org/sub/position_statements/evolution.asp

National Science Teachers Association. (2003). Position statement on the teaching of evolution. Retrieved May 4, 2006 from http://www.nsta.org/159&psid=10

Peloza v. Capistrano Unified School District, 37 F.3d 517 (9th Cir. 1994).

Santorum, R. (2005). Teaching the controversy. Retrieved May 10, 2006 from

Webster v. New Lennox School District #122, 917 F.2d 1003 (7th Cir. 1990).

Wells, J. (2000/2001) Survival of the fakest. *The American Spectator*, Dec 2000/Jan 2001.

Wilson, E. O. (1998). Consilience: *The unity of knowledge*. New York: Knopf.

Young, M., & Edis, T. (Eds.) (2004). *Why intelligent design fails: A scientific critique of the new creationism*. Piscataway, NJ: Rutgers University Press.

Copyright © 2007 by the American Psychological Association.
Reprinted with permission.

American Society of Biological Chemists

Evolutionary theory is concerned with certain past, present, and future biological events. Like other scientific hypotheses, it leads to predictions, many but not all of which are subject to experimental observation and scientific tests. Evolutionary theory is compatible with many, but not all, religious beliefs; by itself it is not, was not meant to be, and should never be presented as a religious belief. Its proper forum is the science classroom.

The term "Creation Science" obscures the profound differences between religious beliefs and scientific theory. The proper education of the nation's youth for citizenship in a technological age demands that the distinction between these two major currents in human affairs be maintained in keeping with the precepts of our Constitution.

25 August 1982. Ballot referendum approved by the ASBC membership by vote of 2624 in favor to 151 opposed. Reported to membership in a memorandum of 30 November 1981 by Charles C. Hancock, Executive Officer.

American Society for Microbiology

Statement on the Scientific Basis for Evolution

Knowledge of the microbial world is essential to understanding the evolution of life on Earth. The characteristics of microorganisms — small size, rapid reproduction, mobility, and facility in exchanging genetic information — allow them to adapt rapidly to environmental influences. In microbiology, the validity of evolutionary principles is supported by [1] readily demonstrated mutation, recombination and selection, which are the fundamental mechanisms of evolution; [2] comparisons based on genomic data that support a common ancestry of life; and [3] observable rates of genetic change and the extent of genomic diversity which indicate that divergence has occurred over a very long scale of geologic time, and testify to the great antiquity of life on Earth. Thus, microorganisms illustrate evolution in action, and microbiologists have been able to make use of the microbes' evolutionary capacity in the development of life-improving and life-saving innovations in medicine, agriculture, and for the environment. By contrast, proposed alternatives to evolution, such as intelligent design and other forms of creationism, are not scientific, in part because they fail to provide a framework for useful, testable predictions.

The use of the supposed "irreducible complexity" of the bacterial flagellum as an argument to endow nonscientific concepts with what appears to be legitimacy, is spurious and not based on fact.

Evolution is not mere conjecture, but a conclusive discovery supported by a coherent body of integrated evidence. Overwhelmingly, the scientific community, regardless of religious belief, accepts evolution as central to an understanding of life and the life sciences. A fundamental aspect of the practice of science is to separate one's personal beliefs from the pursuit of understanding of the natural world. It is important that society and future generations recognize the legitimacy of testable, verified, fact-based learning about the origins and diversity of life.

10/5/2006

American Society of Parasitologists

Society Takes Stand on Creationism and Intelligent Design

The American Society of Parasitologists – a national and international membership organization of 1200 professional scientists – vigorously opposes any state or federal law or any public school board policy that would diminish public education on the principle of evolution, or that would demand comparable funding or treatment of creationism or intelligent design. Some of the society's grounds for this opposition are:

1. Creationism is not a science and cannot become a science

Science is a disciplined method of obtaining naturalistic explanations of the world and universe. God is believed to exist outside the domain of natural law and to transcend its limitations. Creationism inherently rests on belief in this supernatural creator, and no supernatural premise can ever be correctly considered a science.

2. Evolution is not anti-Christian or anti-religious

Science makes no pretense of judging whether or not God exists; science has always acknowledged these questions as being outside the domain of its authority. In their private beliefs, many, perhaps the majority, of scientists who believe the principle of evolution are also Christians, Jews, Moslems, or other theists, and see no contradiction between these beliefs. Many, for example, see evolution as God's mechanism of ongoing creation. Furthermore, the official positions enunciated by American and world leaders of Roman Catholic, Episcopal, Presbyterian, and other churches are that evolution is not a contradiction of Biblical religion. They opine that the Judeo-Christian creation story is "a religious myth system ... neither empirical science nor recorded history, [but] a religious interpretation divinely inspired in a pre-scientific age."

3. Fundamentalist religion is the sole reason for the creationist cause

When the U.S. Supreme Court struck down Arkansas' creationist law in 1968, Justice Fortas ruled that the Arkansas law could not be justified on the grounds of any state policy "other than the religious views of some of its citizens. It is clear that fundamentalist sectarian conviction was and is the law's reason for existence." This is equally true today and the appellation "scientific creationism" cannot disguise that basic intent. See also the ruling of U.S. District Court Judge William R. Overton, in the Arkansas trial on creationism in schools published in Science 215:934-943, 1982), as well as the court decisions regarding the Kitzmiller vs. Dover suit (http://www2.ncseweb.org). Neither science nor public education has any interest in or potential benefit from the passage of such laws, which exist only to benefit a certain denomination of Christians. The 123 year history of creationism clearly shows it to be tied to no other cause but this, and to be overwhelmingly rejected by the majority of Christian denominations and by scientists of all faiths.

4. Creationism infringes on the Unites States Constitution

Because creationism is linked solely with fundamentalist Christianity, all creationist laws infringe on the First Amendment clause prohibiting the establishment of religion, as well as the due process clause of the Fourteenth Amendment which has been judged to imply that no law is constitutional which is too vague or ambiguous to be reasonably obeyed. Creationist bills require instruction in creationism yet prohibit instruction in any religious doctrine. Creationism necessarily implies a supernatural creator, and this is necessarily a religious concept. Creationist laws are therefore unconstitutionally ambiguous or self-contradictory. Instruction in evolution is not unconstitutional despite the claims of creationists that it is so. Evolution has a scientific not a religious basis and is believed by nearly all professional life scientists regardless of their religious beliefs. Evolution does not violate the free exercise clause of the First Amendment, for scientific education in evolution does not prohibit the student from being taught otherwise in the home and church.

5. The business of the science curriculum is only to teach prevailing scientific viewpoints

Any public school science course must cover a large body of knowledge in a short academic term, and is necessarily limited to teaching only those views which are well established and widely accepted by the scientific community. The fact that some scientists reject evolution does not warrant inclusion of their views in lower level science curricula. There are many minority beliefs in science besides creationism that are excluded from consideration or from presentation as valid scientific fact or theory. The scientific community is inherently and traditionally vigorous in its criticism of established beliefs and introduction of new concepts. If the anti-Darwinian views of fundamentalists have any validity as science, they will eventually become widely accepted. If so it will be on their scientific and not their religious merit. Only then will they warrant treatment in the public school curriculum.

6. Creationism is an infringement of academic freedom

Science teachers are already free to mention or discuss creationism in the classroom if they wish, so long as they do not materially compromise the educational objective of the schools to cover the major areas of scientific information. To legislate creationism infringes on the rights of those teachers, students, and parents who believe the curriculum must be religiously neutral and that non-science does not belong in the science class.

7. Evolution is factual and essential to biological education

The word "theory" has different meanings to the scientist and layman. Virtually all scientists accept the evolution of current species from fewer, simpler, ancestral ones as undisputed fact. The "theory" of evolution pertains merely to the mechanisms by which this occurs, and the much-touted arguments among scientists about evolution are over details of these mechanisms, not about the factuality of evolution itself. To call evolution a theory implies no more doubt about its factuality than referring to atomic theory or the theory of gravitation means we doubt the existence of atoms or gravity. To excise evolution from the biology curriculum would reduce biology courses to a series of disconnected facts and severely inhibit those aspects of the discipline which contribute to creative scholarship.

*The above statement is a composite of drafts by Walter M. Kemp
and Kenneth S. Saladin, adopted by the ASP Council
and first published in the ASP Newsletter 4(1):68 in March 1982.
This version has been updated (2006) and edited by several ASP members.*

American Sociological Association

Statement of the American Sociological Association on Creationism and Related Religious Doctrines in U.S. Science Education

The American Sociological Association (ASA) supports the teaching of science methods and content in U.S. public school curricula, and affirms the integrity of science education to include the teaching of evolution, a central organizing principle of the biological sciences that is based upon overwhelming empirical evidence from various scientific disciplines. ASA opposes proposals that promote, support, or advocate religious doctrines or ideologies in science education curricula. Religious doctrines and ideology include, but are not limited to, the non-scientific notion of "creationism," including "intelligent design." In two decades of careful peer-reviewed research, sociologists such as Francis B. Harrold and Raymond A. Eve have documented the relationships among popular cult beliefs, pseudoscientific ideas, and creationism. Creationism, in all its forms, has also been recognized as a religious doctrine by the U.S. federal courts.

ASA respects the right of people to hold diverse religious beliefs, including those that reject evolution and related principles of science, as a matter of faith. Such beliefs, however, should not be promulgated by science educators in the classroom because it would be a disservice to students to present such views as having a basis in science. The United States Constitution articulates the principle of separation of church and state as a means to prevent the government (including public schools) from advocating or imposing specific religious beliefs on our citizens.

Science is an objectively accountable endeavor. It requires systematic, empirical measurements that are intended to be replicated in order to rigorously test the accuracy of observations, concepts, hypotheses, and theories and to encourage further exploration and refinement. The goal of scientists is to determine whether propositions are empirically verifiable using transparent, objective methods of measurement. When scientifically proposed and testable ideas are found not to coincide with objective measures, they are rejected as scientifically unsuitable to explain observations. Creationism includes claims that are empirically un-testable and, therefore, not subjects for examination in the study of the natural and biological sciences.

By contrast, biological evolution is a scientifically developed and well-established principle supported by accumulated scientific knowledge in many fields. Efforts to qualify, limit, or exclude the teaching of biological evolution in U.S. public science curricula would adversely affect national science literacy, academic achievement, and technological and scientific advancement. Such efforts would deprive U.S. public school students of their right to genuine and coherent science education, which they need in a world where science and technology are socially and economically vital areas of knowledge. Similarly, constraints on science curricula addressing theories of the evolution of the universe, the evolution of stars and galaxies, plate tectonics, and the biological development of life would also be detrimental to education and advances in U.S. scientific achievement and literacy.

Creationism, as a social movement and pseudoscientific cognitive process, is a legitimate topic for scientific examination (e.g., exploring social factors that influence social movements or documenting the social and behavioral correlates of cult beliefs). There are suitable curricular venues for teaching about these topics (e.g., contemporary social issues, sociology of religion, other behavioral science courses).

Natural and biological science curricula, however, are not the appropriate place.

There are recognized authorities and respected educational standards and frameworks for teaching natural and biological science content. These standards are provided by organizations such as the National Academies of Science, National Science Teachers Association, and National Association of Biology Teachers.

October 18, 2006

Association of Southeastern Biologists

Regarding the Teaching of Evolution in the Classroom

The Association of Southeastern Biologists is a regional association devoted to the promulgation of biology in all its myriad forms to scientists, students, and the general public. As part of its duties, the Association represents biological scientists from throughout the southeastern region of the United States on various issues of concern. This statement contains the Association's recommendations concerning the teaching of evolution in the classroom.

Evolution is the only currently acceptable scientific theory for the development of life on earth, and is supported by an enormous body of evidence from a wide variety of disciplines, including, but not limited to, biology, chemistry, geology, and physics. Across all of these scientific disciplines, the data are in congruence with regards to the theory of evolution, and there are no data that contradict the fundamental truth of evolution. Such consilience gives credence and support to the concept that all life is related and that it has evolved over time primarily through the process of natural selection. The Association believes that the study of evolution is crucial if students are to gain a proper understanding of life on earth.

In recent years, the public schools have been pressured to teach "alternative" theories to evolution, most notably, creationism and intelligent design. However, both creationism and intelligent design are based in faith and do not follow acceptable scientific principles. Both movements are rooted in preconceived notions about the development of life and its origins, yet fail to present any credible scientific evidence to support those claims. In contrast, the evidence in support for evolution is being added to on a daily basis, and is now so overwhelmingly strong that we can state with certainty that evolution occurs.

Because creationism and intelligent design do not operate within the definitional limits of science, they cannot and should not be treated as such. Neither movement can satisfy the aims of science, which are to make observations and develop questions to explain natural phenomena, to design tests of those hypotheses, and then to either accept or reject those hypotheses, based on a fair and objective evaluation of the evidence accumulated. Creationism and intelligent design offer a mixture of empirically untestable and empirically non-scientific hypotheses, which their proponents fail to retract or modify in the light of contrary evidence. Thus, they do not conform to accepted scientific protocols.

Therefore, since neither creationism nor intelligent design is a scientific endeavor, we oppose any attempts to insert them into the science curricula of any public schools. While religion has played and continues to play a significant role in many people's lives, and in schools' curricula, we object to any attempts to insert religious dogma, such as creationism or intelligent design, into science classes.

Furthermore, we strongly oppose attempts to undermine or compromise the teaching of evolution, whether by eliminating the word 'evolution' from state science standards, requiring textbook disclaimers that misleadingly describe evolution as

Voices for Evolution

"merely" a theory, or by encouraging scientifically unwarranted criticism of evolution under the guise of "analysis," "objectivity," "balance," or "teaching the controversy." Such tactics are clearly intended to leave the false impression that evolution is scientifically precarious and will thus deprive students of a sound scientific education.

In conclusion, the Association of Southeastern Biologists strongly opposes the teaching of any alternative non-scientific theories to evolution that are not based on established scientific concepts, endorses the meaningful teaching of evolution in science classrooms, and opposes any attempts to water down the teaching of evolution by singling out the subject for special treatment not given any other sciences.

April 16, 2004

Association for Women Geoscientists

Policy Paper on Science Curricula and the Teaching of Evolution in K-12 Classrooms

The Association for Women Geoscientists supports the teaching of evolution in the science curriculum and urges the separation of science from religious teaching in public school's science curricula. We believe that all students should be taught the method and principles of modern science, including the method of hypothesis testing by observation, data collection, experimentation, and the difference between scientific theory and hypothesis. Any hypothesis that is not subject to testing, or does not arise from observation and repeatable data, cannot be considered science.

To do otherwise puts students at a disadvantage in understanding and appreciating the wonder of our Earth, as well as in their pursuit of higher education and careers in science.

Passed by the AWG Board of Directors on April 25th, 1998.

Australian Academy of Science

Statement on Creationism

One of the fiercest moral debates witnessed in Europe in the second half of the 19th century was raised by the theory of the evolution of species set out by Charles Darwin in his *Origin of Species.* The theory challenged most established views on the place of humans in the cosmos, on three fundamental points:

- It suggested that *Homo sapiens,* in common with all extant species, arose not by special creation but by evolutionary development from simpler forms of life.

- It suggested that evolution was not guided by some divinity or purpose, but by rules which govern the inheritance of physical characteristics. These rules were not seen as having any moral content, and the theory of evolution did not therefore acknowledge a moral component to the pattern of life.

- The theory of evolution therefore questioned whether *Homo sapiens* holds a supreme place in nature.

In western countries, the debate persisted longest in the United States of America where the theory of evolution clashed with widely held fundamentalist religious views, and in many centres within the US the value of the theory has never been acknowledged. The explanatory power of the theory of evolution has been recognised, however, by all biologists, and their work has expanded and developed it. In Australia, as in all western countries, the theory of evolution has for many years been taught as the most powerful theory available of the origins of the diversity of biology.

Over the last 10-20 years, the fundamentalist rejection of the theory has gained momentum in the United States, and the same thrust has been evident in parts of Australia. The anti-evolution thrust argues two major points:

- that the theory of evolution is flawed; and

- that a sense of balance in the teaching of the scientific basis of life requires that equal consideration be given to the creationist view, that sees the origin of the diversity of life in the specific intention of the Deity.

The following points summarise the view of the Australian Academy of Science on this issue:

- All scientific ideas are theories, imperfect and subject to test. That the theory of evolution is imperfect, and still the subject of study and modification, affirms that the theory is part of science. Many attempts to modify and expand the theory have been successful, showing (since Darwin's day) the gene-basis of inheritance, the basis of gene-reproduction in the double helix structure of DNA, the 'genetic drift' basis of the origin of breeds, and so on. Many challenges to the fundamentals of the theory have failed empirical test. The theory has attracted enormous empirical testing and remains one of the most powerful of scientific ideas.

- The creationist account of the origin of life has been and remains an important idea in human culture. However it is not a *scientific* idea. That is, it is not open to empirical test. It is an article of religious faith.

- The creationist account of the origin of life is not therefore appropriate to a course in the science of biology, and the claim that it is a viable scientific explanation of the diversity of life does not warrant support.

- The Academy sees no objection to the teaching of creationism in schools as part of a course in dogmatic or comparative religion, or in some other non-scientific context. There are no grounds, however, for requiring that creationism be taught as part of a science course.

Biophysical Society

Statement Opposing the Teaching of Alternatives to Evolution in K-12 Science Classrooms

The Biophysical Society is deeply troubled by attempts in the United States to suppress the teaching of evolution in K-12 public schools, or to temper the teaching with disclaimers, or to present evolution as only one of several alternative theories about the origin of human life on earth.

As biophysicists, we are engaged in studying the structure and function of living organisms at a molecular level. Such studies have demonstrated that all life forms on earth obey the laws of chemistry and physics, and that these life forms are built from molecules that show common origins. The hypothesis that binds all these studies, built upon an immense body of evidence accumulated from geology, paleontology, biochemistry and molecular biology, is the theory of evolution. The main mechanism for evolutionary change is genetic variation. Scientists have demonstrated how at the molecular level, imperfections in DNA replication and damage to DNA caused by sunlight and radiation can contribute to genetic variability. One need only look at the progression of influenza to see evolution in action today.

In contrast to the scientific picture of evolution that has emerged from field observations and laboratories, there are some today who argue that alternative views, such as Biblical Creationism or Intelligent Design, should be taught instead of evolution, or alongside evolution in K-12 science classrooms. What distinguishes scientific theories from these theological beliefs is the scientific method, which is driven by observations and deductions, leads to testable predictions, and involves the formulation of hypotheses that can be refuted. This process results in a body of facts that have been repeatedly confirmed by experiments, which in turn result in a theory. Scientific theories are therefore not "guesses," but fact-supported, self-consistent, reliable accounts of the world. The alternative theological explanations for origins are not based on the scientific method, and are, therefore, not in the realm of science. They are in the realm of faith.

The Biophysical Society is strongly opposed to any effort to blur the distinction between science and theology by teaching or presenting non-scientific beliefs in science classrooms. Accepting the evidence that evolution has and continues to take place does not preclude one from believing in theologies, but those beliefs have no place in a science curriculum. Attempts to suppress or compromise the teaching of evolutionary science in the United States are misguided actions that will deprive our youth of a clear understanding of the scientific process, and of the scientific skills that they need to compete in a global economy: one that is increasingly driven by science and technology. Moreover, current efforts to disguise theology as science do a severe disservice to the scientific profession and to the people of the United States.

Adopted by the Biophysical Society Executive Board on November 5, 2005

The Biophysical Society, founded in 1956, is a professional, scientific society established to encourage development and dissemination of knowledge in biophysics. The Society promotes growth in this expanding field through its annual meeting, monthly journal, and committee and outreach activities. Its nearly 8,000 members are located throughout the U.S. and the world, where they teach and conduct research in colleges, universities, laboratories, government agencies, and industry.

Botanical Society of America

Statement on Evolution

The Botanical Society of America has as its members professional scientists, scholars, and educators from across the United States and Canada, and from over 50 other countries. Most of us call ourselves botanists, plant biologists, or plant scientists, and members of our profession teach and learn about botanical organisms using well established principles and practices of science.

Evolution represents one of the broadest, most inclusive theories used in pursuit of and in teaching this knowledge, but it is by no means the only theory involved. Scientific theories are used in two ways: to explain what we know, and to pursue new knowledge. Evolution explains observations of shared characteristics (the result of common ancestry and descent with modification) and adaptations (the result of natural selection acting to maximize reproductive success), as well as explaining pollen:ovule ratios, weeds, deceptive pollination strategies, differences in sexual expression, dioecy, and a myriad of other biological phenomena. Far from being merely a speculative notion, as implied when someone says, "evolution is just a theory," the core concepts of evolution are well documented and well confirmed. Natural selection has been repeatedly demonstrated in both field and laboratory, and descent with modification is so well documented that scientists are justified in saying that evolution is true.

Some people contend that creationism and its surrogate, "intelligent design," offers an alternative explanation: that organisms are well adapted and have common characteristics because they were created just so, and they exhibit the hallmarks of intelligent design. As such, creationism is an all inclusive explanation for every biological phenomenon. So why do we support and teach evolution and not creationism/ "intelligent design" if both explain the same phenomena? Are botanists just dogmatic, atheistic materialists, as some critics of science imply? Hardly, although scientists are routinely portrayed by creationists as dogmatic. We are asked, "Why, in all fairness, don't we teach both explanations and let students decide?"

The fairness argument implies that creationism is a scientifically valid alternative to evolution, and that is not true. Science is not about fairness, and all explanations are not equal. Some scientific explanations are highly speculative with little in the way of supporting evidence, and they will stand or fall based upon rigorous testing. The history of science is littered with discarded explanations, but they weren't discarded because of public opinion or general popularity; each one earned that distinction by being scientifically falsified. Scientists may jump on a "band wagon" for some new explanation, particularly if it has tremendous explanatory power, something that makes sense out of previously unexplained phenomena. But for an explanation to become a mainstream component of a theory, it must be tested and found useful in doing science.

To make progress, to learn more about botanical organisms, hypotheses, the subcomponents of theories, are tested by attempting to falsify logically derived predictions. This is why scientists use and teach evolution; evolution offers testable explanations of observed biological phenomena. Evolution continues to be of paramount usefulness, and so, based on simple pragmatism, scientists use this theory to improve our understanding of the biology of organisms. Over and over again, evolutionary theory has generated predictions that have proven to be true. Any hypothesis that doesn't prove true is discarded in favor of a new one, and so the component hypotheses of evolutionary theory change as knowledge and understanding grow. Phylogenetic hypotheses, patterns of ancestral relatedness, based on one set of data, for example, base sequences in DNA, are generated, and when the results make logical sense out of formerly disparate observations, confidence in the truth of the hypothesis increases. The theory of evolution so permeates botany that frequently it is not mentioned explicitly, but the overwhelming majority of published studies are based upon evolutionary hypotheses, each of which constitutes a test of an hypothesis. Evolution has been very successful as a scientific explanation because it has been useful in advancing our understanding of organisms and applying that knowledge to the solution of many human problems, e.g., host-pathogen interactions, origin of crop plants, herbicide resistance, disease susceptibility of crops, and invasive plants.

For example, plant biologists have long been interested in the origins of crop plants. Wheat is an ancient crop of the Middle East. Three species exist both as wild and domesticated wheats, einkorn, emmer, and breadwheat. Archeological studies have demonstrated that einkorn is the most ancient and breadwheat appeared most recently. To plant biologists this suggested that somehow einkorn gave rise to emmer, and emmer gave rise to breadwheat (an hypothesis). Further evidence was obtained from chromosome numbers that showed einkorn with 14, emmer with 28, and breadwheat with 42. Further, the chromosomes in einkorn consisted of two sets of 7 chromosomes, designated AA. Emmer had 14 chromosomes similar in shape and size, but 14 more, so they were designated AABB. Breadwheat had chromosomes similar to emmer, but 14 more, so they were designated AABBCC. To plant biologists familiar with mechanisms of speciation, these data, the chromosome numbers and sets, suggested that the emmer and breadwheat species arose via hybridization and polyploidy (an hypothesis). The Middle Eastern flora was studied to find native grasses with a chromosome number of 14, and several goatgrasses were discovered that could be the predicted parents, the sources of the BB and CC chromosomes. To test these hypotheses, plant biologists crossed einkorn and emmer wheats with goatgrasses, which produced sterile hybrids. These were treated to produce a spontaneous doubling of the chromosome number, and as predicted, the correct crosses artificially produced both the emmer and breadwheat species. No one saw the evolution of these wheat species, but logical predictions about what happened were tested by recreating likely circumstances. Grasses are wind-pollinated, so cross-pollination between wild and cultivated grasses happens all the time. Frosts and other natural events are known to cause a doubling of chromosomes. And the hypothesized sequence of speciation matches their observed appearance in the archeological record. Farmers would notice and keep new wheats, and the chromosome doubling and hybrid vigor made both emmer and breadwheat larger, more vigorous wheats. Lastly, a genetic change in breadwheat from the wild goatgrass chromosomes allowed for the chaff to be removed from the grain without heating, so glutin was not denatured, and a sourdough (yeast infected) culture of the sticky breadwheat flour would inflate (rise) from the trapped carbon dioxide.

The actual work was done by many plant biologists over many years, little by little, gathering data and testing ideas, until these evolutionary events were understood as generally described above. The hypothesized speciation events were actually recreated, an accomplishment that allows plant biologists to breed new varieties of emmer and breadwheats, and in one instance, create a new cereal grain species, Triticale, by hybridizing wheat and rye and generating a polyploid offspring.

What would the creationist paradigm have done? No telling. Perhaps nothing, because observing three wheat species specially created to feed humans would not have generated any questions that needed answering. No predictions are made, so there is no reason or direction for seeking further knowledge. This demonstrates the scientific uselessness of creationism. While creationism explains everything, it offers no understanding beyond, 'that's the way it was created.' No testable predictions can be derived from the creationist explanation. Creationism has not made a single contribution to agriculture, medicine, conservation, forestry, pathology, or any other applied area of biology. Creationism has yielded no classifications, no biogeographies, no underlying mechanisms, no unifying concepts with which to study organisms or life. In those few instances where predictions can be inferred from Biblical passages (e.g., groups of related organisms, migration of all animals from the resting place of the ark on Mt. Ararat to their present locations, genetic diversity derived from small founder populations, dispersal ability of organisms in direct proportion to their distance from eastern Turkey), creationism has been scientifically falsified.

Is it fair or good science education to teach about an unsuccessful, scientifically useless explanation just because it pleases people with a particular religious belief? Is it unfair to ignore scientifically useless explanations, particularly if they have played no role in the development of modern scientific concepts? Science education is about teaching valid concepts and those that led to the development of new explanations, e.g., inheritance of acquired characters.

Creationism is the modern manifestation of a long-standing conflict between science and religion in Western Civilization. Prior to science, and in all non-scientific cultures, myths were the only viable explanations for a myriad of natural phenomena, and these myths became incorporated into diverse religious beliefs. Following the rise and spread of science, where ideas are tested against nature rather than being decided by religious authority and sacred texts, many phenomena previously attributed to the supernatural (disease, genetic defects, lightening, blights and plagues, epilepsy, eclipses, comets, mental illness, etc.) became known to have natural causes and explanations. Recognizing this, the Catholic Church finally admitted, after 451 years, that Galileo was correct; the Earth was not the unmoving center of the Universe. Mental illness, birth defects, and disease are no longer considered the mark of evil or of God's displeasure or punishment. Epileptics and people intoxicated by ergot-infected rye are no longer burned at the stake as witches. As natural causes were discovered and understood, religious authorities were forced to alter long-held positions in the face of growing scientific knowledge. This does not mean science has disproven the existence of the supernatural. The methodology of science only deals with the material world.

Science as a way of knowing has been extremely successful, although people may not like all the changes science and its handmaiden, technology, have wrought. But people who oppose evolution, and seek to have creationism or intelligent design included in science curricula, seek to dismiss and change the most successful way of knowing ever discovered. They wish to substitute opinion and belief for evidence and testing. The proponents of creationism/intelligent design promote scientific ignorance in the guise of learning. As professional scientists and educators, we strongly assert that such efforts are both misguided and flawed, presenting an incorrect view of science, its understandings, and its processes.

Authored by: J. E. Armstrong and J. Jernstedt, officers of the BSA
Approved by the BSA Council: July 27, 2003

California Academy of Sciences

A Statement Affirming the Central Role of Scientific Principles in the Teaching of Evolutionary Biology

Evolutionary biology, like every other natural science, is a powerful expression of human curiosity and intellect. With techniques for reconstructing the history of life on Earth, Homo sapiens has become uniquely capable of knowing about its own past as well as that of other organisms on this planet. Discoveries in phylogenetics, paleontology, genetics, and developmental and molecular biology give us the capacity to test our theories and to develop new ones, using a vast store of empirical data and increasingly sophisticated methods. Continued opportunity to perform such tests has resulted in further support for descent with modification, justifying the fundamental role that evolution plays in our understanding of humanity's place in nature. It provides a rational basis for dealing with such problems as preserving the quality of our environment, and enhancing the quality of our lives.

Now, more than ever, is a time when intellectual standards need to be upheld. For example, it is crucial that we clearly distinguish between such legitimate natural sciences as astronomy and such pseudosciences as astrology. There is a fundamental difference between testing hypotheses so as to reject some in favor of alternatives, and rationalization in terms of a dogmatic belief system.

The natural sciences have a long history of weeding out notions inherited from pre-scientific culture, often in the face of determined resistance. Repeatedly, old arguments, long since refuted, have been refurbished and presented to new audiences that are ill-equipped to evaluate them. Lately, creationist pseudoscience has been attempting to insinuate itself into the curriculum under the rubric of "intelligent design." Prior to the fundamental contribution of Darwin in 1859, there seemed to be no way to explain the remarkable adaptations of organisms except in terms of a miracle. With the discovery and recognition of natural selection, this argument was shown to depend upon a pre-Darwinian failure of the human imagination to find testable, scientific explanations for the origin and diversity of life. The appropriate place in the science curriculum for the notion that organisms have been designed is the same as that for the notion that the earth is located at the center of the universe.

Science and religion are concerned with different aspects of human life and are evaluated according to fundamentally different criteria. Failing to make this distinction gives the false impression that we are limited to two alternatives when faced with an apparent contradiction.

Insofar as belief in special creation is a part of many religions, it needs to be understood in the context of the comparative and historical study of culture. Religion has played and continues to play an important role in human life, and our citizens need to be well informed about it. In recognizing the rich cultural diversity of beliefs and practices both past and present, schools should teach about all religions, provided that this is done in a fair and objective manner, without proselytizing. All this can be accomplished without compromising the central role that scientific principles must take in the teaching of evolutionary biology.

Adopted unanimously by Curator's Forum, November 16, 1994
Passed by Science Council, November 30, 1994

Committee for the Anthropology of Science, Technology, and Computing

Public Statement on Teaching Evolution in Public Schools

As anthropologists studying science and its cultural contexts, the scholarly work of CASTAC members has often provided analyses of scientific authority in both professional and public life. Recently public schools teaching the theory of evolution have found their curricula challenged by groups who dispute evolution's scientific status, and thus attempt to censor or diminish its place in science education. From the viewpoint of our profession, all scientific theories are products of criticism, re-evaluation and revision by scientific communities. The theory of evolution is not uniquely subject to this critical process. The evidence supporting the theory of evolution is just as strong as the evidence for the existence of sub-atomic particles, the structure of the solar system, or the function of the immune system.

CASTAC encourages public education about the social dynamics of science, including scientific controversies. Many of these controversies have a legitimate role in the science education classroom: global warming, pesticide damage, genetic manipulation, and so on. All of the legitimate controversies concern testable knowledge of natural phenomena (that is, the physical and biological systems of nature as well as technology and culture). "Intelligent Design" (and ideas like it) do not contribute to legitimate scientific controversies: they fail to meet scientific standards since they posit causes that are outside the realm of natural phenomena, and attempt to substitute scientific effort and debate with asserted belief systems for which there can be no test or empirical debate. CASTAC supports the right of public school teachers to convey the scientific community's knowledge in all fields, including that of evolution, without censorship or qualification.

2005

Committee for Scientific Investigation of Claims of the Paranormal

Position Statement on the Teaching of Evolution and the "Scientific" Creationist Challenge

Evolution is the organizing principle of modern biology and is as well established in science as are the principle of gravity and the fact that the earth orbits the sun. Contemporary scientists around the world agree, whatever their national, religious, or cultural affiliations.

Although scientists disagree about such things as the rates, dates, and mechanisms of evolution, virtually no active scientist challenges the fact that evolution has occurred. Furthermore, the fact that scientists debate aspects of evolution is a strong sign that evolution is a healthy science that has not lain dormant in the century since Darwin's death.

The anti-evolutionist "scientific" creationists promote a social and political movement, not a scientific one. They are attempting to impose a sectarian religious view, the literal interpretation of Genesis, upon the public schools. But this is not all: they are claiming to be able to scientifically demonstrate that the world was created suddenly, all at once, a relatively short time ago. Competent scientists, including many Fellows and Scientific Consultants of CSICOP, who have examined the claims of "scientific" creationism, have found them baseless. There is no scientific evidence supporting the instantaneous creation of the earth and all the creatures on it but there is much evidence from many scientific fields that the universe has changed extensively through time.

The gains of the "scientific" creationists have been made through political pressure rather than through the scientific acceptability of their ideas. Science and science literacy suffer greatly when science is subordinated to political pressure. For scientific literacy to increase among Americans, science rather than pseudoscience must be taught to children.

CSICOP urges the public and the mass media to recognize "scientific" creationism as a narrow, religiously based lobby, not a science, and to seek out expert opinion outside the creationist camp when confronted by creationist pseudoscientific claims.

1994

Ecological Society of America

The Ecological Society of America notes with serious concern the Kansas State Board of Education ruling and similar efforts in other states regarding the teaching of evolution and the teaching of religion in science classes. Efforts to weaken the quality of science education should be resisted. Science education is more important than ever before as we prepare students for our increasingly complex world of environmental challenges and technological advances.

ESA Resolution on Science of Evolution

Evolution is a widely accepted scientific theory that all living things have shared ancestors from which they have diverged. It is one of the most fundamental building blocks in science, touching nearly every other discipline including those that directly effect humans, such as medicine and agriculture. Evolutionary science allows us to determine not only how and why living things have become the way they are today, but also what processes are currently acting to change them. Thus, evolutionary biology is vital to our enhanced awareness and prediction of the future of life on earth. Understanding why and how some species change when faced with new challenges is critical to the sustainability of ecosystems upon which humans rely.

Science teaching must include evolutionary biology, which is the core of our understanding of life on Earth. Scientific disciplines such as biology, ecology, and geology cannot be taught with scientific integrity if evolution is not included. The National Science Education Standards recognize the importance of evolution in teaching students to understand the natural world.

Religion-based teachings are not scientific theory. The scientific theory of evolutionary biology has been repeatedly tested and validated. While scientists may debate the mechanisms that drive evolution, they agree that the empirical evidence for it is undeniable. Science has been greatly successful at explaining natural processes, leading to a better understanding of the universe and enormous benefits to society. Science classes should focus on science and not religion.

Adopted by the ESA Governing Board
November 1999

Federation of American Societies for Experimental Biology

FASEB Opposes Using Science Classes to Teach Intelligent Design, Creationism, and other Non-Scientific Beliefs

Representing 22 professional societies and 84,000 scientists in disciplines that range from single molecules to public health, the Federation of American Societies for Experimental Biology (FASEB) affirms that instruction in science is an essential component of education. Science education has become increasingly important in driving innovation and discovery, and in enabling citizens to make informed decisions and to compete in the 21st century workplace. For these reasons, it is critical to preserve the integrity of science education by opposing the mandatory teaching in science classes of creationism, intelligent design, and other concepts not based on sound scientific principles.

Proponents for non-scientific accounts of the development of life, including creationism and intelligent design, contend that evolution alone should not be taught in science classes. Arguing that evolution is "just a theory," rather than a fact, they insist that intelligent design should be offered as an alternative to evolution or given "equal time", and that schools should "teach the controversy" surrounding evolutionary theory.

FASEB does not support these views. We also affirm that these positions seriously undermine science education.

In science, a theory is a coherent explanation of natural phenomena based on direct observation or experimentation. Theories are logical, predictive, and testable. They are open to criticism and when shown to be false, they are modified or dismissed. Using this definition, evolution is categorized with other scientific theories such as gravity or atomic theory, which, like evolution, are universally accepted among scientists.

Evolution is among the most thoroughly tested theories in the biological sciences.

It is supported by volumes of scientific evidence in numerous fields, including genetics, biochemistry, developmental biology, comparative anatomy, immunology, geology, and paleontology. Moreover, evolution lays the foundation for much of what we know about genetics, immunology, antibiotic resistance, human origins, and the adaptation of species to a changing environment. Removing evolution from the classroom, or misrepresenting evolution as a flawed theory, deprives students of one of the most important tenets of science and the basis of our understanding of biology and medicine, including pandemic influenza and AIDS.

In contrast to evolution, intelligent design and creationism are not science because they fail to meet the essential and necessary requirements: they are not based on direct observation or experimentation nor do they generate testable predictions. Therefore, offering these beliefs as alternatives to evolution or giving them equal time in science classes completely misrepresents the nature of science.

Before information is presented as fact in science textbooks, it is tested, evaluated by experts, published in scientific journals, and considered credible by the broader scientific community. Even alternative ideas should have an evidentiary basis and garner at least limited support by scientists before they are incorporated into textbooks. Allowing intelligent design and creationism to circumvent this rigorous process of scientific scrutiny paves the way for other, poorly studied, pseudoscientific ideas to enter science curricula.

Proposals that call for "teaching the controversy" or singling out evolution for criticism are equally objectionable. While there may be some disagreement about the details of evolution, it is not a controversial theory among scientists. Rather, there is overwhelming scientific consensus that evolution is a valid explanation for the development of species. Although students should be encouraged to think critically about all ideas, introducing false controversy into science classes will ultimately impair science education.

FASEB considers evolution a critical topic in science education and strongly supports the teaching of evolution.

FASEB opposes mandating the introduction of creationism, intelligent design, and other non-scientific concepts into the curricula of science.

FASEB opposes introducing false controversies regarding evolution or other accepted scientific theories into the curricula of science.

FASEB calls upon the scientific community and American citizens to defend science education by opposing initiatives to teach intelligent design, creationism, and other non-scientific beliefs in science class.

Adopted by the FASEB Board of Directors on December 19, 2005

Genetics Society of America

The GSA supports educating students in genetics, and consequently feels it important to express its views on the teaching of evolution in elementary and secondary schools. The GSA strongly endorses such teaching, as genetics and evolution are two very closely interwoven disciplines. In fact, evolution might be summarized as population genetics over time.

Some people have been opposed to the teaching of evolution because "it is only a theory." Such opposition rests on a mistaken understanding of what defines a scientific theory.

Science operates first by observation, and then by developing a hypothesis as a preliminary explanation of the data. A theory is a hypothesis that has been subsequently confirmed by abundant, consistent data obtained from tests of the hypothesis. The theory of evolution by natural selection is exactly such a confirmed hypothesis, as developed through the ongoing investigation and understanding of many different areas of biological, chemical, physical and earth science. As such, it is modifiable and constantly refined as new research and information come to light. Without evolutionary theory, we would be forced to completely discard much of what we understand about fields such as genetics, botany, zoology, paleontology, and anthropology.

"Scientific creationism," "intelligent design," and other terms have been offered as alternate explanations for past and present biological processes. However, these represent a collection of beliefs based on a literal interpretation of religious texts, and are thus disguises for religious doctrine, and not scientific theories. They ignore the empirical data around us and fail to provide a testable hypothesis. Consequently, since no testable explanation for biological history has been provided, they cannot be considered scientific theories, and should not be part of school curricula.

As evolution is the only scientific theory to explain the biological history of life and as the GSA supports the education of students in genetics, the GSA hereby endorses the teaching of the facts and theory of evolution at all levels, including in elementary and secondary schools.

Based on a statement by Jeffrey M. Otto, Ph.D. Section of Biochemistry and Molecular Biology, Departments of Biochemistry and Orthopedic Surgery, Rush University at Rush-Presbyterian-St. Luke's Medical Center, Chicago, IL 60612

Geological Society of America (1983)

The Geological Society of America believes in the importance of using scientific documentation and reasoning. Biological evolution is a particularly impressive example of a principle derived in this way; we geologists find incontrovertible evidence in the rocks that life has existed here on Earth for several billions of years and that it has evolved through time. Although scientists debate the mechanism that produced this change, the evidence for the change itself is undeniable.

The ideas of "creationism," on the other hand, lack any similar body of supporting evidence. We oppose including creationism in science courses in public schools on the grounds that its conclusions were not obtained using scientific methods. Creationism weakens the emphasis on scientific reasoning that is essential to the continued advancement of scientific knowledge.

Drafted by GSA Councilors Rosemary J. Vidale, Maria Luisa B. Crawford, and Peter J. Wyllie, and adopted by the Council at its May 1983 meeting. Published in GSA News and Information, November 1983, p. 177.

Geological Society of America (2001)

Evolution

Contributors: Steven M. Stanley – Chair
Patricia Kelley
Richard Bambach
George Fisher
James Skehan
Don Wise
David Dunn

The Geological Society of America recognizes that the evolution of life stands as one of the central concepts of modern science. Research in numerous fields of science during the past two centuries has produced an increasingly detailed picture of how life has evolved on Earth.

The rock record is a treasure trove of fossils, and by 1841, eighteen years before Charles Darwin's published On the Origin of Species, geologists had not only assembled much of the geologic time scale from physical relationships among bodies of rock, but they had also recognized that fossils document profound changes in life throughout Earth's history. Darwin showed that biological evolution provides an explanation for these changes. Since the time of Darwin, geologists have continued to uncover details of life's history, and biologists have continued to elucidate the process of evolution. Thus, our understanding of life's evolution has expanded through diverse kinds of research, much of it in fields unknown to Darwin such as genetics, biochemistry, and micropaleontology. In short, the concept of organic evolution has not only withstood the test of time – the ultimate test of any scientific construct – but it has been greatly enriched.

In recent years, certain individuals motivated by religious views have mounted an attack on evolution. This group favors what it calls "creation science", which is not really science at all because it invokes supernatural phenomena. Science, in contrast, is based on observations of the natural world. All beliefs that entail supernatural creation, including the idea known as intelligent design, fall within the domain of religion rather than science. For this reason, they must be excluded from science courses in our public schools.

This separation of domains does not mean that science and religion are fundamentally incompatible. Many scientists who conduct research on the evolution of life are religious, and many major religions formally accept the importance of biological evolution.

Misinterpreting the Bible's creation narratives as scientific statements, many creationists go so far as to attack the validity of geologic time – time that extends back billions of years. "Deep time" is the foundation of modern geology. It was actually well established, though not quantified, by geologists decades before Darwin published his ideas or most scientists came to accept evolution as the explanation for the history of life. Furthermore, thousands of geologists employing many new modes of research refined the geologic time scale during the Twentieth Century. Near the start of that century, the discovery of naturally occurring radioactive substances provided clocks for measuring actual ages for segments of the geologic record. Today, some billion-year-old rocks can be dated with a precision of less than a tenth of one percent. Moreover, modern geologists can identify particular environments where sediments that are now rocks accumulated hundreds of millions of years ago: margins of ancient oceans where tides rose and fell, for example, and valley floors across which rivers meandered back and forth, and ancient reefs that grew to thicknesses of hundreds of meters but were built by organisms that could not have grown faster than a few millimeters a year. By studying the fossil record that forms part of this rich archive of Earth's history, paleontologists continue to uncover details of the long and complex history of life.

Acceptance of deep time is not confined to academic science. If commercial geologists could find more fossil fuel by interpreting the rock record as having resulted from a single flood or otherwise encompassing no more than a few thousand years, they would surely accept this unconventional view, but they do not. In fact, these profit-oriented geologists have joined with academic researchers in refining the standard geologic time scale and bringing to light the details of deep earth history.

Modern studies of the evolution of Earth and its life are not only aiding us in the search for natural resources, but also helping us to understand how the Earth-life system functions. Annual layers of ice in the Greenland glacier, for example, range back more than a hundred thousand years. These ice records warn that Earth's climate may change with devastating speed in the future. The geologic record also reveals how various forms of life have responded to past environmental change, sometimes migrating, sometimes evolving, and sometimes becoming extinct. In the present world, bacteria are now evolving rapidly in ways that render antibiotics ineffective; to respond to bacterial evolution, we must understand evolution in general.

The immensity of geologic time and the evolutionary origin of species are concepts that pervade modern geology and biology. These concepts must therefore be central themes of science courses in public schools; creationist ideas have no place in these courses because they are based on religion rather than science. Without knowledge of deep time and the evolution of life, students will not understand where they and their world have come from, and they will lack valuable insight for making decisions about the future of their species and its environment.

May 2001

Geological Society of Australia

Science Education & Creationism

The Geological Society of Australia observes a basic policy of non-discrimination and affirms the right of scientists to adhere to or associate with scientific activity without restrictions based on nationality, race, colour, age, religion, political philosophy, ethnic origin, citizenship, language or sex. The Society endorses the universality of science within the natural world.

Scientists, like many others, are touched with awe at the order and complexity of nature. Science seeks to explain natural phenomena using natural laws, verifiable and reproducible observations and logical analysis; it reaches explanations which are always subject to amendment with new evidence.

The Geological Society of Australia considers that notions such as Fundamental Creationism, including so called "Flood Geology", which disregard scientific evidence such as that based on repeatable observations in the natural world and the geological record, are not science and cannot be taught as science.

An essential element in the teaching of science is the encouragement of students and teachers to critically appraise the evidence for notions being taught as science. The Society states unequivocally that the dogmatic teaching of notions such as Creationism within a science curriculum stifles the development of critical thinking patterns in the developing mind and seriously compromises the best interests of objective public education. This could eventually hamper the advancement of science and technology as students take their places as leaders of future generations.

In some parts of Australia the advocacy of notions like Creationism are confronting the integrity and effectiveness of our national education system and the hard-won evidence-based foundations of science. The Geological Society of Australia cannot remain silent. To do so would be a dereliction of our responsibility to intellectual freedom and to the fundamental principles of scientific thought.

As a consequence, the Society dissociates itself from Creationist statements made by any member.

This Policy statement sets out the views of a learned Society dedicated to scientific investigation in earth science, including research, resources exploration, and education. It is made with the agreement of the Society's Executive Committee and the below-listed Past Presidents of the Society which are taken collectively to reasonably represent the sustaining wisdom of the Society in this matter.

Signed: Past Presidents–Prof. R.T. Prider (1958-59) Dr. N.H. Fisher (1959-61), Dr. J.A. Dulhunty (1964-65), Dr. M.R. Banks (1966-67), Dr. N.H. Ludbrook (1968-69), Prof S.W. Carey (1977-78), Dr. C.D. Branch (1980-81), Dr. R.D. Gee (1981-83), Dr. M.J. Rickard (1983-84), Dr. J.B. Waterhouse (1984-86), Prof. D.M. Boyd (1986-88), Mr. I.R. Johnson (1988-90), Prof. D.H. Green (1990-92), Mr. P.J. Legge (1992-94).

1995

Georgia Academy of Science (1980)

Whereas members of the Georgia Academy of Science are duly trained in their respective scientific disciplines by years of education and experience, and

Whereas members of the Georgia Academy of Science have considered creationism in light of their scientific experience and religious beliefs, and

Whereas members of the Georgia Academy of Science have the following concerns about creationism:

1. Philosophically, "scientific creationism" or "divine creationism" is not based upon objectively-gathered data and testing of the model as required by science.

2. Legally, the required teaching of "creationism" might violate the separation of religion and state. It would definitely establish precedent for the legal inclusion of creation narratives of many religions into the science curriculum. The precedent would also be set for other groups to make demands for modifications in the curriculum of disciplines other than science.

3. Pedagogically, problems could result by requiring science teachers to teach as science a model of divine creationism in which they have not been trained. Moreover, various local groups might demand that divine creation be taught according to their own religious beliefs.

Be it, therefore, resolved that the members of the Georgia Academy of Science oppose the teaching of "creationism" in the science curriculum.

Passed unanimously by plenary session of the Georgia Academy of Science on 19 April 1980.

Georgia Academy of Science (1982)

Synoptic Position Statement of the Georgia Academy of Science with Respect to the Forced Teaching of Creation Science in Public School Science Education

The great majority of scientists and teachers of science in the primary schools, high schools, colleges, and universities of Georgia are both evolutionists and Christians, or Jews, or adherents to some other religious preference. A few may adhere to no religion. In a pluralistic society students represent a comparable religious spectrum.

Based upon overwhelming scientifically verifiable evidence to date, most scientists, regardless of religious preference, think that the earth and all forms of life evolved over a period of several billion years. Evolution can be viewed as a creative process continuing over long periods of time. The extensive evidence of evolution is not in opposition to the variety of religious concepts or creation by a supreme being. The causative beginning of primeval appearance of matter or life in our universe is not at issue. The evidence of evolution does not claim to reveal the primal source of energy, matter, or life. The latter is a question which is addressed by the various religions outside the walls of our publicly funded educational institutions.

On January 5, 1982, U.S. Circuit Court Judge William R. Overton ruled Arkansas' "Balanced Treatment for Creation-Science and Evolution-Science" Act to be a violation of the constitutional separation of church and state. The Act had the advancement of religion as its primary goal, in his opinion. A month later, the attorney general of Arkansas announced his decision not to appeal Overton's opinion because the state had little chance of winning in higher federal court. The plaintiffs in this landmark case included components of the Southern Baptist, Presbyterian, United Methodist, Episcopal, and Roman Catholic churches, in addition to the American Jewish Congress, and the Union of Hebrew Congregations. Other plaintiffs included the Arkansas Education Association, the National Association of Biology Teachers, and the National Coalition for Public Education and Religious Liberty.

The Georgia Academy of Science concurs with the following resolution adopted in January of 1982 by the American Association for the Advancement of Science (AAAS) pertaining to the Forced Teaching of Creationist Beliefs in Public School Science Education: AAAS 1982 Statement.

> *The above statement, including the AAAS resolution (page 21), was adopted by the Georgia Academy of Science at its plenary session on 24 April 1982 and published in the Georgia Journal of Science 40:91-92, 1982.*

Georgia Academy of Science (2003)

Endorsement of AAAS Board Resolution on Intelligent Design Theory

Whereas, the Georgia Academy of Science, established in 1922 and affiliated with the American Association for the Advancement of Science (AAAS), has as its purpose "the promotion of the interests of science, particularly in Georgia";

Whereas, opponents of evolution, including proponents of so-called "intelligent design theory," have attempted to circumscribe the teaching of evolution in public schools in Georgia;

Whereas, the AAAS Board of Directors has issued a resolution on "intelligent design theory," stating that the lack of scientific warrant for so-called "intelligent design theory" makes it improper to include as a part of science education; that AAAS urges citizens across the nation to oppose the establishment of policies that would permit the teaching of "intelligent design theory" as a part of the science curricula of the public schools; that AAAS calls upon its members to assist those engaged in overseeing science education policy to understand the nature of science, the content of contemporary evolutionary theory and the inappropriateness of "intelligent design theory" as subject matter for science education; and that AAAS encourages its affiliated societies to endorse this resolution and to communicate their support to appropriate parties at the federal, state and local levels of the government;

And whereas, the Georgia Academy of Science has previously addressed issues surrounding the teaching of evolution (in 1980 and in 1982);

Therefore Be It Resolved, that the Georgia Academy of Science endorses the AAAS Board resolution on "intelligent design theory";

Therefore Be It Further Resolved, that the Georgia Academy of Science publishes this resolution in the Georgia Journal of Science, that it shares this resolution with members of the Georgia Junior Academy of Science, and that it communicates this resolution to appropriate parties at the state and local levels.

Passed by the plenary session of the Georgia Academy of Science on 22 March 2003.

History of Science Society

Statement on Evolution and Related Matters

The history of science can teach us much about the nature and development of science over time. As the National Academy of Sciences explains in its National Science Education Standards, "In learning science, students need to understand that science reflects its history and is an ongoing, changing enterprise. The standards for the history and nature of science recommend the use of history in school science programs to clarify different aspects of scientific inquiry, the human aspects of science, and the role that science has played in the development of various cultures."

The History of Science Society endorses this view, developed as part of a process that involved over 18,000 scientists and all the major scientific organizations and funding agencies. The history of science helps us understand scientific processes and is important for informing the way that science is used publicly, for example, in the courts and in the development of educational standards in those states and countries that have chosen to develop such standards for their public schools. In such cases it is important to draw on the best available understanding of science and its social context.

Recent discussions about educational standards in public schools have focused on the teaching of evolution and related issues. The history of science shows that such concepts as evolution and geological change are well established and belong in science curricula along with other basic scientific ideas. The history of science has generated a rich literature exploring the development of these concepts as well as the relationship between science and religion; this discussion is available to inform ongoing public discussion.

In view of this historical perspective, the History of Science Society disapproves of recent efforts by state school boards effectively to remove evolution as a subject from the secondary school curriculum, either through textbook disclaimers or censorship. Such efforts will only hinder students from developing a historical appreciation for

Voices for Evolution

science as a process of intellectual inquiry and from understanding the place of science in society, both past and present.

The History of Science Society, which explores the nature of science and scientific change, provides a valuable resource of over 2,900 members, many of whom are available to serve as consultants in public arenas. Through its publications and other activities, the Society provides scholars, decision makers, educators, and the public with historical perspectives on science policy and on the potentials, achievements, and the limitations of basic and applied science.

2000

Idaho Scientists for Quality Science Education

As scientists, employed in the State of Idaho, we are very concerned and deeply committed to maintaining the integrity and quality of science education in Idaho. As such, we wish to advise the Legislative Committee that we strongly support the exiting standards for science in general and evolution in particular as they are presently written. We also highly commend the State Board of Education for approving these standards by a majority vote of seven to one–an endorsement for good science that few states can match.

At a time when Idaho is trying to move from a resource-based economy to a knowledge-based economy, it is imperative that the State of Idaho strive to achieve the best education possible for its students. Recently, in recognition of the importance of science, Governor Dirk Kempthorne appointed a special science adviser. As Idaho moves forward confidently to the 21st century we must ensure that our students receive the best science education possible. Teaching the theory of evolution, like teaching the theory of gravitation, is an excellent way to make that happen.

The Theory of Evolution ranks as one of the great discoveries in the intellectual history of science. Its impact on biology is analogous to that of Newton's law on physics, Copernicus' heliocentric (Sun-centered) theory of the universe on astronomy and the theory of plate tectonics on geology. As defined by the National Academy of Sciences (1999), "biological evolution concerns changes in living things during the history of life on Earth. It explains that living things share common ancestors. Over time, biological processes such as natural selection give rise to new species."

The National Academy of Sciences, the most prestigious scientific organization in the United States, has noted that "the teaching of science in the nation's public schools often is marred by a serious omission. Many students receive little or no exposure to the most important concept in modern biology, a concept essential to understanding key aspects of living things – biological evolution."

Understanding the theory of evolution is crucial in the development of new drugs to fight microbial infections. The theory of evolution, in its broadest sense, unites such disparate disciplines as cosmology, astronomy, anthropology, biology, physics, chemistry, and geology. The fossil evidence alone supports the theory that life has evolved over billions of years from simpler to more complex organisms. Mainstream American religious organizations spanning Christianity, Judaism, and Islam have supported the teaching of evolution in science classes. These religious organizations see in evolution the wonder of their Creator's work. U.S. courts have consistently ruled that teaching creationism amounts to inflicting a narrow, unscientific religious dogma into the public schools, which is contrary to the U.S. and Idaho Constitutions.

Biological evolution accounts for three of the most fundamental features of the world around us: the similarities among living things, the diversity of life, and many features of the physical world we inhabit. Evidence for biological evolution comes from all parts of biology (molecular biology, comparative anatomy, biodiversity, and embryology), geology, paleontology, biochemistry, and physics. Thus, evolution is the central organizing principle that biologists use to understand the natural world. As Time magazine (12/31/99) recently said, "Yet Darwinism remains one of the most successful scientific theories ever promulgated. There is hardly an element of humanity-not capitalism, not gender relations, certainly not biology-that can be fully understood without its help."

In conclusion, we heartily support the teaching of scientifically accepted concepts in science, including the theory of evolution in Idaho's public schools.

2000

Inter-Academy Panel

Statement on the Teaching of Evolution

We, the undersigned Academies of Sciences, have learned that in various parts of the world, within science courses taught in certain public systems of education, scientific evidence, data, and testable theories about the origins and evolution of life on Earth are being concealed, denied, or confused with theories not testable by science. We urge decision makers, teachers, and parents to educate all children about the methods and discoveries of science and to foster an understanding of the science of nature. Knowledge of the natural world in which they live empowers people to meet human needs and protect the planet.

We agree that the following evidence-based facts about the origins and evolution of the Earth and of life on this planet have been established by numerous observations and independently derived experimental results from a multitude of scientific disciplines. Even if there are still many open questions about the precise details of evolutionary change, scientific evidence has never contradicted these results:

1. In a universe that has evolved towards its present configuration for some 11 to 15 billion years, our Earth formed approximately 4.5 billion years ago.

2. Since its formation, the Earth – its geology and its environments – has changed under the effect of numerous physical and chemical forces and continues to do so.

3. Life appeared on Earth at least 2.5 billion years ago. The evolution, soon after, of photosynthetic organisms enabled, from at least 2 billion years ago, the slow transformation of the atmosphere to one containing substantial quantities of oxygen. In addition to the release of the oxygen that we breathe, the process of photosynthesis is the ultimate source of fixed energy and food upon which human life on the planet depends.

4. Since its first appearance on Earth, life has taken many forms, all of which continue to evolve, in ways which palaeontology and the modern biological and biochemical sciences are describing and independently confirming with increasing precision. Commonalities in the structure of the genetic code of all organisms living today, including humans, clearly indicate their common primordial origin.

We also subscribe to the following statement regarding the nature of science in relation to the teaching of evolution and, more generally, of any field of scientific knowledge:

Scientific knowledge derives from a mode of inquiry into the nature of the universe that has been successful and of great consequence. Science focuses on (i) observing the natural world and (ii) formulating testable and refutable hypotheses to derive deeper explanations for observable phenomena. When evidence is sufficiently compelling, scientific theories are developed that account for and explain that evidence, and predict the likely structure or process of still unobserved phenomena.

Human understanding of value and purpose are outside of natural science's scope. However, a number of components – scientific, social, philosophical, religious, cultural and political – contribute to it. These different fields owe each other mutual consideration, while being fully aware of their own areas of action and their limitations.

While acknowledging current limitations, science is open ended, and subject to correction and expansion as new theoretical and empirical understanding emerges.

1. Albanian Academy of Sciences
2. National Academy of Exact, Physical and Natural Sciences, Argentina
3. Australian Academy of Science
4. Austrian Academy of Sciences
5. Bangladesh Academy of Sciences
6. The Royal Academies for Science and the Arts of Belgium
7. Academy of Sciences and Arts of Bosnia and Herzegovina
8. Brazilian Academy of Sciences
9. Bulgarian Academy of Sciences
10. RSC: The Academies of Arts, Humanities and Sciences of Canada
11. Academia Chilena de Ciencias
12. Chinese Academy of Sciences
13. Academia Sinica, China, Taiwan
14. Colombian Academy of Exact, Physical and Natural Sciences
15. Croatian Academy of Arts and Sciences
16. Cuban Academy of Sciences
17. Academy of Sciences of the Czech Republic
18. Royal Danish Academy of Sciences and Letters
19. Academy of Scientific Research and Technology, Egypt
20. Académie des Sciences, France
21. Union of German Academies of Sciences and Humanities
22. The Academy of Athens, Greece
23. Hungarian Academy of Sciences
24. Indian National Science Academy
25. Indonesian Academy of Sciences
26. Academy of Sciences of the Islamic Republic of Iran
27. Royal Irish Academy
28. Israel Academy of Sciences and Humanities
29. Accademia Nazionale dei Lincei, Italy
30. Science Council of Japan
31. Kenya National Academy of Sciences
32. National Academy of Sciences of the Kyrgyz Republic
33. Latvian Academy of Sciences
34. Lithuanian Academy of Sciences
35. Macedonian Academy of Sciences and Arts
36. Academia Mexicana de Ciencias
37. Mongolian Academy of Sciences
38. Academy of the Kingdom of Morocco
39. The Royal Netherlands Academy of Arts and Sciences
40. Academy Council of the Royal Society of New Zealand
41. Nigerian Academy of Sciences
42. Pakistan Academy of Sciences
43. Palestine Academy for Science and Technology
44. Academia Nacional de Ciencias del Peru
45. National Academy of Science and Technology, The Philippines
46. Polish Academy of Sciences
47. Académie des Sciences et Techniques du Sénégal
48. Serbian Academy of Sciences and Arts
49. Singapore National Academy of Sciences
50. Slovak Academy of Sciences
51. Slovenian Academy of Sciences and Arts
52. Academy of Science of South Africa

53. Royal Academy of Exact, Physical and Natural Sciences of Spain
54. National Academy of Sciences, Sri Lanka
55. Royal Swedish Academy of Sciences
56. Council of the Swiss Scientific Academies
57. Academy of Sciences, Republic of Tajikistan
58. The Caribbean Academy of Sciences
59. Turkish Academy of Sciences
60. The Uganda National Academy of Sciences
61. The Royal Society, UK
62. US National Academy of Sciences
63. Uzbekistan Academy of Sciences
64. Academia de Ciencias Físicas, Matemáticas y Naturales de Venezuela
65. Zimbabwe Academy of Sciences
66. African Academy of Sciences
67. The Academy of Sciences for the Developing World (TWAS)
68. The Executive Board of the International Council for Science (ICSU)

21 June 2006

Iowa Academy of Science (1986)

Statement of the Position of the Iowa Academy of Science on Pseudoscience

The Iowa Academy of Science strongly opposes the public promotion of pseudoscience, whether through the media, the legislature, or classrooms of accredited educational institutions of Iowa.

"Pseudoscience" is a catch-all term for any mistaken or unsupported beliefs that are cloaked in the disguise of scientific credibility. Examples include assertions of scientific creationism, the control of actions at a distance through meditation, and the belief in levitation, astrology, or UFO visitors. While the IAS opposes the promotion of such beliefs, it does not oppose critical examination of them, either in the public media or in classrooms. Indeed, there is much to be learned from critical examination of pseudoscience.

One main concern is public confusion over what science is and what it is not. This cannot be resolved merely by contriving tighter definitions of science or its methods. In fact, authoritative definitions inadvertently provide a model that counterfeiters need in order to better fashion their "cloaks of scientific credibility". To clear up the confusion between real and bogus science we must focus not on their definitions, but on their differences.

In contrast to pseudoscientists, scientists seek out, expose, and correct any logical fallacies or others errors which could weaken their theories or interpretations. To assure complete scrutiny, open criticism is not only tolerated but often rewarded, particularly when it results in significant revisions of established views. The debate is held in refereed scientific journals and in meetings, and anyone, well-known or not, can submit pro or con arguments for publication or presentation before peers.

By contrast, open criticism is not welcomed by pseudoscientists. They usually avoid publishing in refereed scientific journals, and subsequently their theories are not self-correcting; thus they fail to experience the progressive changes characteristic of science. Astrology and creationism, for example, have experienced nothing comparable to Copernican or Darwinian revolutions (paradigm shifts) which have occurred in astronomy and biology.

The Iowa Academy of Science is prepared to assist citizens, teachers, public officials and the media who seek information on issues involving science and pseudoscience.

1986

Statement of the Position of the Iowa Academy of Science on the Validity of Evolutionary Science and on the Status of Creationism as a Scientific Explanation of Natural Phenomena

Current attempts to introduce "scientific creationism", "creationism", or the Judeo-Christian biblical account of creation, as well as to reframe the discussion around terms such as "abrupt appearance theory", "intelligent design theory", or other disguised forms of creationism into the science classroom along with or instead of evolutionary science are strongly opposed by The Iowa Academy of Science on the grounds that creationism, in whatever form, is a religious doctrine and not science.

Creationist organizations that are advocating the teaching of "scientific creationism" or equal time for creationism along with evolution in the science classrooms include members purported to be scientists who have examined the evidence and have found creationism to be a superior alternative to evolution. They claim to know of evidence that supports the idea of a young earth and that shows evolution to be impossible. Much of this "evidence" is inaccurate, out of date, and not accepted by recognized paleontologists, geologists, astronomers, and biologists. The total membership of these "scientific" creationist groups constitutes only a fraction of one percent of the scientific personnel in this country, and the major scientific organizations of this country all support evolutionary concepts as valid. Most "scientific creationists", are not trained in biology or geology, the area in which professional judgments are made in the field of evolutionary theory. The "scientific creationists" often misrepresent the positions of respected scientists and quote them out of context to support their own views before audiences and government bodies. They are driven by the notion that all explanations of natural events must conform to their preconceived views. These tactics are used to give the uninformed public the false impression that science itself is confused. Then a supernatural explanation is proposed to bring order out of apparent chaos. Not only are the arguments offered by creationists misrepresentations, they also include distortions and misconception of scientific facts and concepts. This includes the meaning of the word "theory" which scientists use to describe the integrating group of fundamental principles underlying a science. The evidence in support of evolutionary science has accumulated for over one hundred years, and the evidence has been strengthened further by molecular techniques developed since the 1970s. While science continually reexamines and reevaluates theory as new evidence is presented, the basic tenets of evolutionary theory have never been in doubt.

The Iowa Academy of Science urges legislators, school administrators, educators, and the general public not be misled by the tactics of these so-called "scientific creationists." The Academy respects the right of persons to hold diverse religious beliefs, including those that reject evolution, but only as matters of theology or faith, not as secular science. Creationism is not science and the Academy deplores and opposes any attempt to disguise it as science. Most recognized scientists find no conflict between religious faith and the acceptance of evolution. They do not view evolution as being anti-religious. They have no vested interest in supporting evolution as do the "scientific creationists" in supporting creationism, but merely consider evolution as being most consistent with the best evidence.

The Iowa Academy of Science feels strongly that the distinction between science and religion must be maintained. A state with one of the highest literacy rates and with the highest scientific literacy scores in the nation, and one which prides itself on the individuality of its citizens, should discriminate in its public education system between what is science and what is not science.

Approved 31 January 1981
Updated and approved by Board of Directors 13 October 1999

Kansas Academy of Science

Position on teaching evolution in public schools

Gregory A. Liggett
Northern California Natural History Museum,
College of Natural Sciences, California State University, Chico,
Chico, California 95929-0555 and
Sternberg Museum of Natural History,
Fort Hays State University, Hays, Kansas 67601

The Kansas Academy of Sciences, like all scientific organizations, continues to be deeply concerned about an assault against the teaching of science in public schools, particularly the principles of biological evolution. Several years ago Kansas became a national lighting rod of controversy when the State Board of Education voted to approve science standards that deemphasized the teaching of evolution. The whole debate continues to rear its ugly head across the nation.

Over the last year or more, members of the Executive Committee and science supporters of all stripes have offered testimony at public hearings, written letters, and done all the usual time-consuming steps necessary in our democracy to ensure that science education is strong in Kansas. This position statement is just one small part of that ongoing effort.

This paper includes the position statement of the Kansas Academy of Sciences on the teaching of evolution in public schools and two additional parts. The two additional sections move beyond simply stating a position. The first additional section is for school boards at the local, state, and national levels, and was written to provide a non-emotional argument for why this debate should not be happening in a public school forum at the expense of our public school students. Perhaps it will provide school board members some ammunition to defeat measures designed to undermine science education.

The last part is aimed at helping the nonscientist understand the scientific process in general. There is not, of course, space in this short essay to lay out all of scientific history and philosophy, and realistically it will not likely change the minds of those who oppose the scientific understanding of evolution because of deeply held personal beliefs, whatever their origin. The section is presented in the hope of helping those who are genuinely confused by the whole issue, and are willing to be intellectually honest enough to seek a deeper understanding.

Position Statement

The Kansas Academy of Science is a professional organization of scientists representing all areas of scientific inquiry. Science is the systematic, empirical investigation of the natural world. As a group, the Academy clearly asserts that biological evolution, or descent with modification by natural processes, is a central organizing principle in modern biology. As such, the teaching of evolution should be of paramount importance to state and local boards of education to ensure a well-educated and productive citizenry. The Academy strongly supports education standards and efforts that support the teaching of the predominant scientific theories, particularly biological evolution, and opposes any changes that diminish the teaching of science in general.

Message to State and Local Boards of Education

Thank you. Thank you for your hard work and dedication to the educational future of our children. Yours is the difficult task of balancing complex budgetary concerns, complying with federal, state, and local guidelines, and making sure that the curricular content offered in schools will ensure that our young people have a solid foundation for lifelong learning and will be educated citizens as adults. Agreeing to serve on a BOE is a selfless sacrifice of your time and energy.

From time to time proposals are made to change, or even eliminate, certain subjects in the school curriculum. Evolution is currently a chief example. Arguments against evolution are often made that in the interest of "fairness" we need to present a "complete" picture to our students, exposing them to "alternative" or "competing" theories to biological evolution. However, ideas that involve a supernatural agent are not scientifically testable, and therefore not scientific. Scientific ideas are complex, with technical contributions from many disciplines, and you may be presented with many scientific-sounding arguments in support of one theory over another. So how can you, as a BOE member and likely a non-scientist, choose the best course of action for the educational wellbeing of our youth?

The fact is that the answer is surprisingly simple. A science school teacher's job is to present the consensus view of the scientific discipline to students in an age-appropriate manner. Teachers find the consensus views in the articles, text books, and other materials communicated by professional scientists. And professional scientists are united in their acceptance of biological evolution as a powerful, unifying scientific theory.

It is unfair, and even inappropriate, for the BOE or a classroom teacher to be placed in the position of having to decide which of several competing theories in science is the most "correct." We don't expect that teachers in other science subjects should take on this task which normally is left to the entire scientific process. Why ask biology teachers to do anything different?

The scientific process continuously tests and evaluates the current prevailing and alternative scientific theories. Every scientific theory is the best current explanation of natural phenomena, and as such is subject to further testing and refinement. That is the scientific process. Therefore, the appropriate venue for challenges and changes to any theory is within the halls of academia and the journals of science – in other words, within the dialogue that encompasses the scientific process. Those who argue that the current theory is not correct should take the discussion up in that appropriate venue, not with the local school BOE or science teacher.

So, please strive to ensure that the prevailing, widely-accepted scientific theories are taught to our children in science class so that they are properly prepared to be competitive and productive in the future. Do not be seduced by false notions of "fairness," or weaken your resolve to provide the best science education for our children. Allow the scientific process to do its job so you can do yours. Thank you.

The Scientific Process: The Rationale for Support of Biological Evolution

Science is a process that provides for an ever-improving understanding of the physical world. A good example of this is the theory of plate tectonics. Many people living today went to school prior to the conception of plate tectonics theory. In studying the Earth they learned the then-current theory of how mountains were formed and why volcanoes erupted. However, those older ideas have since been supplanted by a new theory, plate tectonics, because it has far more explanatory power than older ideas. Now plate tectonics is a central concept in Earth science, taught at every level.

Use of the scientific method has proven to be a powerful tool in learning about and understanding the physical world around us. Every day we enjoy the fruits of scientific discovery as the basis of technology. Science classes tend to have a lot of facts about the world around us, but those facts are only the stepping stones for scientific ideas, not the process of science itself. Science is a process of discovery, a way of gathering and organizing information into coherent concepts about the world.

The steps of science are familiar, and most people have been introduced to the "scientific method." Often the method is elucidated as containing the steps of observation, analysis, hypothesis formation, and evaluation of the hypothesis. The method is a guide for systematically framing questions and exploring ideas – a repeated cycle of discovery.

Because information gained in the hypothesis-testing stage can be added to the original data set, the scientific method is self-correcting, and this is among its most powerful attributes. Say we have made observations on a phenomenon that we wish to study. The method helps to guide our actions to form a natural explanation for what we observe, then to devise tests of that explanation. In effect, we seek to disprove our ideas.

After the experiment, if the outcome predicted by our hypothesis is observed, the hypothesis still stands as a possible explanation. If, on the other hand, the expected outcome is not observed, all is not lost. In fact, the potential is there for real progress, because new data has been acquired that did not fit the original hypothesis, allowing for a new, more inclusive hypothesis to be generated that can explain all the observations. In this way the scientific process is cumulative, always adding new bits of knowledge to the pool, and providing self-correcting course changes along our path toward understanding.

Scientists present their results to their peers and to society through a dialogue process in peer-reviewed journals. There the ideas are subjected to critique by other scientists, and suggestions are made and weaknesses and strengths of the new ideas are addressed. Only if the work is a sound contribution to the body of knowledge will it be published. If it has significant flaws, it will not. This provides a checks-and-balances system, and always keeps scientists on their toes.

It recently has been suggested that science is somehow afraid of challenges to cherished theories, that somehow scientists will not admit "alternative" views into the dialogue. Frankly, this is nonsense. Every practicing scientist would relish the chance to "turn the world upside down" with a dramatically better theory. We remember those scientific greats of the past who have done so. Names like Einstein, Newton, and Darwin are household names, all of whom have more "staying" power in our cultural consciousness than the latest pop-star gracing the covers of tabloids.

Science does not shy away from radical ideas – quite the opposite. The fact is that paradigm-altering scientific ideas do not come around often. However, when they do come, they are challenged, tested, and – if proven better than current theories – are ultimately adopted. Do not believe that alternative scientific theories to evolution would threaten a comfortable status quo. If those alternate theories were scientific and had any substance they would come to be embraced if they were better than the current theory. No such scientific theories relative to biological evolution, however, exist at present.

Plate tectonics and biological evolution are examples of ideas that were radical when they were introduced and have come to be embraced, now forming the centers of their sciences because they are more satisfying explanations for the world around us. Tectonics comprehensively explains observed phenomena like earthquakes, volcanoes, and the shape of the continents. Likewise, the biological theory of evolution is strongly supported and robust in its power to explain of the attributes and geographic distribution of living organisms.

The observation that species change over time was not Charles Darwin's novel concept. Observers of nature had previously noted similarities and differences in living things that suggested close relationships and diversification from common ancestors. In other words, noting that species changed over time was the observation that Darwin was working to understand. What was lacking was a clear explanation of how species could naturally diversify over time.

Darwin's magnificent contribution was the recognition of natural selection as the process driving the change of living organisms, by which species become highly adapted to their environments. The modern theory of evolution incorporates natural selection and provides a powerful and consistent explanation that unifies all areas of the biological sciences such as ecology, anatomy, systematics, paleontology, genetics, cellular and molecular biology, and biochemistry.

Since Darwin first proposed the idea, the concept of natural selection has been rigorously tested in all the sub-disciplines of biology, and the concept has proven to be a robust unifying theory.

Theories are never complete explanations – they cannot be complete given the nature of scientific discovery. Both plate tectonics and evolution have been, and will continue to be, modified and improved upon from their original conceptions as new data are incorporated into the theories. Indeed, our modern understanding of evolution is significantly different from Darwin's original outline. For example, because of the period in which he worked, Darwin knew little about genetics and inheritance or the fossil record and geologic time. Advances in those areas have refined the original concept, but have not fundamentally altered its grand contribution to science.

The magnificence of Darwin's basic concept of natural selection is that it has held up well as new data are added, that it is applicable across biology as a fundamental principle, and that it is congruent with other areas of science. For example, the patterns of species distributions through space and time are consistent with the changing configuration of the continents as explained by plate tectonics. As such, the elucidation of biological evolution is among humankind's greatest scientific achievements. Evolution should hold a central place in the teaching of biology at all levels of science education.

The fact that we as a nation are even having a debate about teaching evolution in our science classrooms is evidence of the need to strengthen the public's understanding of science, the scientific process, and what science is not. The scientific method as described above is the tool of choice for unraveling the workings of the physical world around us. Science by definition limits itself to the empirical – that which can be tested, measured, or observed, either with the naked senses or aided by technology. Therefore, the scientific method, by design, cannot address topics which are outside the physical world, namely the religious, esthetic, ethical, and moral realms, and therefore cannot be a threat to those endeavors. Those non-empirical ways of exploring the human experience are not less significant, but we must not allow them to be taught to our children as some twisted definition of science.

Ultimately, the nation's future economic growth and prosperity, and even our national security, depends on how well we educate our children in general, and in science in particular. We must rise to this challenge. If the United States is to remain a world leader in science and technological development our children need the best possible foundation in science. It starts in the best possible science classrooms.

Acknowledgements

I would like to thank the Kansas Academy of Science Executive Committee for allowing me to present the unanimous position statement on their behalf. Comments from many people helped clarify and strengthen this paper, including Mike Everhart, Kansas Academy of Science and Fort Hays State University (FHSU) Sternberg Museum of Natural History, and Richard Packauskas, FHSU Department of Biological Sciences. I especially wish to thank Cameron Liggett, FHSU Sternberg Museum of Natural History for significant editorial assistance.

2006

Kentucky Academy of Science

At the annual business meeting of the KAS, on November 11, 2005, the KAS reviewed and reaffirmed past resolutions in support of the teaching of Evolution and unanimously endorsed the American Association for the Advancement of Science's "Resolution on Intelligent Design Theory"

The following resolution, already adopted by the Kentucky Academy of Science at the annual business meeting on November 12, 1983, was unanimously approved again at its annual business meeting on November 11, 2005:

Resolution In Support of Evolution

The Kentucky Academy of Science is opposed to any attempt by legislative bodies to mandate specific content of science courses. The content of science courses should be determined by the standards of the scientific community. Science involves a continuing systematic inquiry into the manifold aspects of the biological and material world. It is based upon testable theories which may change with new data; it cannot include interpretations based on faith or religious dogma. As scientists, we object to attempts to equate "scientific creationism" or "intelligent design" with evolution as scientific explanations of events. Teaching faith-based models implies that these views are equivalent alternatives among scientists; doing so would be misleading to students. "Scientific creationism" and "intelligent design" are not equivalent to evolution. There is overwhelming acceptance by scientists of all disciplines that evolution (the descent of modern specifies of animals and plants from different ancestors that lived millions of years ago) is consistent with the weight of a vast amount of evidence. The understanding of the processes underlying evolution has provided the foundation upon which many of the tremendous advances in agriculture and medicine and theoretical biology have been built. Differences among scientists over questions of how evolution was accomplished do not obscure the basic agreement that evolution has occurred.

Most people who subscribe to religious views have developed belief systems that are compatible with evolution. There is a widespread consensus among theologians that biblical accounts of creation are misunderstood if they are treated as literal scientific explanations. We fully respect the religious views of all person but we object to attempts to require any religious teachings as science.

We join the National Academy of Sciences, the American Association for the Advancement of Science, and the academies of science in many other states in calling for the rejection of attempts to require the teaching of "scientific creationism" and "intelligent design" as a scientific theory.

It is further recommended that the Kentucky Academy of Science encourages its members and other professional scientific groups to give support and aid to those

Voices for Evolution

classroom teachers who present the subject matter of evolution fairly and encounter community objection. We also encourage administrators and individual teachers to oppose the inclusion of nonscientific concepts in the science classroom.

Passed KAS Annual Business Meeting, 14 November 1981.

And,

A Resolution of the Kentucky Academy of Science In Regard to Omitting Evolution Terminology and Teaching in the Public Schools (1999):

Whereas the Kentucky Academy of Science, founded in 1914, is an organization that encompasses all of the accepted scientific fields, and

Whereas the Scientific Method exemplifies that search for Scientific Understanding, and

Whereas this methodology has consistently provided the means of questioning dogma, authoritarianism, and deliberate deception, by championing the spirit of inquiry based on testing, analysis, honest review, criticism and counter criticism and designs for further testing, and

Whereas the advancements of our understanding of the interconnection of the physical properties of our universe coupled with the life forms which together compose our biosphere clearly support that the evolutionary process has functioned and does function in the development, control, and survival of the earth's living beings, and

Whereas to deny the concepts of the known theoretical basis of the evolutionary process to the education arena of our public schools by avoiding or eliminating from the science curriculum any mention of the term evolution and evolutionary concepts would be an affront to an objective inquiry and the understanding of science,

Thereby be it resolved that the Kentucky Academy of Science, in the strongest and most determined ways possible deplores the decision to substitute "change over time" for "evolution" in the state teaching standards, urges that the original working be reinstated, and decries any attempt to remove the teaching of basic evolutionary theory or any scientific concept that may be tested and examined in concert with the basic scientific laws and principles that comprise the Scientific Method, and furthermore be it resolved that the public supported education systems of the Commonwealth be enhanced with complete support of seeking knowledge by every means possible commensurate with known principles of scientific theory, fact, and understanding.

Adopted by the KAS Governing Board November 6, 1999
Passed unanimously by KAS membership November 6, 1999
Both resolutions reviewed and reaffirmed by the KAS membership
at the annual KAS business meeting on November 12, 2005.

Kentucky Paleontological Society

Statement on the Teaching of Evolution

The Kentucky Paleontological Society was founded in 1993 for the purpose of promoting interest in and knowledge of the science of paleontology. The Society is a network for the exchange of data between professionals and serious amateurs in the field. The KPS and its members have worked with world-class paleontologists on exciting projects ranging from the discovery of a new genus of extinct echinoderm, and the excavation of a rare early land vertebrate in Kentucky to helping excavate dinosaurs and other vertebrate fossils in New Mexico and Montana. Our mission is to advance science by bringing untapped talent into the field, and to help create a more scientifically literate public through our educational efforts. Correcting misunderstandings about science is clearly part of any educational mission. We think that it is vital that all scientific organizations, including the KPS, stand against pseudoscience. On October 12, 1999, the KPS issued the following statement:

The Kentucky Paleontological Society (KPS) is opposed to any attempt to teach creationism or omit mention of evolution from public school instruction. Furthermore, evolution should be called "evolution" in curriculum guidelines and other documents; euphemisms such as "change over time" are intellectually dishonest for they attempt to conceal the terminology used by scientists. Paleontology relies for its evidence on two different but historically related fields, biology and geology. Biological evolution is the central organizing principle of biology, understood as descent with modification. Evolution is equally basic to geology, because the pattern of fossil distribution in the rock record makes no sense without evolution. Evidence for the progressive replacement of fossil forms has been adequate to support the theory of evolution for over 100 years. Paleontologists may dispute, on the basis of the available evidence, the tempo and mode of evolution in a particular group at a particular time, but they do not argue about whether evolution took place. The record of the evolution of life is exciting, instructive, and enjoyable, and it is our view that everyone should have the opportunity and the privilege to understand it as paleontologists do.

Kentucky's students deserve and require a high-quality science education, grounded in scientific evidence and free of sectarian influence. The content of science courses should be determined by the standards of the scientific community.

Most people who subscribe to religious views have developed belief systems that are compatible with evolution. We fully respect the religious views of all persons, but we object to attempts to require any religious teachings as science.

Our Executive Committee approved this statement. We wish to make it clear that we do not restrict our membership to avowed evolutionists. We insist only that our members conduct themselves responsibly and safely when doing field work and collecting specimens.

The KPS encourages its members and other professional scientific groups to give support and aid to those classroom teachers who present the subject matter of evolution fairly and encounter community objection. We also encourage administrators and individual teachers to oppose the inclusion of nonscientific concepts in the science classroom.

October 12, 1999

Voices for Evolution

Louisiana Academy of Sciences

Whereas the stated goal of the Louisiana Academy of Sciences is to encourage research in the sciences and disseminate scientific knowledge, and

Whereas such pursuits are based on the scientific method requiring the testing of hypotheses before their inclusion in the body of scientific knowledge, and

Whereas organic evolution is amenable to repeated observation and testing, and

Whereas the ideas of Intelligent Design are not amenable to verification by observation and experimentation, and

Whereas the Academy respects and supports the right of people to possess beliefs in Intelligent Design and other matters that are not encompassed by the subject matter of science,

Therefore be it resolved that the term "Intelligent Design" does not denote a hypothesis, theory, or method of inquiry that falls within the realm of science, and

Be it further resolved that the members of the Louisiana Academy of Sciences urge fellow Louisianans, political leaders, and educators to oppose the inclusion in state science programs of Intelligent Design or other similar ideas which cannot be tested, accepted, or rejected by the scientific method.

March 10, 2006

National Academy of Sciences (1972)

Whereas we understand that the California State Board of Education is considering a requirement that textbooks for use in the public schools give parallel treatment to the theory of evolution and to belief in special creation; and

Whereas the essential procedural foundations of science exclude appeal to supernatural causes as a concept not susceptible to validation by objective criteria; and

Whereas religion and science are, therefore, separate and mutually exclusive realms of human thought whose presentation in the same context leads to misunderstanding of both scientific theory and religious belief; and

Whereas, further, the proposed action would almost certainly impair the proper segregation of teaching and understanding of science and religion nationwide, therefore

We, the members of the National Academy of Sciences, assembled at the autumn 1972 meeting, urge that textbooks of the sciences, utilized in the public schools of the nation, be limited to the exposition of scientific matter.

Passed by members of the National Academy of Sciences at the
business session of the autumn meeting, 17 October 1972.

Science and Creationism: A View from the National Academy of Sciences

State legislatures are considering, and some have passed, bills that would require the introduction of biblical creationism in science classes. Local school boards have passed ordinances to restrict the teaching of evolution or to require what is called a "balanced treatment" of creationism and evolution. Publishers of science textbooks are under pressure to deemphasize evolution while adding course material on "creation science."

The teaching of creationism as advocated by the leading proponents of "creation science" includes the following judgments: (1) the earth and universe are relatively young, perhaps only 6,000 to 10,000 years old; (2) the present form of the earth can be explained by "catastrophism," including a worldwide flood; and (3) all living things (including humans) were created miraculously, essentially in the forms we now find them. These teachings may be recognized as having been derived from the accounts of origins in the first two chapters of Genesis.

Generations of able and often devout scientists before us have sought evidence for these teachings without success. Others have given us hypotheses about the origin and history of the earth and the universe itself. These hypotheses have been tested and validated by many different lines of inquiry. With modifications to include new findings, they have become the central organizing theories that make the universe as a whole intelligible, lend coherence to all of science, and provide fruitful direction to modern research. The hypothesis of special creation has, over nearly two centuries, been repeatedly and sympathetically considered and rejected on evidential grounds by qualified observers and experimentalists. In the forms given in the first two chapters of Genesis, it is now an invalidated hypothesis. To reintroduce it into the public schools at this time as an element of science teaching would be akin to requiring the teaching of Ptolemaic astronomy or pre-Columbian geography.

Confronted by this challenge to the integrity and effectiveness of our national educational system and to the hard-won evidence-based foundations of science, the National Academy of Sciences cannot remain silent. To do so would be a dereliction of our responsibility to academic and intellectual freedom and to the fundamental principles of scientific thought. As a historic representative of the scientific profession and designated advisor to the Federal Government in matters of science, the Academy states unequivocally that the tenets of "creation science" are not supported by scientific evidence, that creationism has no place in a science curriculum at any level, that its proposed teaching would be impossible in any constructive sense for well-informed and conscientious science teachers, and that its teaching would be contrary to the nation's need for a scientifically literate citizenry and for a large, well-informed pool of scientific and technical personnel.

The Central Scientific Issues

Five central scientific issues are critical to consideration of the treatment in school curricula of the origin and evolution of the universe and of life on earth . . . .

The Nature Of Science

It is important to clarify the nature of science and to explain why creationism cannot be regarded as a scientific pursuit. The claim that equity demands balanced treatment of the two in the same classroom reflects misunderstanding of what science is and how it is conducted. Scientific investigators seek to understand natural phenomena by direct observation and experimentation. Scientific interpretations of facts are always provisional and must be testable. Statements made by any authority, revelation, or appeal to the supernatural are not germane to this process in the absence of supporting evidence. In creationism, however, both authority and revelation take precedence over evidence. The conclusions of creationism do not change, nor can they be validated when subjected to test by the methods of science. Thus, there are profound differences between the religious belief in special creation and the scientific explanations embodied in evolutionary theory. Neither benefits from the confusion that results when the two are presented as equivalent approaches in the same classroom. . . .

Special creation is neither a successful theory nor a testable hypothesis for the origin of the universe, the earth, or of life thereon. Creationism reverses the scientific process. It accepts as authoritative a conclusion seen as unalterable and then seeks to support that conclusion by whatever means possible.

In contrast, science accommodates, indeed welcomes, new discoveries: its theories change and its activities broaden as new facts come to light or new potentials are recognized. Examples of events changing scientific thought are legion. . . . Prior acceptance of the fixed ad hoc hypothesis of creationism – ideas that are certified as untestable by their most ardent advocates – would have blocked important advances that have led to the great scientific achievements of recent years. Truly scientific understanding cannot be attained or even pursued effectively when explanations not derived from or tested by the scientific method are accepted.

Scientific Evidence On The Origin Of The Universe And The Earth

The processes by which new galaxies, stars, and our own planetary system are formed are sometimes referred to as the "evolution" of the universe, the stars, and the solar system. The word evolution in this context has a very different meaning than it does when applied to the evolution of organisms.

Evidence that the evolution of the universe has taken place over at least several billion years is overwhelming. Among the most striking indications of this process are the receding velocities of distant galaxies. This general expansion of the universe was first noted in the late 1920s and early 1930s. Astronomers today estimate that the expansion probably began some 10 to 20 billion years ago.

The invariant spontaneous decay of the radioactive isotopes of some elements provides further evidence that the universe is billions of years old. Analyses of the relative abundances of radioactive isotopes and their inert decay products in the earth, meteorites, and moon rocks all lead to the conclusion that these bodies are about 4.5 billion years old.

A major assertion for the creationists' opposition to the geological record and evolution is their belief that earth is relatively young, perhaps only a few thousand years old. In rejecting evidence for the great age of the universe, creationists are in conflict with data from astronomy, astrophysics, nuclear physics, geology, geochemistry, and geophysics. The creationists' conclusion that the earth is only a few thousand years old was originally reached from the timing of events in the Old Testament. . . .

The Scientific Standing Of Biological Evolution

Although it was Darwin, above all others, who first marshaled the convincing critical evidence for biological evolution, earlier alert scholars recognized that the succession of living forms on the earth had changed systematically within the passage of geological time.

As applied to biology, a distinction is to be drawn between the questions (1) whether and (2) how biological evolution, happened. The first refers to the finding, now supported, by an overwhelming body of evidence, that descent with modification occurred during more than 2.7 billion years of earth's history. The second refers to the theory explaining how those changes developed along the observed lineages. The mechanisms are still undergoing investigation; the currently favored theory is an extensively modified version of Darwinian natural selection.

With that proviso we will now consider three aspects of biological evolution in more detail....

Relation by Common Descent: Evidence for relation by common descent has been provided by paleontology, comparative anatomy, biogeography, embryology, biochemistry, molecular genetics, and other biological disciplines. The idea first emerged from observations of systematic changes in the succession of fossil remains found in a sequence of layered rocks. . . .

In Darwin's time, however, paleontology was still a rudimentary science, and large parts of the geological succession of stratified rocks were unknown or inadequately studied. Darwin, therefore, worried about the rarity of truly intermediate forms. Creationists have then and now seized on this as a weakness in evolutionary theory. Indeed, although gaps in the paleontological record remain even now, many have been filled with the researches of paleontologists since Darwin's time. Hundreds of thousands of fossil organisms found in well-dated rock sequences represent a succession of forms through time and manifest many evolutionary transitions...There have been so many discoveries of intermediate forms between fish and amphibians, between amphibians and reptiles, between reptiles and mammals, and even along the primate line of descent that it is often difficult to identify categorically the line to which a particular genus or species belongs.

Although creationists claim that the entire geological record, with its orderly succession of fossils, is the product of a single universal flood that lasted a little longer than a year and covered the highest mountains to a depth of some 7 meters a few thousand years ago, there is clear evidence in the form of intertidal and terrestrial deposits that at no recorded time in the past has the entire planet been under water. The belief that all this sediment with its fossils was deposited in an orderly sequence in a year's time defies all geological observations and physical principles concerning sedimentation rates and possible quantities of suspended solid matter. We do not doubt that there were periods of unusually high rainfall or that extensive flooding of inhabited areas has occurred, but there is no scientific support for the hypothesis of a universal, mountain-topping flood.

Inferences about common descent derived from paleontology have been reinforced by comparative anatomy. The skeletons of humans, dogs, whales, and bats are strikingly similar, despite the different ways of life led by these animals and the diversity of environments in which they have flourished. The correspondence, bone by bone, can be observed in every part of the body, including the limbs. Yet a person writes, a dog runs, a whale swims, and a bat flies – with structures built of the same bones. Scientists call such structures homologous and have concurred that they are best explained by common descent.

Biogeography also has contributed evidence for common descent. . . . Creationists contend that the curious facts of biogeography result from the occurrence of a special creationary event. A scientific hypothesis proposes that biological diversity results from an evolutionary process whereby the descendants of local or migrant predecessors became adapted to their diverse environments. A testable corollary of that hypothesis is that present forms and local fossils should show homologous attributes indicating how one is derived from the other. Also, there should be evidence that forms without an established local ancestry had migrated into the locality. Whenever such tests have been carried out, these conditions have been confirmed.

Embryology, the study of biological development from the time of conception, is another source of independent evidence for common descent. Barnacles, for instance, are sedentary crustaceans with little apparent similarity to such other crustaceans as lobsters, shrimps, or copepods. Yet barnacles pass through a free-swimming larval stage, in which they look unmistakably like other crustacean larvae. The similarity of larval stages supports the conclusion that all crustaceans have homologous parts and a common ancestry.

Molecular Biology and the Degree of Relationship: Very recent studies in molecular biology have independently confirmed the judgments of paleontologists and classical biologists about relationships among lineages and the order in which species appeared within lineages. They have also provided detailed information about the mechanisms of biological evolution.

DNA, the hereditary material within all cells, and the proteins encoded by the genes in the DNA both offer extensive information about the ancestry of organisms. Analysis of such information has made it possible to reconstruct evolutionary events that were previously unknown, and to confirm and date events already surmised but not precisely dated.

In unveiling the universality of the chemical basis of heredity, molecular biology has profoundly affirmed common ancestry. In all organisms – bacteria, plants, and animals, including humans – the hereditary information is encoded in DNA, which is in all instances made up of the same four subunits called nucleotides. The genetic code by which the information contained in the nuclear DNA is used to form proteins is essentially the same in all organisms. Proteins in all organisms are invariably composed of the same 20 amino acids, all having a "left-handed" configuration, although there are amino acids in nature with both "right-" and "left-handed" configurations. The metabolic pathways through which the most diversified organisms produce energy and manufacture cell components are also essentially the same. This unity reveals the genetic continuity of living organisms, thereby giving independent confirmation of descent from a common ancestry. There is no other way consistent with the laws of nature and probability to account for such uniformity. . . .

Human Evolution

Studies in evolutionary biology have led to the conclusion that mankind arose from ancestral primates. This association was hotly debated among scientists in Darwin's day, before molecular biology and the discovery of the now abundant connecting links. Today, however, there is no significant scientific doubt about the close evolutionary relationships among all primates or between apes and humans. The "missing links" that troubled Darwin and his followers are no longer missing. Today, not one but many such connecting links, intermediate between various branches of the primate family tree, have been found as fossils. These linking fossils are intermediate in form and occur in geological deposits of intermediate age. They thus document the time and rate at which primate and human evolution occurred.

The Origin Of Life

Scientific research on the origin of life is in an exploratory phase, and all its conclusions are tentative. We know that the organisms that lived on earth 2 billion or more years ago were simply microbial forms. . . . Experiments conducted under plausible primitive-earth conditions have resulted in the production of amino acids, large protein-like molecules made from long chains of amino acids, the nucleotide components of DNA, and DNA-like chains of these nucleotides. Many biologically interesting molecules have also been detected by astronomers using radiotelescopes. We can, therefore, explain how the early oxygen-free earth provided a hospitable site for the accumulation of molecules suitable for the construction of living systems.

For those who are studying aspects of the origin of life, the question no longer seems to be whether life could have originated by chemical processes involving nonbiological components but, rather, what pathway might have been followed. The data accumulated thus far imply selective processes. Prebiological chemical evolution is seen as a trial-and-error process leading to the success of one or more systems built from the many possible chemical components. The system that evolved with the capability of self-replication and mutation led to what we now define as a living system.

Conclusion

Scientists, like many others, are touched with awe at the order and complexity of nature. Religion provides one way for human beings to be comfortable with these marvels. However, the goal of science is to seek naturalistic explanations for phenomena – and the origins of life, the earth, and the universe are, to scientists, such phenomena – within the framework of natural laws and principles and the operational rule of testability.

It is, therefore, our unequivocal conclusion that creationism, with its account of the origin of life by supernatural means, is not science. It subordinates evidence to statements based on authority and revelation. Its documentation is almost entirely limited to the special publications of its advocates. And its central hypothesis is not subject to change in light of new data or demonstration of error. Moreover, when the evidence for creationism has been subjected to the tests of the scientific method, it has been found invalid.

No body of beliefs that has its origin in doctrinal material rather than scientific observation should be admissible as science in any science course. Incorporating the teaching of such doctrines into a science curriculum stifles the development of critical thinking patterns in the developing mind and seriously compromises the best interests of public education. This could eventually hamper the advancement of science and technology as students take their places as leaders of future generations.

Excerpts from "Science and Creationism: A View from the National Academy of Sciences," National Academy Press, Washington, DC 1984. Omissions of short phrases are not identified, but omissions of several sentences or more, usually of examples and argumentation in support of the central point, are indicated by ellipses. The editor has not made any additions.

National Academy of Sciences (1999)

Science and Creationism: A View from the National Academy of Sciences, Second Edition

Science is a particular way of knowing about the world. In science, explanations are limited to those based on observations and experiments that can be substantiated by other scientists. Explanations that cannot be based on empirical evidence are not a part of science.

In the quest for understanding, science involves a great deal of careful observation that eventually produces an elaborate written description of the natural world. Scientists communicate their findings and conclusions to other scientists through publications, talks at conferences, hallway conversations, and many other means. Other scientists then test those ideas and build on preexisting work. In this way, the accuracy and sophistication of descriptions of the natural world tend to increase with time, as subsequent generations of scientists correct and extend the work done by their predecessors.

Progress in science consists of the development of better explanations for the causes of natural phenomena. Scientists never can be sure that a given explanation is complete and final. Some of the hypotheses advanced by scientists turn out to be incorrect when tested by further observations or experiments. Yet many scientific explanations have been so thoroughly tested and confirmed that they are held with great confidence.

The theory of evolution is one of these well-established explanations. An enormous amount of scientific investigation since the mid-19th century has converted early ideas about evolution proposed by Darwin and others into a strong and well-supported theory. Today, evolution is an extremely active field of research, with an abundance of new discoveries that are continually increasing our understanding of how evolution occurs.

[…]

The theory of evolution has become the central unifying concept of biology and is a critical component of many related scientific disciplines. In contrast, the claims of creation science lack empirical support and cannot be meaningfully tested. These observations lead to two fundamental conclusions: the teaching of evolution should be an integral part of science instruction, and creation science is in fact not science and should not be presented as such in science classes.

Terms Used in Describing the Nature of Science*

Fact: In science, an observation that has been repeatedly confirmed and for all practical purposes is accepted as "true." Truth in science, however, is never final, and what is accepted as a fact today may be modified or even discarded tomorrow.

Hypothesis: A tentative statement about the natural world leading to deductions that can be tested. If the deductions are verified, it becomes more probable that the hypothesis is correct. If the deductions are incorrect, the original hypothesis can be abandoned or modified. Hypotheses can be used to build more complex inferences and explanations.

Law: A descriptive generalization about how some aspect of the natural world behaves under stated circumstances.

Theory: In science, a well-substantiated explanation of some aspect of the natural world that can incorporate facts, laws, inferences, and tested hypotheses.

The contention that evolution should be taught as a "theory, not as a fact" confuses the common use of these words with the scientific use. In science, theories do not turn into facts through the accumulation of evidence. Rather, theories are the end points of science. They are understandings that develop from extensive observation, experimentation, and creative reflection. They incorporate a large body of scientific facts, laws, tested hypotheses, and logical inferences. In this sense, evolution is one of the strongest and most useful scientific theories we have.

* Adapted from Teaching About Evolution and the Nature of Science by the National Academy of Sciences (Washington, D.C.: National Academy Press, 1998).

Modified from the introduction to Science and Creationism: A View from the National Academy of Sciences Second Edition, National Academy Press, Washington, DC 1999. To read or order copies of the booklet, please visit the National Academy Press website at http://www.nap.edu/catalog/6024.html.

The New Mexico Academy of Science

Statement Concerning Evolution

For more than 100 years the New Mexico Academy of Science has been a strong voice for the teaching of sound science, both in New Mexico's schools and to the general public. This specifically includes the understanding of what science is, and how science is used to learn about the natural world using natural causality. In this spirit, the Academy adopts the following resolution:

Whereas the Theory of Evolution is one of the most thoroughly tested and confirmed scientific theories in existence, and

Whereas the Theory of Evolution has been derived from sound experimental methods and discovery of natural data and is based on natural laws of causality, and

Whereas the process of science requires that only natural causality be considered in science, and

Whereas the natural mechanistic explanations incorporated into the Theory of Evolution are sufficient to explain the presence of the diversity of life on earth, both past and present, and

Whereas the Theory of Evolution has proven to be predictive and evolution, itself, is observed in both nature and in the laboratory, and

Whereas other explanations of the diversity of life known by such names as creationism, intelligent design, and further expressions such as evidence against evolution, alternate interpretations of the data, and so forth, are based not in science but rather in a belief in supernatural causality, unsupported by scientific data, and in opposition to the use of established scientific methods,

Therefore be it resolved that the New Mexico Academy of Science supports all state and national leaders and public officials in their efforts to stop any attempt at replacing or supplementing the teaching of the Theory of Evolution in public education science class venues with any of the above named unscientific beliefs of how life on earth has come to be as it is over several billions of years.

Furthermore be it known that the New Mexico Academy of Science does not present this resolution so as to oppose the practice or beliefs in any religion; the intent of this resolution is to assure that science teaching remains independent of religious, social, and political pressures.

7 June 2006

Science and Evolution vs Creationism and Louisiana Act 685 (1981): "Balanced Treatment For Evolution-Science and Creation-Science In Public School Instruction"

The New Orleans Geological Society, an organization of professional earth scientists, takes the position that science classes in Louisiana public schools should teach scientifically accurate and scientifically relevant material. The Society, therefore, disagrees with Louisiana Act 685 of 1981, the law for "Balanced Treatment of Creation-Science and Evolution-Science in Public School Instruction."

"Science" generally is defined as the systematic study of the activities of nature by accumulation of evidence that allows people to understand natural processes. A scientific theory is an idea, based upon a wealth of evidence, that describes and predicts conditions in nature. "Theory" – to a scientist – is a concept firmly grounded in and based upon facts, contrary to the popular conception that it is a hazy notion or undocumented hypothesis. Theories do not become facts; they explain facts. A theory must be verifiable; if evidence is found that contradicts the stated theory, the theory must be modified or discarded. In this manner, general knowledge is advanced. Scientific theories must provide new avenues for investigation and cannot be accepted on faith. Scientific facts supporting theories are presented to the scientific community in the form of published literature for examination by peers and by anyone else interested in the subject. In summary, science is not a belief system. It is simply a method for studying and accumulating knowledge about nature.

Louisiana Act 685 defines "creation-science" as "...the scientific evidences for creation and inferences from those scientific evidences." However, creation-science does not meet the foregoing rigorous standards. Creation-science data almost invariably are of questionable quality, obsolete, or taken out of context from the scientific literature. Even well-known creation scientists such as Duane Gish of the Institute for Creation Research have readily admitted that creation-science is not at all scientific.

Documentation refuting scientific creationism has been presented by the National Academy of Sciences, the Geological Society of America and by members of the American Association for the Advancement of Science and of the United States Geological Survey. Their findings and the findings of this Society are:

The bulk of creation-science literature is not devoted to the presentation of any positive evidence for creationism. Most of its material is an attempt to refute the evidence for the age of the Earth and organic evolution as documented by the geologic record and detailed biological studies, as if such a refutation would, by itself, leave creationism as the only logical alternative.

It is easily demonstrable that fossils are the remains of once living organisms that can be placed in a taxonomic hierarchy supporting evolution. It is also proved that strata of a given geological age contain certain fossil types that are of distinctive character and that over a wide geographical area occur in the same sequences. These are observable facts despite creationist claims that paleontological data do not support evolution.

The age of the Earth as determined by various methods including radiometric dating of meteorites and of the Earth's rocks is approximately 4.6 billion years. Creationist criticisms of that age are based upon misinterpretation of valid data and upon obsolete data. Creationists have failed to produce one single reliable dating technique that supports their idea of a young (6,000-year-old) Earth.

Creationists, in their charge that the "gaps" in the fossil record refute evolution, ignore the hundreds of identifiable transition species that have been catalogued. Concentrating their criticism only on vertebrate fossil finds, creationists neglect the detailed fossil record of invertebrates, microfauna, and microflora whose evolutionary change over time is well documented. That evolution has occurred is a documented fact, not disputed within the scientific community.

Creationist statistics "proving" that the origin of life from inanimate matter is impossible are inaccurate. Such statistical calculations do not take into account laboratory evidence showing that organic matter does organize itself, and that organic molecules can carry on processes similar to life-sustaining biochemical actions outside the cell. Also omitted are astronomical observations that demonstrate the ubiquitous nature of organic matter throughout the solar system and the galaxy.

Arguments stating that thermodynamics precludes the evolution of life because evolution would run against the trend of order to disorder in nature misrepresent the science of thermodynamics. Such arguments are not based on any mathematical calculations. Thermodynamics does in fact show that entropy reversals can and do occur in a biological system that is open with respect to energy input, which is the case for the biosphere of the Earth.

Creationism, as a scientific concept, was dismissed over a century ago and subsequent research has only confirmed that conclusion. Scientific creationism threatens to do great damage to the credibility of legitimate scientific research and to data accumulated from the many varied and unrelated scientific disciplines that independently support organic evolution as a verifiable scientific concept because of its misuse of those data.

The Society, as stated in the introduction to this document, is against the teaching of creationism in our public schools as science along with evolution on an equal basis. The creationist concept of "equal time" has no place in the advancement of science. If an idea can be shown to have no scientific merit, it must either be modified in light of available facts or new data or discarded regardless of how much its proponents believe in it. Creationism is such an idea. It is based on a preconceived notion, not upon any observations of nature and the world around us. The Society has no objection to people wanting to believe that the universe, the Earth, and its residents were created in 6 days, 6,000 years ago. However, those people must realize that such ideas are religious in nature and cannot be called scientific.

By advocating this position, the Society is not taking a stand against any particular religious belief. Science and religion are two different disciplines that are not in conflict with one another. Science is not atheistic; it is non-theistic, and it makes no judgment of religion. The Society feels that religious views have no place in the science classroom.

At the same time, the Society supports the teaching of evolution in science classes precisely because it is legitimate science. As a nation, we live in a society heavily influenced by science and technology. Evolution is a basic scientific concept. People do not have to "believe" in it, but they should understand evolution and how and why it came about.

It is because the system of scientific education in this country has declined in recent years that laws such as Act 685 became possible. Legislation such as this Act, that attempts to legislate what should be taught as science in public schools, ignore one simple fact: scientific findings cannot be altered by public opinion. It is irrelevant that some public opinion polls show approval of creationism being taught alongside evolution. Laws that require non-scientific ideas such as creationism to be taught as current scientific thought alongside established scientific principles such as evolution, or teach neither, do not promote free inquiry–they stifle it. Scientific research and education cannot take place in such a coercive atmosphere.

1985

New York Academy of Sciences

Mandating the study of scientific creationism in the public schools of New York State, as embodied in New York State Assembly Bill 8569 and New York State Senate Bill 8473, by legislative mandate is viewed by the New York Academy of Sciences as an attempt to introduce, by fiat, religious dogma into an arena where verifiability is paramount to the subject matter. It would constitute a very serious breach of the concept of the separation of Church and State. Scientific Creationism is a religious concept masquerading as a scientific one.

Science attempts to explain the physical world through verifiable and repeatable data. Through its rigorous application of inductive and deductive logic, science asks how physical phenomena occur. It attempts to explain the processes that bring about the phenomena that exist now or have existed in the past.

The concept of evolution in biology is an attempt to ascertain how life may have originated, developed and diversified on the planet Earth. Concepts such as that of evolution are developed within the framework of natural laws. The methodology of science aims to ascertain these laws from experimental data. Science accepts the theories or hypotheses that best "fit" these data.

Science modifies established theories in the light of new experimental data. It is receptive to new theories, if they withstand the tests of scientific methodology.

The concept of evolution is incorporated within many scientific disciplines. Scientific data supplied from these many disciplines have contributed to a more thorough understanding of the mechanism of evolution. The theory itself does not rest on any single branch of science.

Because of inherently different methodologies of science and of religion, there is no overlapping area where the methods of science can be applied to religion or vice versa. There is no way for science to test the various accounts of creation held by the world's religions. These accounts depend upon the acceptance of supernatural phenomena and are not subject to scientific investigation. Their proponents demand that these accounts be accepted on faith, and are properly the province of religion. The methodologies of science cannot be used for their evaluation.

The subject known as "Scientific Creationism" is lacking in scientific substance; we reject it for inclusion in science curricula.

For these reasons, the New York Academy of Sciences strongly opposes the introduction of "Scientific Creationism" into any science curricula of the public schools of New York State.

Passed by the Board of Governors of the New York Academy of Sciences on
22 May 1980.

North American Benthological Society

Statement Endorsing Evolution by Natural Selection

The North American Benthological Society recognizes Biological Evolution, including common ancestry of life of earth, descent with modification, speciation through lineage splitting, and the mechanism of natural selection as facts supported by empirical evidence. Moreover, since evolution by natural selection is the central unifying theory of biology, we recognize the importance of incorporating evolution into ultimate causal explanations of ecological, biogeographical and physiological phenomena within aquatic ecosystems. We strongly endorse the teaching of evolution as science in schools.

July 9, 2001

North Carolina Academy of Science

Intellectual freedom and the quality of science education in North Carolina, and the competency of future generations of North Carolinians to make wise decisions concerning science and technology, are being threatened by groups pressuring educators to present creationism as a scientifically viable alternative to evolution. Textbooks are being censored; authors, science teachers, and school boards are being intimidated; and science curricula are being modified in ways that accommodate non-scientific points of view and reject principles accepted by the scientific community.

The North Carolina Academy of Science strongly opposes any measure requiring or coercing public school educators either to include creationism in science curricula or to limit the inclusion of evolution in those same curricula. Principles and concepts of biological evolution are basic to the understanding of science. Students who are not taught these principles, or who hear creationism presented as a scientific alternative to them, will not be receiving an education based on modern scientific knowledge. Their ignorance about evolution will seriously undermine their understanding of the world and the natural laws governing it, and their introduction to creationism as "scientific" will give them false ideas about scientific methods and criteria. Yet we must give students who will face the problems of the 20th and 21st centuries the best possible education.

Creationists claim that biological evolution is a religious tenet; in fact it is one of the cornerstones of modern science. More than 50 years ago the North Carolina Academy of Science adopted a resolution declaring evolution an established law of nature, and since then extensive data have accumulated which further reinforce the confidence of the scientific community in the validity of evolution and help clarify the mechanisms through which evolution operates. Scientists agree that organisms now living on the earth are derived from preexisting organisms which, over long periods of time measured in billions of years, have changed from the simplest ancestors to the diverse and complex biota now in existence. Scientists further agree that there was a time when the earth was devoid of life, and that life developed through natural processes. The evidences supporting these conclusions are extensive, are drawn from many disciplines of science, and are mutually corroborative. They have withstood tests and searching criticism as rigorous as that to which any scientific principles have been subjected. No scientific hypothesis suggested as an alternative to evolution has succeeded in explaining relevant natural phenomena. Moreover, insights provided by evolutionary principles have been the basis for progress in the biological and bio-medical sciences which has benefited mankind in many ways.

There are important questions remaining, of course, about how evolution operates. We have made progress in this area during the past century, but debates about evolutionary mechanisms still go on today. Some creationists, in an attempt to discredit the principles of evolution, have emphasized these disagreements between scientists about how evolution takes place. But such discussion is a normal part of how science works; fruitful controversy plays an important role in stimulating scientific investigation and furthering scientific knowledge. Debate about evolutionary mechanisms in no way undermines scientists' confidence in the reality of evolution, any more than disagreement about the behavior of subatomic particles would lead scientists to doubt the existence of atoms.

Creationists contend that creationism is a scientific theory and therefore a valid alternative to evolution. But to quote from a statement by the National Science Teachers Association, "The true test of a theory in science is threefold: (1) its ability to explain what has been observed; (2) its ability to predict what has not been observed; and (3) its ability to be tested by further experimentation and to be modified by the acquisition of new data." Viewed in the context of these criteria, creationism is not scientific. There should be opportunity for full discussion of such non-scientific ideas in appropriate forums, but they have no place in science classes. The content of science courses must meet scientific criteria; to require equal time for discussion of non-science topics would destroy the integrity of science education.

Therefore, we the members of the North Carolina Academy of Science declare the following to be the position of the Academy on this issue:

The North Carolina Academy of Science strongly opposes the mandated inclusion of creationist views of origins in public school science classes. Furthermore, the Academy is strongly opposed to any mandated exclusion of the principles of evolution from public school instruction. We totally reject the concept, put forth by certain pressure groups, that evolution is itself a tenet of religion. And we assert that evolution is the only strictly scientific explanation for changes in the biota of the earth over time and for the existence and diversity of living organisms.

January 1982

Ohio Academy of Science

Advocacy for Teaching Cosmic, Geological and Biological Evolution and Opposition to Forced Teaching of Creationist Beliefs in Public School Science Education

WHEREAS, it is a responsibility of the Ohio Academy of Science to preserve the integrity of science; and

WHEREAS, science is a systematic method of continuing investigation, based on observation, hypothesis testing, measurement, experimentation, and theory building, which leads to more adequate explanations of natural phenomena, explanations that are open to further testing, revision, and falsification, and while not "believed in" through faith may be accepted or rejected on the basis of evidence; and

WHEREAS, the theory of evolution, as presently defined, fully satisfies these criteria, especially when its teaching considers the remaining debates concerning its detailed mechanisms; and

WHEREAS, the Academy respects the right of people to hold diverse beliefs about creation that do not come within the definitions of science; and

WHEREAS, some Creationist groups are intent on imposing religious beliefs disguised as science upon teachers and students to the detriment and distortion of public education in the United States;

THEREFORE, BE IT RESOLVED that because "Creation Science" and "Intelligent Design" have no scientific validity, they should not be taught as science, and further that the OAS views legislation requiring such religious views to be taught in public schools, as though these were legitimate arguments against evolution that should be included as part of a so-called balanced treatment approach, to be a real and present threat to the integrity of education and the teaching of science; and

BE IT FURTHER RESOLVED that the OAS urges citizens, educational authorities, and legislators to oppose the compulsory inclusion in the curricula, the state competencies or proficiency tests for science education of religious beliefs that are not amenable to the process of scrutiny, testing, and revision that is indispensable to science.

BE IT FURTHER RESOLVED that the OAS urges citizens, educational authorities, and legislators to include, explicitly, cosmic, geological and biological evolution in the curricula, state competencies and proficiency tests for science education.

Revised and Approved February 28, 2000 by the Executive Committee of The Ohio Academy of Science; based on a similar resolution adopted by the Academy on April 23, 1982.

Ohio Mathematics and Science Coalition

Position Statement on Intelligent Design as an Academic Science Topic

The Ohio Mathematics and Science Coalition recommends the following criteria for deliberation prior to the addition or deletion of a topic to or from the Ohio Academic Content Standards for Science.

What should or should not be part of an Ohio Academic Standard for Science must be judged in the context of the nature and processes that legitimize science as an area of learning and as a discipline unique from others.

We urge that the decision to include or exclude any topic in the Ohio Academic Content Standards for Science be given consideration according to the American Heritage Dictionary definition that states "Science is the observation, identification, description, experimental investigation and theoretical explanation of natural phenomena" (adopted by the Ohio Mathematics and Science Coalition) and the following three criteria:

1. The topic must be consistent with the body of scientific knowledge, the processes employed by science, and the ways of reasoning scientifically that constitute acceptable scientific professional practices, and with the discipline of science.

2. The topic must contribute to the curriculum enabling a student to think and function as a person who is well versed in scientific literacy, understands the nature of science and the tools a person employs in drawing conclusions, and making conjectures through science.

3. Science must be the appropriate discipline in the curriculum where a student should engage the topic.

The Ohio Mathematics and Science Coalition believes that "Intelligent Design" does not meet the above criteria and, therefore, does not have a place in the Ohio academic content standards for science.

2002

The Paleontological Society

Position Statement: Evolution

Evolution is both a scientific fact and a scientific theory. Evolution is a fact in the sense that life has changed through time. In nature today, the characteristics of species are changing, and new species are arising. The fossil record is the primary factual evidence for evolution in times past, and evolution is well documented by further evidence from other scientific disciplines, including comparative anatomy, biogeography, genetics, molecular biology, and studies of viral and bacterial diseases.

Evolution is also a theory – an explanation for the observed changes in life through Earth history that has been tested numerous times and repeatedly confirmed. Evolution is an elegant theory that explains the history of life through geologic time; the diversity of living organisms, including their genetic, molecular, and physical similarities and differences; and the geographic distribution of organisms. Evolutionary principles are the foundation of all basic and applied biology and paleontology, from biodiversity studies to studies on the control of emerging diseases.

Because evolution is fundamental to understanding both living and extinct organisms, it must be taught in public school science classes. In contrast, creationism is religion rather than science, as ruled in recent course cases, because it invokes supernatural explanations that cannot be tested. Consequently, creationism in any form (including "scientific creationism," "creation science," and "intelligent design") must be excluded from public school science classes. Because science involves testing hypotheses, scientific explanations are restricted to natural causes.

This difference between science and religion does not mean that the two fields are incompatible. Many scientists who study evolution are religious, and many religious denominations have issued statements supporting evolution. Science and religion address different questions and employ different ways of knowing.

The evolution paradigm has withstood nearly 150 years of scrutiny. Although the existence of evolution has been confirmed many times, as a science evolutionary theory must continue to be open to testing. At this time, however, more fruitful inquiries address the tempo and mode of evolution, various processes involved in evolution, and driving factors for evolution. Through such inquiry, the unifying theory of evolution will become an even more powerful explanation for the history of life on Earth.

Revised 4/3/03

Pennsylvania Academy of Science

Resolution on Teaching of Evolution

Be it resolved on this 2nd day of April, in the year 2006, the Executive Board of the Pennsylvania Academy of Science passed the following resolution on the teaching of science based evolution in accredited elementary and secondary schools (K-12) in the Commonwealth of Pennsylvania.

The theory of evolution is based on sound scientific principles and supported by over 145 years of research in all biological disciplines. It is the cornerstone of biological education around the world.

The scientific evidence and well supported data for evolution, as proposed by Darwin (1859) and refined through the modern synthesis by Dobzhansky, Chetverikov,

Fisher, Wright, Simpson, Stebbins, Babcock, Gould, Freeman, Miller, Mayr and others, are overwhelming.

In contrast, there is no scientific evidence or supporting data for the idea of intelligent design. This theological/philosophical concept does not belong in the science curriculum, but perhaps in cultural, philosophical, or theological comparative studies.

Accordingly, be it resolved that the Executive Board of the Pennsylvania Academy of Science rejects the idea that intelligent design as an alternative to modern evolutionary theory be taught in science/biology classes in accredited elementary and secondary (K-12) schools across the Commonwealth of Pennsylvania.

Be it also resolved, that the Executive Board of the Pennsylvania Academy of Science supports the teaching of evolution, as supported by valid scientific evidence, in science/biology classes in accredited elementary and secondary schools (K-12) across the Commonwealth of Pennsylvania.

April 2, 2006

Pennsylvania Council of Professional Geologists

The Role of Science and Scientific Standards in Pennsylvania Public School Curricula

The Pennsylvania Council of Professional Geologists, representing more than 500 practicing geologists in the Commonwealth of Pennsylvania, opposes educational proposals and/or actions which would dilute the quality and quantity of science education by incorporating non-scientific concepts or methods into public school biology curricula as alternative explanations to biological evolution. In particular, PCPG opposes the introduction or instruction of the concept of 'intelligent design' as an alternative to biological evolution, but is equally opposed to the inclusion of any positions or philosophies in science curricula which are not based on scientific methods and accepted by the scientific community.

PCPG is an advocacy organization which actively promotes science education in Pennsylvania. As such, and in light of its mission to increase the protection of public welfare through continued improvements in the awareness and application of science within the Commonwealth, PCPG supports the Pennsylvania Department of Education standards on science education which specify a curriculum including biological evolution as the accepted scientific explanation of the diversity of life on Earth.

Biological evolution is a fact. Evolution is change to populations over time and the constituent species of life on Earth have undeniably changed over geologic time. The theory of biological evolution, the lengthy explanation of the accepted fact of evolution, is supported by a myriad of scientific facts. Establishing many of those facts has been, and remains the purview of geologists. PCPG does not imply that the scientific community is in complete accord regarding the rate of evolutionary change, or which of the several mechanisms provides the greatest contribution to change under different circumstances. PCPG does hold that the theory of evolution, in its totality, is the only scientifically accepted explanation of the diversity of life on earth.

The Scientific Method places no bounds or limits on the scope or direction of scientific inquiry into the natural world. Inquiry within the construct of intelligent design, however, is bounded and limited. Intelligent design, therefore, can never be considered a science and its conclusions are, as a result, unscientific. Consequently, intelligent design and/or other non-scientific alternatives to any scientifically derived and supported theory have no established place in science curricula.

The claim that intelligent design should be taught, or even mentioned, as part of science curricula in schools because there is "scientific controversy regarding the theory of evolution" is not supported by facts. Controversies surrounding biological evolution and/or its inclusion in educational curricula are not based on scientifically derived facts or on competing scientific theories of which there are none.

As the premier organization which promotes the education and professional application of Earth Sciences in the Commonwealth of Pennsylvania, PCPG encourages and fosters science education and specifically opposes any educational proposals or reforms which would dilute the quality and quantity of scientific tutelage by the mandatory introduction of non-scientific concepts. Likewise, PCPG opposes the adoption and use of educational disclaimers, written or stated, which:

- infer that biological evolution is "only a theory" and not, therefore, a fact;

and/or which

- state or imply that there is controversy within the scientific community in general, and the community of researching and published biologists and geologists in particular, regarding the naturalistic explanation of the diversity of life provided by the comprehensive theory of evolution.

2005

Philosophy of Science Association

The Testing of Evolution in Kansas Schools

The American Association for the Advancement of Science requested that their constituent societies (which includes PSA) write letters of protest to the Governor of Kansas regarding the State Board of Education's decision to de-emphasize the testing (and thereby, presumably, the teaching) of evolution and cosmology. After discussion, the Officers of the Association composed and sent the following message to the Governor. As of the present date (1 Feb 00), the Governor has not seen fit to respond to our message.

George Gale, Executive Secretary
The Honorable Bill Graves, Governor
State Capitol, 2nd Floor
Topeka, KS 66612

Dear Governor Graves:

The President and Governing Board of the Philosophy of Science Association deplore the recent decision by the Kansas State Board of Education to remove references to evolution and cosmology from its state education standards and assessments. In our judgment, this decision is likely to decrease the quality of education in Kansas in three important ways.

First, the omission of important and well-established parts of science from the curriculum directly affects the ability of future citizens to understand questions that will affect the well-being of their families and communities. In addition, the students of Kansas will not be given our best answers to questions about the history of our species, the history of life on our planet, and the history of the universe, questions that are of concern to all thoughtful people. There is no more reason to deny them these answers than to leave them with the belief that the Earth is flat.

Second, by pretending that there are serious controversies in areas where a massive body of evidence supports contemporary scientific views, and insisting that this evidence should not be presented and assessed, students are deprived of the opportunity for open critical discussion. An educational system should foster habits of inquiry by giving a fair account of the evidence for rival points of view, and by showing how important questions can be resolved.

Third, by allowing the religious beliefs of a particular group to dictate the form of the science curriculum, the recent decision gives notice to those teaching in Kansas High Schools that they are not to be allowed to impart what they know. They will also understand that they are likely to encounter further pressure to conform to the demands of a very specific faith. Under these circumstances, it is probable that Kansas schools will fail to attract the most thoughtful and dedicated teachers, so that Kansas students will be further disadvantaged.

For these reasons we align ourselves with the AAAS resolution, and urge that this ill-conceived decision be reconsidered.

Yours sincerely,
Richard Jeffrey, President

Originally printed in the PSA newsletter, February 2000

Research!America

Teaching of Intelligent Design in Science Classrooms

Research!America supports the scientific community's unanimous position that intelligent design does not meet the criteria of a scientific concept and thus should not be presented as one in the classroom. Evolution is backed by a substantial body of scientific evidence, whereas intelligent design is a matter of belief and not subject to proof.

Opinion polls commissioned by Research!America and others show a woeful lack of appreciation among the public that biological evolution is well-supported by scientific evidence. At a time of heightened global competition in science and technology, the American public deserves, now more than ever, nothing less than the best science education in the world.

8/4/2005

Royal Astronomical Society of Canada - Ottawa Centre

Science & Evolution

The RASC Ottawa Centre supports high standards of scientific integrity, academic freedom and the free exchange of ideas. It also respects the scientific method and recognizes that the validity of any scientific model comes only as a result of rational hypotheses, sound experimentation, and findings that can be replicated by others.

The RASC Ottawa Centre, then, is unequivocal in its support of contemporary evolutionary theory that has its roots in the seminal work of Charles Darwin and has been refined by findings accumulated over 140 years.

Some dissenters from this position are proponents of non-scientific explanations of the nature of the universe. These may include "creation science", "creationism", "in-

Voices for Evolution

telligent design" or other non-scientific "alternatives to evolution". While we respect the dissenters' right to express their views, these views are theirs alone and are in no way endorsed by the RASC Ottawa Centre. It is our collective position that these explanations do not meet the characteristics and rigour of scientific empiricism.

Therefore the science agenda of the RASC Ottawa Centre and its publications will not promote any non-scientific explanations of the nature of the universe.

Approved by RASC Ottawa Centre Council, April 26, 2007

The Royal Society

A statement by the Royal Society on evolution, creationism and intelligent design

The Royal Society was founded in 1660 by a group of scholars whose desire was to promote an understanding of ourselves and the universe through experiment and observation. This approach to the acquisition of knowledge forms the basis of the scientific method, which involves the testing of theories against observational evidence. It has led to major advances of understanding over more than 300 years. Although there is still much left to be discovered, we now have a broad knowledge of how the universe developed after the 'Big Bang' and of how humans and other species appeared on Earth.

One of the most important advances in our knowledge has been the development of the theory of evolution by natural selection. Since being proposed by Charles Darwin nearly 150 years ago, the theory of evolution has been supported by a mounting body of scientific evidence. Today it is recognised as the best explanation for the development of life on Earth from its beginnings and for the diversity of species. Evolution is rightly taught as an essential part of biology and science courses in schools, colleges and universities across the world.

The process of evolution can be seen in action today, for example in the development of resistance to antibiotics in disease-causing bacteria, of resistance to pesticides by insect pests, and the rapid evolution of viruses that are responsible for influenza and AIDS. Darwin's theory of evolution helps us to understand these problems and to find solutions to them.

Many other explanations, some of them based on religious belief, have been offered for the development of life on Earth, and the existence of a 'creator' is fundamental to many religions. Many people both believe in a creator and accept the scientific evidence for how the universe, and life on Earth, developed. Creationism is a belief that may be taught as part of religious education in schools, colleges and universities. Creationism may also be taught in some science classes to demonstrate the difference between theories, such as evolution, that are based on scientific evidence, and beliefs, such as creationism, that are based on faith.

However, some versions of creationism are incompatible with the scientific evidence. For instance, a belief that all species on Earth have always existed in their present form is not consistent with the wealth of evidence for evolution, such as the fossil record. Similarly, a belief that the Earth was formed in 4004 BC is not consistent with the evidence from geology, astronomy and physics that the solar system, including Earth, formed about 4600 million years ago.

Some proponents of an alternative explanation for the diversity of life on Earth now claim that their theories are based on scientific evidence. One such view is presented as the theory of intelligent design. This proposes that some species are too complex to have evolved through natural selection and that therefore life on Earth must be the product of a 'designer'. Its supporters make only selective reference to the overwhelming scientific evidence that supports evolution, and treat gaps in current knowledge which, as in all areas of science, certainly exist–as if they were evidence for a 'designer'. In this respect, intelligent design has far more in common with a religious belief in creationism than it has with science, which is based on evidence acquired through experiment and observation. The theory of evolution is supported by the weight of scientific evidence; the theory of intelligent design is not.

Science has proved enormously successful in advancing our understanding of the world, and young people are entitled to learn about scientific knowledge, including evolution. They also have a right to learn how science advances, and that there are, of course, many things that science cannot yet explain. Some may wish to explore the compatibility, or otherwise, of science with various religious beliefs, and they should be encouraged to do so. However, young people are poorly served by deliberate attempts to withhold, distort or misrepresent scientific knowledge and understanding in order to promote particular religious beliefs.

April 2006

Royal Society of Canada

Dear Colleagues:

The RSC office has received some calls requesting that it state its position in the debate about Intelligent Design vs Evolution. Through publications over the last decades [...] and the RSC support of the IAP Statement on the Teaching of Evolution, the Society has made its position explicit.

Intelligent Design is a religious belief, and Evolution is the only credible scientific position that is defensible. The RSC position in support of evolution has been consistent: from a scientific point of view, the teaching of Evolution is a benchmark for legitimacy. Other theories or positions, such as Intelligent Design, are not scientific in basis or nature.

On March 27, 2006, the Society was signatory to the IAP Statement of international Academies of Sciences. The Statement, whose full text will appear on our website toward the end of May, urges "decision makers, teachers, and parents to educate all children about the methods and discoveries of science and to foster an understanding of the science of nature." It underscores the importance of "evidence-based facts about the origins and evolution of the Earth and of life on this planet."

Consequently the position of the RSC is clear on this matter.

Patricia Demers
President

April 2006

Academy of Science of the Royal Society of Canada

The Academy of Science of the Royal Society of Canada considers that "scientific creationism" has nothing to do with science or the scientific method. "Scientific creationism" does not belong in any discussion of scientific principles or theories, and therefore should have no place in a science curriculum.

Science provides knowledge of the natural world in the form of evidence gathered by observation and experiment. Analysis of this evidence allows scientists to generate hypotheses that link and explain different phenomena. Scientific hypotheses must be capable of being tested by further research. If a hypothesis is found to explain many different facts, and even to allow accurate predictions of subsequent discoveries, greater confidence is placed in it, and it is called a theory.

The theory of evolution by natural selection was first clearly formulated in 1859, and for over a century it has been tested and improved by the research of many thousands of scientists: not only by biologists and geologists, but also by chemists and physicists. From deductions based on abundant data, the theory has been developed to explain the changes that have taken place in living things over much of the Earth's history. In its modern form, it remains the only explanation for the diversity of life on this planet that is acceptable to the scientific community.

Science itself evolves, since it must continuously modify existing explanations to incorporate new information. The theory of evolution continues to be refined as new evidence becomes available. Only one thing in science is not open to change: its demand that every explanation be based on observation or experiment, that these be in principle repeatable, and that new evidence be considered.

Scientific creationists adopt an entirely different approach in their attempt to explain the natural world. They accept either biblical or some other authority as overriding other kinds of evidence. They reject much of the accumulated scientific knowledge, and commonly deny the validity of deductions based on directly observable phenomena such as radioactive decay. This is because their philosophy is rooted in a different aspect of human culture. If their claim, that the Earth and all its living things were created only several thousand years ago, was correct, many of the central concepts of modern science would have to be abandoned. The methodology and conclusions of scientists and "scientific creationists" are therefore incompatible, and the term "scientific creationism" is a contradiction in terms, since it has no basis in science.

Delivered by Fellows of the Academy to each Provincial Minister of Education in Canada. Published in Geotimes, November 1985, p. 21.

Sigma Xi, Louisiana State University Chapter, Baton Rouge, Louisiana

The LSU Chapter of Sigma Xi urges the reconsideration and repeal of the "Balanced Treatment for Creation-Science and Evolution-Science Act" which in 1981 became part of Louisiana law.

The current science curriculum is the result of numerous discoveries and critical studies by scientists over many decades. The scientific process affords equal treatment to every theory by requiring it to face the evidence successfully before it becomes part of the science curriculum. The theory called "creation science" cannot successfully face the evidence. The Act constitutes intervention by the State to give that theory a standing it has not earned. The Act, if put into effect, would violate academic freedom and weaken science education. This is a time for strengthening educational standards and programs, particularly in science.

Approved by mail ballot of the membership and released 15 February 1982.

Society for Amateur Scientists

The Society for Amateur Scientists was founded to place the power, process, and promise of science within reach of everyone. SAS links science enthusiasts of all backgrounds and interests with world-class professional scientists, to empower amateurs to take part in the great scientific debates of our time as full members of the scientific community. Our mission is two-fold: to advance science by bringing untapped talent into the field, and to help create a more scientifically literate public.

The debate about teaching evolution and scientific creationism in the public schools has raged for decades. Is it appropriate for a grass roots science organization like ours to comment on this debate? Absolutely. The Society for Amateur Scientists was founded to educate people about how science works, what science tells us about our world, and how everyday people can take an active part in fascinating scientific issues. Some participants in this debate constantly distort science and misinform the public. Correcting misunderstandings is clearly part of any educational mission.

But there is a deeper concern. Our democracy depends on an informed and educated electorate. As science literacy suffers, so does our country. This is truer today then ever before as the voting public is faced with ever more technical issues about which they are asked to make informed choices. By not opposing bad science whenever we can, SAS would be implicitly aiding the forces of unreason to distort fundamental principles of science in the public mind. We believe that it is vital that all scientific organizations, including SAS, stand against bad science.

In the last 100 years, science has forged a profound understanding of many different fields which bear on the question of our origin. Genetics, astronomy, geology, paleontology, biology, physiology, anatomy and physics all speak with one voice. The universe is ancient, perhaps 15 billion years old. The earth too is ancient, perhaps 5 billion years old. And life is ancient, perhaps 2 billion years old.

The evidence is abundant and irrefutable. Life has changed drastically over earth's history. Since the first complex multi-cellular forms appeared about 650 million years ago organisms have lived, died and adapted to their environments through many violent upheavals on the planet. The one constant has been the process of change itself – of mutation and natural selection, the hammer and anvil by which nature has sculpted her handiwork into the imperfectly beautiful and intricate web of life that now covers the planet.

Voices for Evolution

On the question of humanity, the data support only one conclusion – humans arose like all other beings with which we share the earth; through the random mutations altering our ancestors' bodies over eons, and natural selection blindly and mercilessly cutting away the chaff. Evolution is the great shaper of all life on earth.

Today, evolution is the unifying principle of biology. Nothing makes sense without it. True, it remains a very active field of research and many subtle and fascinating questions remain to be answered. However, that life has adapted and changed through time is as well established as the fact that the earth goes round the sun.

Evolution is science, and as such belongs in science classrooms. By contrast scientific creationism just doesn't make the grade. None of the arguments which scientific creationists make against evolution withstand scrutiny and most were first refuted nearly a century ago. And the creationists have never been able to marshal quality evidence that strongly supports their ideas.

This statement was approved by our Board of Directors. Amateur scientists are often fiercely independent, and some of our members do not accept evolution. While the Board of Directors respects their views and values their input, we wish to make it clear that SAS will never participate in creationist research. However, we do not restrict our membership to avowed evolutionists. As a scientific organization, we insist only that our members be willing to consider any position that can be supported by empirical evidence. In this we are quite unlike the Institute for Creation Research (ICR), the primary promoter of Scientific Creationism in public school, which requires its members to sign a statement attesting to their belief in the literal truth of the Bible. ICR's agenda is religion concealed in the guise of science. Their materials in particular have no place in a science classroom.

Shawn Carlson, Ph.D.
Elizabeth Arsem
Paul MacCready, Ph.D.
Glenn T. Seaborg, Ph.D.

1994

Society for Integrative and Comparative Biology

Nothing in biology makes sense except in the light of evolution. Insofar as the life sciences are critical to human health, well-being, and knowledge, evolutionary biology is and must be a fundamental component of an excellent science education. Moreover, awareness of current views concerning evolutionary history and mechanisms, including natural selection, is an essential part of modern literacy for all citizens. Excellence in education requires that teachers and students can explore, investigate, and criticize scientific ideas. However, learning and inquiry are inhibited when educators feel pressured to alter their teaching of fundamental concepts of science in response to demands external to the scientific disciplines. The Society for Integrative and Comparative Biology is committed to these principles and will support the teaching of fundamental concepts and ideas in science, including those related to evolution and the nature of scientific inquiry.

Approved January 6, 2001.

Society for Neuroscience

Statement on Evolution versus Intelligent Design

Recognizing that the theory of evolution is fundamental to understanding and studying the origins and diversity of living things, the Society for Neuroscience opposes the assertion that teaching intelligent design theory is a valid scientific alternative to teaching evolution in science classrooms.

The theory of evolution is accepted with remarkable consensus throughout the scientific community. The evidence in its support has accumulated over the past 160 years – from fields as disparate as paleontology and genomics – and is overwhelming. Scientific advances in the field of evolution, as in every other field of science, are obtained on the basis of respectful debate, the continuous search for truth, and meticulous investigation to accept or reject ideas supported by evidence. In this regard, education on evolution and on science in general provides tools for a better understanding of ourselves and the world and also provides individuals with a language for universal understanding, mutual respect, and tolerance.

Intelligent design is the most recent attempt by creationists to undermine the theory of evolution in the science classroom. Thwarted by past legal decisions upholding the separation of church and state, proponents of intelligent design have resorted to masking their religious beliefs with the pseudo-scientific language of this theory. By invoking "intelligent forces" to account for biological diversity, however, intelligent design presents a theory that is as supernatural and unscientific as the traditional creationist one. In fact, intelligent design theory runs counter to the established principles of science in that it is not based on evidence or testable through the scientific method. Intelligent design is not science, and has no place in the science classroom.

The process underpinning evolution – natural selection – has been widely and thoroughly documented. As in all areas of active research, scientists continue to debate the details. Yet these disagreements should not be misconstrued, as they have been by creationists, as evidence of fundamental problems with the theory. There is consensus within the scientific community about the overall validity of Darwin's theory. In fact, evolution is still evident today; with bacterial resistance to antibiotics and potential mutations in influenza that could impact avian flu transmission as examples that profoundly affect world health. Evolution is an essential component of modern science education. K-12 science education based on anything other than tested and accepted scientific theory is detrimental to the education of America's youth.

Creationists often argue that religious and scientific worldviews are incompatible, asserting that it is impossible to be both actively religious and accept the theory of evolution. However, many people, including prominent scientists, embrace both evolution and a belief in God. SfN strongly disputes the claims made by advocates of intelligent design that subscribing to a scientific view of the world is incompatible with religious experience.

The Society for Neuroscience supports the teaching of evolution, and opposes the teaching of intelligent design in science classrooms. Education about evolution is essential to our future competitiveness as a nation, so it is imperative that an understanding of this fundamental scientific theory be shared with the school children of America. The mixing of faith or religious belief with the scientific method is not a sound lesson for our children's education.

2006

Society of Physics Students

Statement on Evolution and Science Education

Recently, some political and educational groups have attempted to undermine the importance of teaching the concepts of biological and cosmological evolution, thereby rejecting the consensus of the scientific community. Ideas about the structure and evolution of the universe, including Earth and its life forms, are unifying concepts in science. The development of students' informed views about these concepts is essential to a knowledge of science. These concepts should therefore be included and emphasized as a part of science frameworks and curricula for all students.

The Society of Physics Students (SPS) recognizes that decisions about science education standards are the purview of state and local authorities; however, the position of SPS is that such decisions should involve education experience and scientific expertise, and be based on the body of research in science, pedagogy, and cognitive development. SPS encourages science educators and scientists to participate in the development of science education standards by involving themselves in the decision-making processes of state and local school boards.

2003

Society for the Study of Evolution

In 1952, Ernst Mayr stated that "the aims of the Society [for the Study of Evolution], through its journal and otherwise, reflect the conviction, that the evolutionary approach will clarify many unsolved biological problems and will provide common goals and mutual comprehension among all the life sciences." The history of evolutionary studies has as its basis empirical documentation of biogeographical distribution of species. Contributing to its development are rigorous horticultural and agricultural programs that have led to substantial improvements in world food supplies. More recently, evolutionary studies have been applied to conservation and to health-related fields such as disease epidemiology. Increasingly, evolutionary studies are used to predict how the biological world responds to changing environments – environments that indisputably have changed over time. Evolutionary studies supply scientific explanations for past and present biological processes, based on currently observed biological processes. They have directly provided information, techniques, and even products that contribute to the improvement of human conditions and ecological welfare.

The study of evolution is an empirically based science which employs the scientific process of hypothesis testing. Hypotheses are either accepted or rejected, depending on the empirical evidence. The Society for the Study of Evolution employs a rigorous critical review process to ensure that these procedures are followed – that the empirical data support the conclusions – before a study is accepted as scientific. No hypothesis that cannot be tested empirically is acceptable as scientific to the Society. "Scientific creationism" cannot be empirically refuted. Rather, it has as its basis the unquestioned authority of a literal interpretation of religious texts. "Scientific creationism" does not employ hypothesis testing, does not use unbiased empirical data to support or refute hypotheses, and it has no scientific review process. It therefore cannot be considered to be scientific by the Society. The attitude that "scientific creationism" is an alternative hypothesis to evolution is scientifically untenable. Its inclusion in state-sponsored school curricula as a scientifically based hypothesis rather than as a religious faith is not acceptable. The Society for the Study of Evolution maintains that evolutionary studies should be promoted in schools as a scientific approach to explaining biological phenomena – one that has contributed much to biotechnological advances, and one which has the potential to solve important problems in the physical relationship of human beings to the rest of the biological world.

The Society of Systematic Biologists

Support for the Teaching of Evolution and Scope of Systematic Biology

The historical fact of evolution, as common descent with modification for life on earth, and the concepts used to study evolutionary change in living systems, provide the unifying theme for all biological knowledge. This is aptly summarized in Dobzhansky's statement that "nothing in biology makes sense except in the light of evolution." The corollary that nothing in evolution makes sense except in the light of phylogeny is broadly recognized as well.

SSB affirms that evolutionary biology is a fundamental and necessary component of an excellent science education. SSB strongly supports the teaching of evolution and teaching about the process of science in classrooms, museums, and science centers. Modern research in global environmental change, agriculture, medicine, and the spread and control of disease all depend on understanding evolutionary concepts. Thus, understanding biological systems, their evolutionary history and their mechanisms of change is crucial to human health and well-being. Awareness of current views concerning evolutionary biology, including natural selection, is an essential part of modern cultural and scientific literacy for all citizens. Excellence in education requires that teachers and students continually evaluate scientific ideas in light of evidence; however, learning and inquiry are inhibited when educators feel pressured to alter their teaching of fundamental concepts of science in response to demands external to the scientific disciplines.

Systematic biology is the scientific study of the diversity of organisms and of any and all relationships among them.

Concerns of systematic biologists include:

- phylogenetic analysis to produce or test hypotheses of genealogical relationship among groups of organisms, and using those hypotheses to:

- discover patterns of structural, developmental, or molecular evolution;

- learn about processes that underlie the origin and maintenance of taxonomic diversity;

- conduct studies of biogeographical, co-evolutionary, and paleobiological patterns to learn about the diversification, distribution, and extinction of taxa;

- learn about the tempo and mode of evolutionary change;

- conduct studies leading to improved classifications, better methods of taxonomic identification and nomenclatural reform.

SSB is dedicated to the advancement of the science of systematic biology in all aspects of theory and practice, for all living and extinct organisms. In its journal, "Systematic Biology", the society publishes original contributions regarding the theory, principles, and methods of systematics as well as evolution, morphology, biogeography, paleontology, genetics, and classification.

SSB encourages its members to stay informed about local science education issues and to promote rigorous and comprehensive teaching in the sciences, including evolutionary biology, for students at all levels.

Approved by SSB Council and Officers, 26 June 2001

Society of Vertebrate Paleontology (1986)

Be it resolved, that the Society of Vertebrate Paleontology opposes the teaching of so-called "creation science" or "scientific creationism" as a viable alternative to evolutionary explanations of the origin and history of the earth and of life, on the grounds that "creation science" or "scientific creationism" is in its essentials a body of religious doctrines rather than an embodiment of scientific process.

Be it further resolved, that the officers of the Society of Vertebrate Paleontology are hereby authorized to investigate the feasibility of associating the Society with one of the briefs of *amicus curiae* in the Louisiana creationism case now pending before the United States Supreme Court; and that, if feasible, the Society of Vertebrate Paleontology formally associate itself with such a brief opposing the teaching of "scientific creationism" as science.

Unanimously passed at the general business meeting held during the 46th annual meeting in Philadelphia, on 7 November 1986, and distributed by letter over the signature of SVP President Bruce J. MacFadden

Society of Vertebrate Paleontology (1994)

The fossil record of vertebrates unequivocally supports the hypothesis that vertebrates have evolved through time, from their first records in the early Paleozoic Era about 500 million years ago to the great diversity we see in the world today. The hypothesis has been strengthened by so many independent observations of fossil sequences that it has come to be regarded as a confirmed fact, as certain as the drift of continents through time or the lawful operation of gravity.

Paleontology relies for its evidence on two different but historically related fields, biology and geology. Evolution is the central organizing principle of biology, understood as descent with modification. Evolution is equally basic to geology, because the patterns of rock formations, geomorphology, and fossil distributions in the world make no sense without the underlying process of change through time. Sometimes this change has been gradual, and sometimes it has been characterized by violent upheaval. These processes can be seen on the Earth today in the forms of earthquakes, volcanoes, and other tectonic phenomena. Vertebrates have also evolved at a variety of rates, some apparently gradual, and some apparently rapidly. Although the fossil record is not complete, and our knowledge of evolution will always be less than entire, the evidence for the progressive replacement of fossil forms has been adequate to support the theory of evolution for over 150 years, well before genetic mechanisms of evolutionary change were understood. Paleontologists may dispute, on the basis of the available evidence, the tempo and mode of evolution in a particular group at a particular time, but they do not argue about whether evolution took place: that is a fact.

The fossil record has long been seen as a search for "ancestors" of living forms and of other fossil forms. Some fossil vertebrates appear to have no features that debar them from ancestry to other groups, and so could be seen as potential ancestors. Nevertheless, paleontologists do not focus on a search for direct ancestors, but rather look for sets of evolutionarily derived characters that are shared by fossil taxa that can then be linked as each other's closest known relatives. Proceeding in this way, paleontologists have clarified in recent years a great many mysteries about the origins and interrelationships of major groups of vertebrates, including birds, dinosaurs and their relatives, lizards and snakes, Mesozoic marine reptiles, turtles, mammals and their relatives, amphibians, the first tetrapods, and many groups of fishes. At the same time, techniques of geologic dating, including magnetostratigraphy, radiometric dating of many different isotopes of common elements, lithostratigraphy, and biostratigraphy, have provided independent lines of evidence for determining age relationships of the sediments in which fossils are found. This evidence from the principles and techniques of chemistry and physics support the finds of paleontology based on paleobiological and geological analyses, making the theory of evolution the only robust scientific explanation for the patterns of life on Earth.

Evolution is fundamental to the teaching of good biology and geology, and the vertebrate fossil record is an excellent set of examples of the patterns and processes of evolution through time. We therefore urge the teaching of evolution as the only possible reflection of our science. Any attempt to compromise the patterns and processes of evolution in science education, to treat them as less than robust explanations, or to admit "alternative" explanations not relying upon sound evolutionary observations and theory, misrepresents the state of our science and does a disservice to the public. Textbooks and other instructional materials should not indulge in such misrepresentation, educators should shun such materials for classroom use, and teachers should not be harassed or impeded from teaching vertebrate evolution as it is understood by its practitioners. The record of vertebrate evolution is exciting, inspirational, instructive, and enjoyable, and it is our view that everyone should have the opportunity and the privilege to understand it as paleontologists do.

Adopted November, 1994

Southern Anthropological Society

The Southern Anthropological Society deplores the intrusion of a particular religious doctrine into public school classrooms under the guise of so-called "scientific creationism."

These doctrines claim that a literalist reading of the account of the origins of the earth and life on it, as contained in the initial chapters of the book of Genesis, is supported by acceptable scientific evidence.

This interpretation treats a religious text as a scientific theory, which would seem to misrepresent both religion and science. The overwhelming evidence of the sciences – cosmology, geology, biology, anthropology, among others – indicates that the earth and all living forms on it have evolved from a simpler state, although, as in all ongoing science, theories as to how this took place continue to be revised in detail.

There is no necessary conflict between religious belief and inquiry into the natural world.

The institutionalization of creationist doctrine in the school curriculum will lead to the crippling of scientific inquiry as well as to the blurring of the important constitutional distinction between church and state.

Passed at the general business meeting of the Southern Anthropological Society on 16 April 1982 and published in The Southern Anthropologist *(SAS newsletter),* 10(1):1,7.

Tallahassee Scientific Society

A Statement of Resolution On the Teaching of Intelligent Design as Science

Recognizing that the concept of intelligent design (ID) represents a serious threat to the quality of science education in Florida and throughout the United States, the Board of Directors of the Tallahassee Scientific Society adopts the following resolution:

WHEREAS intelligent design was found in the 2005 federal court case *Kitzmiller et al v. Dover Area School District* to be the religious-based doctrine of creation science masquerading under another name and, specifically, not a scientific theory;

WHEREAS the teaching of creation science as a suitable alternative to standard science instruction in public classrooms was banned on constitutional grounds by the U.S. Supreme Court in 1987;

WHEREAS, to date, ID proponents have failed to offer any credible scientific evidence to support their claims about life's origins or proposed any scientific means of testing these claims;

WHEREAS the vast majority of scientists throughout the world hold that evolutionary theory is the only testable scientific theory in existence on how life developed over time and therefore is a major unifying force in contemporary science;

WHEREAS the theory of evolution is among the most tested theories in the life sciences and is supported by volumes of evidence in such fields as anthropology, genetics, biochemistry, developmental biology, comparative anatomy, immunology, geology, and paleontology;

WHEREAS the most eminent scientific societies in the United States, including the National Academy of Sciences, the American Association for the Advancement of Science, the American Chemical Society, the American Institute of Physics, the American Geophysical Union, the National Association of Biology Teachers, the American Society for Biochemistry and Molecular Biology and the Federation of American Societies for Experimental Biology – a consortium of 22 national scientific organizations with a combined membership of 85,000 scientists – have all passed resolutions condemning the promulgation of ID as science and as part of science education;

THEREFORE BE IT RESOLVED that the TSS supports the teaching of evolutionary theory as the only plausible scientific approach yet known to understanding the biological, chemical and physical underpinnings of how life developed and changed over time;

THEREFORE BE IT ALSO RESOLVED that the TSS opposes any reference to ID in Florida science education textbooks or science classroom instruction as anything other than a theological concept worthy of study only in such courses as religion, philosophy or history;

THEREFORE BE IT FURTHER RESOLVED that in the name of promoting public scientific literacy the TSS is committed to combating any effort aimed at placing ID, creation science or any other religion-based belief system on the same intellectual and scientific footing as the theory of evolution in any science education setting in Florida or elsewhere.

Approved by the Tallahassee Scientific Society Board of Directors on June 4, 2007

Position Statement: The Teaching of
Human Evolution in the High School Classroom

It has recently come to our attention that with the inclusion of the Gateway standards in the Tennessee high school biology curriculum, which require the coverage of evolutionary principles, many teachers are choosing to exclude human-related examples. We support and applaud the effort that administrators have made to insure the inclusion of evolution in the curriculum of high schools across the state. However, while we are sensitive to the fact that broaching this topic may be difficult for many individuals because of cultural beliefs or religious convictions, we find the exclusion of human evolution to be incompatible with the goal of integrating evolution throughout the biology curriculum. We are further disappointed because there are excellent examples from humans and closely related lineages that uniquely illustrate many evolutionary principles. Many students would find the discussion of these topics both relevant and intriguing, and their inclusion would help students appreciate relationships between ourselves and other organisms living on this planet. These points are outlined in more detail below:

1) Exclusion of human examples is incompatible with an accurate presentation of key ideas in biology in the curriculum.

Discussion of evolution in a topical framework is inadequate. Instead all topics in biology should be presented with an historical perspective. This approach makes the discussion of our historical relationships to other organisms inevitable. For example, all subjects in biology are enhanced by an evolutionary context from molecular (e.g., the universal nature of the genetic code), cellular (e.g., the origin of mitochondria), to developmental biology (e.g., similarity in early embryonic development among mammals) and the discussion of whole organisms (e.g., homological relationships in the anatomy of appendages in birds, bats, whales, etc.). Discussion of biology in an evolutionary framework would not only be more accurate, but would also render the subject matter intrinsically more interesting to students.

2) Examples from human evolution uniquely illustrate many evolutionary principles.

In humans and closely related species we have a relatively complete and well documented data base supporting evolutionary relationships. This is particularly true for a range of molecular and DNA sequence analyses that have been completed for humans and other primates from around the world. These molecular data combined with the available fossil evidence provide a substantial picture of the origin and migration patterns for human ancestors and related lineages. Presentation of salient examples from this information base (e.g., the disappearance of the Neandertals) would emphasize the "branchy" nature of our family tree and help erase inaccurate perceptions of linear progressions of fossil types that are still prevalent in the popular media.

3) Inclusion of human examples is crucial to communicate the relevance of evolutionary principles.

Much of the typical high school biology curriculum concentrates on human biology and human health issues. The delegation of evolution to a limited and focused presentation (the topical approach mentioned above) during which only non-human examples were used would provide the false impression that these principles have only limited application. Obviously teachers and textbook authors have chosen to provide a human focus for high school level because it facilitates increased interest and learning for these students. Utilization of human examples would emphasize the relevance of historical relationships among organisms and would be more likely to promote discussion and consideration of evolutionary principles in the broader context of biology.

Mitch Cruzan, President
Massimo Pigliucci
Tennessee Darwin Coalition
Department of Ecology and Evolutionary Biology
University of Tennessee, Knoxville

September 12, 2001

Virginia Academy of Science

Statement of the Position of the Virginia Academy of Science on the Teaching of Evolution

Science is three-fold. It consists of a body of information, a theoretical structure for organizing that information, and a method for generating new information and testing new theories. An acceptable scientific theory must be consistent with the available data and be subject to experimental verification. Any theory that cannot be tested lies outside the domain of science.

The central organizing principle of biology is the theory of evolution. It is consistent with the data of systematics, comparative anatomy and biochemistry, genetics, embryology and paleontology. It has been tested by the methods of population genetics and experimental breeding. Its detailed interpretation is subject to revision by the normal methods of science in the course of experimentation and peer review.

It is the duty of the scientific community to resist unwarranted political and religious intrusion into the domain of science. The Virginia Academy of Science, therefore, affirms the propriety of teaching the theory of evolution in secondary schools, colleges, and universities, and maintains that the curricula should conform to the highest professional standards of the various scientific disciplines.

Approved unanimously by the VAS Council, May 13, 1981

West Virginia Academy of Science

Be it resolved that the West Virginia Academy of Science adopts the following position statement on the relation between science and religion, and on their places in science classrooms in public schools.

In the modern world, science is one important way of organizing human experience. That there are other important ways is evident from the existence of diverse religions and other nonscientific systems of thought.

Our nation requires well trained scientists and scientifically literate citizens who understand the values and limitations of science. Therefore, science courses should not only convey the important conclusions of modern science, but should also help students to understand the nature of scientific thought, and how it differs from other modes of thought.

Teachers are professionally obligated to treat all questions as objectively as possible. Questions regarding the relation between science and various religions may arise. To the extent that a teacher feels competent to do so, he or she should be free to respond to such questions. It is appropriate to show why science limits itself to ways of reasoning that can only produce naturalistic explanations. However, teachers and students should be free to challenge the presuppositions of science and to question their adequacy as a basis for a religion or world view. Ideas offered seriously by students deserve a serious response. They will never be ridiculed by teachers with high professional standards. Furthermore, teachers should make it clear that students will be evaluated on their understanding of the concepts studied, and not on their personal beliefs regarding those concepts.

Dogmatic assertions are inconsistent with objective consideration of any subject. Science is always tentative and does not pretend to offer ultimate truth. Nevertheless, there is an overwhelming consensus among scientists that the earth is several billion years old, that living organisms are related by descent from common ancestors, and that interpretation of all available evidence by *scientific* standards renders contrary claims highly implausible.

"Scientific creationism," which does challenge these conclusions, is a point of view held only by those who insist that the principle of biblical inerrancy and perspicuity must take precedence over all scientific considerations. This viewpoint is religious. Their claim that scientific creationism is independent of biblical creationism, which they admit is religious, is demonstrably false. The consistently poor scholarship of their attempts to defend scientific creationism suggests that their dominating principle can be accepted on faith but is not compatible with scientific standards of reasoning. It is clear that scientific creationism and science are two distinct systems of thought. It should be noted that other religions, including other varieties of Christianity, are also distinct from science, but are compatible with it.

Scientific creationists have defined the issue in such a way that their point of view on one side is contrasted with all other points of view lumped together on the other side, even though some of these other points of view also consider themselves creationist. Their demand that public schools devote equal time and resources to scientific creationism is in effect a demand that their religion be accorded special status and that schools purchase large quantities of books from their publishing houses, even though these books demonstrably represent poor scholarship. It is an attempt to win by legislative decree what they have been unable to win through scholarly argument. Proposals for equal time legislation are unwise.

Be it resolved that the West Virginia Academy of Science endorses and adopts the AAAS (American Association for the Advancement of Science) resolution on Forced Teaching of Creationist Beliefs in Public School Science Education. This resolution, adopted by the AAAS Board of Directors and AAAS Council in January, 1982, read as follows: [AAAS 1982 Statement]

Passed at the WVAS annual business meeting on 3 April 1982 and published in the Proceedings of the West Virginia Academy of Science, *54:154-155.*

PART THREE

RELIGIOUS ORGANIZATIONS

Voices for Evolution

African Americans for Humanism

In recent years, religious fundamentalists have increased their efforts to teach Creationism in the public schools as an alternative to the theory of evolution. But though Creationism is pushed by religious adherents, the real conflict is not merely between religion and science, but between science and pseudoscience. Creationism does not qualify as a scientific theory because it begins with a conclusion (i.e., God created the universe) and seeks to support it, while scientific theories are prone to change (and may even be dismissed) in the light of new evidence. Creationism may or may not be good religion, but it is not good science, and should have no place in the public schools.

Many Creationists assert that evolution is used to further racism. But the scientific evidence has not led to racist conclusions in reputable scientific circles. On the contrary, human diversity is regarded as a product of genetic processes and natural selection, and "races" are always changing, often as a result of intermarriage among various peoples.

Conversely, many Creationists have propagated the racist "myth of Ham," or the belief that the "colored" peoples (who are supposedly descended from the eponymous Ham, the son of Noah) are cursed by God with servitude to whites. (Not surprisingly, such thinking spawned counter-myths among some black groups, such as the Nation of Islam, whose members have asserted that whites are a race of devils.) Evolution, far from supporting such notions, helps to dispel them.

Moreover, AAH is concerned that Blacks and other minorities are woefully underrepresented in the sciences. It will become increasingly difficult to attract and retain minority students to the sciences if they are constantly bombarded with pseudoscientific misinformation and unscientific methods of investigation. For these reasons, AAH opposes the introduction of Creationism into all science curricula of the U.S. public schools.

1994

American Humanist Association

A Statement Affirming Evolution as a Principle of Science

For many years it has been well established scientifically that all known forms of life, including human beings, have developed by a lengthy process of evolution. It is also verifiable today that very primitive forms of life, ancestral to all living forms, came into being thousands of millions of years ago. They constituted the trunk of a "tree of life" that, in growing, branched more and more; that is, some of the later descendants of these earliest living things, in growing more complex, became ever more diverse and increasingly different from one another. Humans and other highly organized types of today constitute the present twig-ends of that tree. The human twig and that of the apes sprang from the same apelike progenitor branch.

Scientists consider that none of their principles, no matter how seemingly firmly established - and no ordinary "facts" of direct observation either - are absolute certainties. Some possibility of human error, even if very slight, always exists. Scientists welcome the challenge of further testing of any view whatever. They use such terms as firmly established only for conclusions, founded on rigorous evidence, that have continued to withstand searching criticism.

The principle of biological evolution, as just stated, meets these criteria exceptionally well. It rests upon a multitude of discoveries of very different kinds that concur and complement one another. It is therefore accepted into humanity's general body of knowledge by scientists and other reasonable persons who have familiarized themselves with the evidence.

In recent years, the evidence for the principle of evolution has continued to accumulate. This has resulted in a firm understanding of biological evolution, including the further confirmation of the principle of natural selection and adaptation that Darwin and Wallace over a century ago showed to be an essential part of the process of biological evolution.

There are no alternative theories to the principle of evolution, with its "tree of life" pattern, that any competent biologist of today takes seriously. Moreover, the principle is so important for an understanding of the world we live in and of ourselves that the public in general, including students taking biology in school, should be made aware of it, and of the fact that it is firmly established in the view of the modern scientific community.

Creationism is not scientific; it is a purely religious view held by some religious sects and persons and strongly opposed by other religious sects and persons. Evolution is the only presently known strictly scientific and nonreligious explanation for the existence and diversity of living organisms. It is therefore the only view that should be expounded in public-school courses on science, which are distinct from those on religion.

We, the undersigned, call upon all local school boards, manufacturers of textbooks and teaching materials, elementary and secondary teachers of biological science, concerned citizens, and educational agencies to do the following:

- Resist and oppose measures currently before several state legislatures that would require that creationist views of origins be given equal treatment and emphasis in public-school biology classes and text materials.

- Reject the concept, currently being put forth by certain religious and creationist pressure groups, that alleges that evolution is itself a tenet of a religion of "secular humanism," and as such is unsuitable for inclusion in the public-school science curriculum.

- Give vigorous support and aid to those classroom teachers who present the subject matter of evolution fairly and who often encounter community opposition.

Composed by Bette Chambers, Isaac Asimov, Hudson Hoagland, Chauncey D. Leake, Linus Pauling, and George Gaylord Simpson; published over the signatures of 163 scientists, theologians, philosophers, and others in The Humanist, 37(1):46 (Jan/Feb 1977). © American Humanist Association. Reprinted with permission.

The American Jewish Committee

Creationism

Creationism or "creation science" – the belief that the origin of the world and the development of life were due to divine intervention – is not a scientific theory, but rather a matter of religious faith. As such, AJC has opposed its being taught in public school science classes and filed an amicus brief in the case of Edwards v. Aguillard in which the Supreme Court in 1987 struck down a state law mandating the teaching of creationism whenever the Darwinian theory of evolution was taught in public schools. In recent years, the forces determined to put creationism back in the public school curricula have been very active. AJC continues to oppose the teaching of "creation science" in public school science classes and opposes laws mandating its instruction alongside the theory of evolution. However, AJC does not oppose reference to "creationism" as a religious belief in elective courses, for example on comparative religion, at an age-appropriate level.

American Jewish Congress

The American Jewish Congress is a national organization committed to the vigorous enforcement of the First Amendment provision requiring separation of church and state. The First Amendment provides "Congress shall make no law respecting an establishment of religion." This provision – often called the establishment clause – forbids the government from performing or aiding in the performance of a religious function.

Our appearance at this hearing today arises from our concern that Proclamation 60 (both alone and together with Board Rule 5) abrogates the establishment clause in three fundamental ways. The first constitutional deficiency lies in the Proclamation's glaring omission of any reference to the Darwinian theory of evolution. The second constitutional deficiency lies in the Board Rule's requirement that evolution be singled out for a special negative treatment not required in connection with the teaching of any other scientific theory. The third constitutional deficiency arises from the fact that the proposed textbook standards allow for the teaching of scientific creationism. Despite attempts to describe scientific creationism as scientific theory, it is our position that scientific creationism is a religious theory and that, therefore, the First Amendment's establishment clause prohibits its being taught as science in public school classes.

It seems apparent that, in establishing the proposed textbook standards, the intent of the State Board of Education has been to avoid conflict with a particular religious doctrine and to allow for the inclusion of religious theory in the science curriculum. The United States Supreme Court has made clear that the approach employed by Proclamation 60 is unconstitutional. In 1968, in a case titled *Epperson vs Arkansas*, an Arkansas biology teacher asked the Supreme Court to declare void a state statute which prohibited the teaching of evolution and which prohibited the selection, adoption or use of textbooks teaching that doctrine. The Supreme Court held that the statute was unconstitutional. In its opinion the Supreme Court stated:

"The First Amendment's prohibition is absolute. It forbids alike the preference of a religious doctrine or the prohibition of a theory which is deemed antagonistic to a particular dogma."

Under the standards so clearly articulated by the Supreme Court, Proclamation 60 and Board Rule 5, as presently written, fail to satisfy the constitutional requirement of separation of church and state. In order to comply with the applicable constitutional provisions, the proclamation and board rule should be revised in three ways. First, evolution should be clearly included in the science curriculum. Second, evolution should be taught as are all scientific theories and should not be singled out for special negative comment. Finally, the proposed textbook standards should make clear that scientific creationism is not to be taught as scientific theory. Rather, because there is no constitutional objection to teaching about religion, public school teachers should simply tell their students, when evolution is taught, that there are

Voices for Evolution

certain religious groups whose members do not accept the Darwinian theory and advise them to consult with their parents or religious advisors for further guidance on the subject.

The American Jewish Congress believes that this approach is not only fully consistent with the Constitution but is also an effective means by which to resolve objections to the teaching of evolution.

Should the Board of Education fail to take the steps necessary to make the Proclamation constitutional, then the result could lead to textbooks which do not meet constitutional standards. And that mistake would be a costly one to the taxpayers.

> *Testimony in behalf of the American Jewish Congress by spokesperson*
> *Nina Cortell before the Texas State Board of Education, responding to*
> *Proclamation 60, setting forth specific content rules for biology and science*
> *textbooks to be adopted in 1984*

American Scientific Affiliation

A Voice for Evolution As Science

... After polling the membership on its views, the *Executive Council of the American Scientific Affiliation* hereby directs the following *Resolution* to public school teachers, administrators, school boards, and producers of elementary and secondary science textbooks or other educational materials:

Because it is our common desire to promote excellence and integrity in science education as well as in science; and

Because it is our common desire to bring to an end wasteful controversy generated by inappropriate entanglement of the scientific concept of evolution with political, philosophical, or religious perspectives;

We strongly urge that, in science education, the terms *evolution* and *theory of evolution* should be carefully defined and used in a consistently scientific manner; and

We further urge that, to make classroom instruction more stimulating while guarding it against the intrusion of extra-scientific beliefs, the teaching of *any* scientific subject, including evolutionary biology, should include (1) forceful presentation of well-established scientific data and conclusions; (2) clear distinction between evidence and inference; and (3) candid discussion of unsolved problems and open questions.

ASA was founded in 1941 as a nationwide fellowship of evangelical Christians trained in science. Its vision is "To have science and theology interacting and affecting one another in a positive light." The 1991 resolution was preceded by a background statement citing various definitions of evolution and identifying "scientific creationism" at one extreme and "evolutionary naturalism" at the other as "essentially religious doctrine masquerading as science." First published in ASA's journal, *Perspectives on Science & Christian Faith* (Vol. 44, No. 4, p. 252, Dec. 1992), the resolution and its background statement also appear in the 1993 edition of *Teaching Science in a Climate of Controversy*, a guidebook for high school teachers from ASA, P.O. Box 668, Ipswich, MA 01938.

> *Adopted by the Executive Council of the American Scientific Affiliation on*
> *December 7, 1991.*

Center for Theology and the Natural Sciences

The universe is more mysterious than either science or religion can ever fully disclose, and the urgencies of humankind and the natural environment demand an honest interaction between the discoveries of nature, the empowerment afforded us by appropriate technology, the inherent value of the environment, and the demand that we commit ourselves to a future in which all species can flourish. We can no longer afford the stalemate of past centuries between theology and science, for this leaves nature Godless and religion worldless. When this happens, our culture, hungering after science for something to fill the void of its lost spiritual resources, is easy prey to New Age illusions wrapped in scientific-sounding language – the 'cosmic self-realization movement' and the 'wow of physics' – while our 'denatured' religion, attempting to correct social wrong and to provide meaning and support for life's journey, is incapable of making its moral claims persuasive or its spiritual comfort effective because its cognitive claims are not credible. Nor can we allow science and religion to be seen as adversaries, for they will be locked in a conflict of mutual conquest, such as "creation science" which costs religion its credibility or a philosophical stance of "scientific materialism" which costs science its innocence....

Excerpted from the Mission Statement of the Center for Theology and the Natural Sciences, Berkeley, California

Central Conference of American Rabbis

On Creationism in School Textbooks

Whereas the principles and concepts of biological evolution are basic to understanding science; and

Whereas students who are not taught these principles, or who hear "creationism" presented as a scientific alternative, will not be receiving an education based on modern scientific knowledge; and

Whereas these students' ignorance about evolution will seriously undermine their understanding of the world and the natural laws governing it, and their introduction to other explanations described as "scientific" will give them false ideas about scientific methods and criteria,

Therefore be it resolved that the Central Conference of American Rabbis commend the Texas State Board of Education for affirming the constitutional separation of Church and State, and the principle that no group, no matter how large or small, may use the organs of government, of which the public schools are among the most conspicuous and influential, to foist its religious beliefs on others;

Be it further resolved that we call upon publishers of science textbooks to reject those texts that clearly distort the integrity of science and to treat other explanations of human origins for just what they are – beyond the realm of science;

Be it further resolved that we call upon science teachers and local school authorities in all states to demand quality textbooks that are based on modern, scientific knowledge and that exclude "scientific" creationism;

Be it further resolved that we call upon parents and other citizens concerned about the quality of science education in the public schools to urge their Boards of Education, publishers, and science teachers to implement these needed reforms.

Adopted at the 95th Annual Convention of the Central Conference of American Rabbis, 18-21 June 1984, at Grossinger's, New York.

Voices for Evolution

Clergy Letter Project

Within the community of Christian believers there are areas of dispute and disagreement, including the proper way to interpret Holy Scripture. While virtually all Christians take the Bible seriously and hold it to be authoritative in matters of faith and practice, the overwhelming majority do not read the Bible literally, as they would a science textbook. Many of the beloved stories found in the Bible - the Creation, Adam and Eve, Noah and the ark - convey timeless truths about God, human beings, and the proper relationship between Creator and creation expressed in the only form capable of transmitting these truths from generation to generation. Religious truth is of a different order from scientific truth. Its purpose is not to convey information but to transform hearts.

We the undersigned, Christian clergy from many different traditions, believe that the timeless truths of the Bible and the discoveries of modern science may comfortably coexist. We believe that the theory of evolution is a foundational scientific truth, one that has stood up to rigorous scrutiny and upon which much of human knowledge and achievement rest. To reject this truth or to treat it as 'one theory among others' is to deliberately embrace scientific ignorance and transmit such ignorance to our children. We believe that among God's good gifts are human minds capable of critical thought and that the failure to fully employ this gift is a rejection of the will of our Creator. To argue that God's loving plan of salvation for humanity precludes the full employment of the God-given faculty of reason is to attempt to limit God, an act of hubris. We urge school board members to preserve the integrity of the science curriculum by affirming the teaching of the theory of evolution as a core component of human knowledge. We ask that science remain science and that religion remain religion, two very different, but complementary, forms of truth

The Clergy Letter Project is an endeavor designed to demonstrate that religion and science can be compatible and to elevate the quality of the debate of this issue. This statement was signed by 11,107 members of the clergy as of December 19, 2007.

Council for Democratic and Secular Humanism

Concerning the origin and historical diversity of life on earth, secular humanists accept the fact of evolution as the essential framework of modern biology. Physico-chemical development paved the way for the origin of life about four billion years ago. Subsequent organic evolution is now documented by empirical evidence from geology, paleontology, biogeography, anthropology and genetics as well as comparative studies in taxonomy, biochemistry, embryology, anatomy and physiology. The ages of rock strata, with their fossils and artifacts in the geological column, are determined by radiometric dating techniques. Grounded in science and reason, evolution has descriptive and explanatory powers free from supernatural claims and dogmatic religious beliefs. Concerning models, mechanisms and interpretations, the present Neodarwinian synthesis in biological evolution is always subject to modification and expansion in light of new discoveries in science and widening perspectives in philosophy.

Defending the constitutional separation of church and state, secular humanists deplore the efforts of biblical fundamentalists or so-called scientific creationists to invade science classrooms and pressure textbook publishers with their religious myth and political agenda. We reject the teaching of religious fundamentalism as a viable alternative to organic evolution in science texts and biology classes. In fact, all religious beliefs and practices have evolved throughout human socio-cultural development. Clearly, a strict and literal interpretation of Genesis is merely a religious account for the origin of life that is not subject to testing by evidence, experience and experimentation. Consequently, biblical creationism is an ongoing and serious threat to science education, responsible research, critical thought and free inquiry. Authority and revelation are not reliable substitutes for the scientific method and logical procedure. In short, rigorous scrutiny shows evolutionary science and scriptural literalism, with its appeals to miraculous causes, to be opposing explanations for the appearance of all life forms on this planet.

Furthermore, secular humanists boldly accept the far-reaching consequences of evolution and extinction for understanding and appreciating the place our species occupies within earth history and this dynamic universe. The human animal is a product of, dependent upon, and totally within organic evolution. Comparative DNA studies show that humankind shares a common ancestry with the three great apes (orangutan, chimpanzee and gorilla). Fossil hominid evidence recently found in central East Africa documents the emergence of our species over the past four million years. No doubt, future discoveries will shed additional light on the origin and history of humankind from ape-like ancestors.

Religious beliefs in a personal god, human immortality, and a divine destiny for our species are inadmissible as scientific statements. And questions concerning metaphysics, epistemology, ethics and values are best answered in terms of science, reason and human experience within a humanist framework and a naturalist worldview.

Drafted for CODESH by H. James Birx, Ph.D. Executive Director for the Alliance of Secular Humanist Societies (ASHS), October, 1994. This organization has since changed its name to the Council for Secular Humanism.

Episcopal Bishop of Atlanta, the Rt. Rev. Bennett J. Sims

A Pastoral Statement on Creation and Evolution

Grace to you and peace from God our Father and from the Lord Jesus Christ.

Legislation is pending before the Georgia State Legislature which calls for the public financing and teaching of Scientific Creationism as a counter-understanding to Evolution, wherever the evolutionary view is taught in the public schools.

Scientific Creationism understands the cosmos and the world to have originated as the Bible describes the process in the opening chapters of Genesis.

The 74th Annual Council of the Diocese of Atlanta, in formal action on January 31, 1981, acted without a dissenting vote to oppose by resolution any action by the Georgia Legislature to impose the teaching of Scientific Creationism on the public school system. A copy of the resolution is attached to this Pastoral.

It seems important that the Episcopal Church in this diocese add to its brief resolution a statement of its own teaching. The office of Bishop is historically a teaching office, and I believe it is timely to offer instruction as to this Church's understanding of what has become a contested public issue.

To begin with creation is a fact. The world exists. We exist. Evolution is a theory. As a theory, evolution expresses human response to the fact of creation, since existence raises questions: how did creation come to be, and why?

The question of why is the deeper one. It takes us into the realm of value and purpose. This urgent inquiry is expressed in human history through religion and statements of faith. Christians cherish the Bible as the source book of appropriating the point and purpose of life. We regard the Bible as the Word of God, His revelation of Himself, the meaning of His work and the place of humanity in it.

The question of how is secondary, because human life has been lived heroically and to high purpose with the most primitive knowledge of the how of creation. Exploration of this secondary question is the work of science. Despite enormous scientific achievement, humanity continues to live with large uncertainty. Science, advancing on the question of how, will always raise as many questions as it answers. The stars of the exterior heavens beyond us and the subatomic structure of the interior deep beneath us beckon research as never before.

Religion and science are therefore distinguishable, but in some sense inseparable, because each is an enterprise, more or less, of every human being who asks why and how in dealing with existence. Religion and science interrelate as land and water, which are clearly not the same but need each other, since the land is the basin for all the waters of the earth and yet without the waters the land would be barren of the life inherent to its soil.

In the Bible the intermingling of why and how is evident, especially in the opening chapters of Genesis. There the majestic statements of God's action, its value and the place of humanity in it, use an orderly and sequential statement of method. The why of the divine work is carried in a primitive description of how the work was done.

But even here the distinction between religion and science is clear. In Genesis there is not one creation statement but two. They agree as to why and who, but are quite different as to how and when. The statements are set forth in tandem, chapter one of Genesis using one description of method and chapter two another. According to the first, humanity was created, male and female, after the creation of plants and animals. According to the second, man was created first, then the trees, the animals and finally the woman and not from the earth as in the first account, but from the rib of the man. Textual research shows that these two accounts are from two distinct eras, the first later in history, the second earlier.

From this evidence, internal to the very text of the Bible, we draw two conclusions.

First, God's revelation of purpose is the overarching constant. The creation is not accidental, aimless, devoid of feeling. Creation is the work of an orderly, purposeful Goodness. Beneath and around the cosmos are the everlasting arms. Touching the cosmos at every point of its advance, in depth and height, is a sovereign beauty and tenderness. Humanity is brooded over by an invincible Love that values the whole of the world as very good; that is the first deduction: God is constant.

Second, creation itself and the human factors are inconstant. Creation moves and changes. Human understanding moves and changes. Evolution as a contemporary description of the how of creation is anticipated in its newness by the very fluidity of the biblical text by the Bible's use of two distinct statements of human comprehension at the time of writing. As a theoretical deduction from the most careful and massive observation of the creation, the layers and deposits and undulations of this ever-changing old earth, evolution is itself a fluid perception. It raises as many questions as it answers. Evolution represents the best formulation of the knowledge that creation has disclosed to us, but it is the latest word from science, not the last.

If the world is not God's, the most eloquent or belligerent arguments will not make it so. If it is God's world, and this is the first declaration of our creed, then faith has no fear of anything the world itself reveals to the searching eye of science.

Insistence upon dated and partially contradictory statements of how as conditions for true belief in the why of creation cannot qualify either as faithful religion or as intelligent science. Neither evolution over an immensity of time nor the work done in a six-day week are articles of the creeds. It is a symptom of fearful and unsound religion to contend with one another as if they were. Historic creedal Christianity joyfully insists on God as sovereign and frees the human spirit to trust and seek that sovereignty in a world full of surprises.

Episcopal Church, General Convention (1982)

Whereas, the state legislatures of several states have recently passed so called "balanced treatment" laws requiring the teaching of "Creation-science" whenever evolutionary models are taught; and

Whereas, in many other states political pressures are developing for such "balanced treatment" laws; and

Whereas, the terms "Creationism" and "Creation-science" as understood in these laws do not refer simply to the affirmation that God created the Earth and Heavens and everything in them, but specify certain methods and timing of the creative acts, and impose limits on these acts which are neither scriptural nor accepted by many Christians; and

Whereas, the dogma of "Creationism" and "Creation-science" as understood in the above contexts has been discredited by scientific and theologic studies and rejected in the statements of many church leaders; and

Whereas, "Creationism" and "Creation-science" is not limited to just the origin of life, but intends to monitor public school courses, such as biology, life science, anthropology, sociology, and often also English, physics, chemistry, world history, philosophy, and social studies; therefore be it

Resolved, the House of Bishops concurring, That this 67th General Convention affirm its belief in the glorious ability of God to create in any manner, and in this affirmation reject the rigid dogmatism of the "Creationist" movement, and be it further

Resolved, That we affirm our support of the scientists, educators, and theologians in the search for truth in this creation that God has given and entrusted to us.

67th General Convention of the Episcopal Church, 1982

Episcopal Church, General Convention (2006)

Resolution A129: Affirm Creation and Evolution

Resolved, That the 75th General Convention affirm that God is Creator, in accordance with the witness of Scripture and the ancient Creeds of the Church; and be it further,

Resolved, That the theory of evolution provides a fruitful and unifying scientific explanation for the emergence of life on earth, that many theological interpretations of origins can readily embrace an evolutionary outlook, and that an acceptance of evolution is entirely compatible with an authentic and living Christian faith; and be it further

Voices for Evolution

Resolved, That Episcopalians strongly encourage state legislatures and state and local boards of education to establish standards for science education based on the best available scientific knowledge as accepted by a consensus of the scientific community; and be it further

Resolved, That Episcopal dioceses and congregations seek the assistance of scientists and science educators in understanding what constitutes reliable scientific knowledge.

Explanation

The theory of evolution is broadly accepted by the overwhelming majority in the scientific community as the most adequate explanation for the emergence of life on earth, and the ongoing adaptation of life to changes in environments. For example, knowledge of how evolution functions is essential in understanding the resistance of bacteria to antibiotics, the resistance of insects to insecticides, and the appearance of viruses such as HIV and influenza.

The teaching of evolution is a crucial contribution to the development of scientific literacy among the nation's youth, yet state legislators and state and local school boards continue to challenge, limit, or seek to supplant the teaching of evolution. Limiting the teaching of evolution in our schools has the potential to compromise students' ability to understand constantly changing living systems, and may undermine, for instance, the understanding and treatment of diseases of the future.

Since the sixteenth century, Anglicans have described their faith in terms of the "three-legged stool" of Scripture, Tradition and Reason. The quest to understand the origins of life on earth, and the forces that drive the ongoing changes in living organisms involves Reason and is in no way incompatible with the central truths of Scripture and Christian Tradition. Episcopalians generally accept that it is appropriate to seek to understand, through scientific probing, the origins both of the cosmos and life on earth, and that evolution is a valid explanation of the development of all living things, including humanity. Several leading Anglican theologians, past and present, among them priest-scientists William G. Pollard, Arthur Peacocke, and Sir John Polkinghorne, have shown how an evolutionary world view can be integrated with a theology of creation. The 67th General Convention affirmed a belief "in the glorious ability of God to create in any manner", and its "support of scientists, educators, and theologians in the search for truth" (GC Resolution 1982-D090).

Passed at the 75th General Convention, June 13-21, 2006 in Columbus, Ohio

Humanist Association of Canada

Evolution is the basis of modern biology. A student cannot possibly understand any of the life sciences without understanding the process of evolution that is the foundation of these sciences. It is the unifying web that links them together. Without evolution, biology is only a series of disconnected facts. With evolution, comes a comprehension of adaptation to local ecologies, the relationships among species, and the relationships among plants and animals and environments.

The physical sciences also depend on an accurate knowledge of the origins of the universe, radioactive decay, the age of the earth, chemical reactions and many physical relationships that change uniformly over time.

All these facts complement and reinforce each other. To comprehend the age of the universe, students must learn about the speed of light, what a red shift is, and something about spectroscopy. To understand the age of the earth, they must understand sedimentation, fossilization, and radioactive decay. To understand human origins they must understand genetic drift, carbon dating, archeology and linguistic change. Then they can begin to appreciate how these different systems reinforce each other and mutually confirm many diverse facts. They will then appreciate how a scientific hypothesis must fit in with all the observed and confirmed facts of the universe. Gravitation, relativity, radioactive decay, molecular genetics; one odd observation or a new theory cannot overturn these well-established truths. For instance, Einstein's relativity did not change the observations Newton had made. Newton's laws of gravity and motion still work correctly, unless one is dealing with objects moving nearly at the speed of light. Students must learn that a new theory must still fit in with the old facts, while explaining observations that were previously unexplained.

Evolution is an area where great strides are being made yearly, especially in the area of human origins. Students should learn how science changes because of new information.

Students should learn how science progresses through the accumulation of facts, through testing theories to see if they explain the facts, or if any facts disprove the theory.

Science education must avoid implying that science is a received and unchangeable set of dogmas for students to memorize, but must also teach those facts that are true.

So-called creation science is merely misnamed religious propaganda. There is nothing of science in it beyond the name. Creationists do not accept any evidence that goes against their case and will not listen to any arguments that don't go their way. Science is interested in the truth, and seeks out tests that might disprove a new theory. Creationists do not recognize anything that contradicts their beliefs. They have simply decided in advance what the conclusion must be, and head toward it without consideration of any contrary evidence that may be in the path. Creationism is an attempt to sneak a narrow sectarian religious creed into public classrooms and impose it on everyone. It is based, despite denials, upon the Genesis texts of the Jewish and Christian bible. Only a few Christian denominations, and a few Jewish sects, demand literal interpretation of these myths. Creation science is a religious dogma. Most of all, it is false and it is inaccurate. There is no evidence to support the creationist argument.

There is no room in science for believing without evidence. The whole of humanity's scientific enterprise is based on testing every belief and relinquishing those that fail the tests. Any public school teacher or public school board that lets "creation science" into a classroom, has abandoned teaching and taken up preaching and should be stopped.

Lexington Alliance of Religious Leaders

The following ministers and religious leaders are very much concerned with and opposed to the possibility of "Scientific Creationism" being taught in the science curriculum of Fayette County Schools.

As religious leaders we share a deep faith in the God who created heaven and earth and all that is in them, and take with utmost seriousness the Biblical witness to this God who is our Creator. However, we find no incompatibility between the God of creation and a theory of evolution which uses universally verifiable data to explain the probable process by which life developed into its present form.

We understand that you may shortly receive considerable pressure from groups advocating the teaching of "Scientific Creationism" alongside of the theory of evolution. However, we feel strongly that to introduce such teaching into our schools would be both divisive and offensive to many members of the religious community of Fayette County, as well as to those not identified with any religious group.

Please be assured of our continuing interest in this issue, and of our strong desire that the Fayette County Public Schools not permit the teaching of "Scientific Creationism" as an alternative "theory" to evolution in science courses.

1981; signed by 78 Kentucky ministers and religious leaders

The Lutheran World Federation

Symbolic of the prominence of the evolutionary idea in contemporary thought is the occurrence of "evolved" as the last word of the famous closing paragraph of Darwin's *The Origin of Species,* 1859. While not original with the emergence of Darwinism, evolution has nevertheless been intimately associated with it and has in the intervening century become one of the most comprehensive concepts of the modern mind. Consequently the issue cannot be stated in terms of the restricted alternative whether any one phase of evolution (especially the biological) is still "only a scientific theory" or long since "an established fact." Neither is it a matter of holding out the hope that if only enough fault can be found with Darwin the church's doctrine of creation will automatically be accepted and religion can then be at peace with science.

Rather, the evolutionary dynamisms of today's world compel a more realistic confrontation. One area of reality after another has been analyzed and described on the basis of some kind of progressive change until the whole may be viewed as a single process. The standpoint of the one who views this unitary development may be avowedly atheistic in the sense of ruling out the supernatural (Sir Julian Huxley) or just as avowedly Christian in the sense of finding in evolution an infusion of new life into Christianity, with Christianity alone dynamic enough to unify the world with God (Teilhard de Chardin).

In whatever way the process may be ultimately explained, it has come about that an idea which has been most thoroughly explored in the field of biology (lower forms of life evolving into higher) has by means of organismic analogy found universal application. Phenomena thus accounted for range from physical realities (evolution of the atoms and expanding galaxies) to man and his social experience (the evolution of cultural values) including his understanding of time and history (the evolutionary vision of scientific eschatology). Hence there is posited a movement of cumulative change in the organic and the inorganic; in the evolution of life and of man, of social institutions and political constitutions, of emerging races and nations, of language and art forms, of school systems and educational methods, of religion and doctrine; and of science and of the theory of evolution itself.

In the 1959 University of Chicago Centennial Discussions of *Evolution After Darwin* a working definition given to the term evolution was that of a long temporal process, operating everywhere, in which a unidirectional and irreversible natural development generates newness, variety, and "higher levels of organization" (Vol. I, p. 18; Vol. III, p. 111). A noteworthy feature of these discussions was the forthrightness with which at least some of the participants presented evolution in an uncompromising opposition to any notion of the supernatural and in a consistent upholding of naturalistic self sufficiency in a cosmos which was not created but which has evolved.

With biological evolution (ostensibly a matter of pure science) thereby becoming a metaphysics of evolution it needs to be determined whether religion's proper quarrel is with the science which permits itself such dogmatic extension or whether the misgivings are primarily with the particular philosophical interpretation involved. To the evolutionary concept in general there are however (in spite of innumerable variations) basically two religious reactions.

1. As in the days of the Scopes trial all evolution may still be denied on the grounds of a literalistic interpretation of the Bible, especially Genesis 1-11. Not content with the commitment of faith in the Creator expressed in the First Article of the Apostles' Creed this interpretation may demand a specific answer also to the questions of when creation occurred and how long it took. On the premise of a literal acceptance of the Scriptures as authoritative also in matters of science the whole of past existence is comprehended within the limited time span of biblical chronologies and genealogies. The vastness of astronomical time with its incredible number of light years may be accounted for as an instantaneous arrival of light and the eras of geological and biological time with their strata, fossils, and dinosaurs pointing to the existence of life and death on the earth ages before the arrival of man may be reduced to one literal week of creative activity.

2. On the other hand there are those who can no more close their eyes to the evidence which substantiates some kind of lengthy evolutionary process in the opinion of the vast majority of those scientists most competent to judge than they could deny the awesome reality of God's presence in nature and their own experience of complete dependence upon the creative and sustaining hand of God revealed in the Scriptures. In reference to creation, Langdon Gilkey (*Maker of Heaven and Earth*, 1959, pp. 30 f.) interprets the doctrine as affirming ultimate dependence upon God and distinguishes it from scientific hypotheses which properly deal with finite processes only. Among Lutheran theologians George Forell (*The Protestant Faith*, 1960, p. 109) sees the doctrine of creation not as expressing "a theory about the origin of the world" but as describing man's situation in the world, and Jaroslav Pelikan (*Evolution After Darwin*, Vol. III, p. 31) presents the creation accounts of Genesis as "not chiefly cosmogony" and furthermore sketches a development in the church which by the 19th century had emphasized those aspects of the doctrine of the creation to which Darwin represented a particular challenge and had neglected other important aspects which could be maintained independently of biological research.

An assessment of the prevailing situation makes it clear that evolution's assumptions are as much around us as the air we breathe and no more escapable. At the same time theology's affirmations are being made as responsibly as ever. In this sense both science and religion are here to stay, and the demands of either are great enough to keep most (if not all) from daring to profess competence in both. To preserve their own integrity both science and religion need to remain in a healthful tension of respect toward one another and to engage in a searching debate which no more permits theologians to pose as scientists than it permits scientists to pose as theologians.

Edwin A. Schick, "Evolution", in The Encyclopedia of the Lutheran Church, *Vol. I J. Bodensieck, ed., 1965 Minneapolis: Augsburg Publishing House. The* Encyclopedia *is a publication of the Lutheran World Federation.*

National Council of Jewish Women

The National Council of Jewish Women (NCJW) supports quality education in public schools and strongly opposes efforts to add faith-based interpretations of the creation of the universe to the curriculum. Specifically, "intelligent design" is not a scientific theory, but rather an effort to explain the origins of the earth and human life in religious terms. As such, it has no place in the public schools that are funded by tax dollars.

The constitutional separation of religion and state protects the rights of all citizens regardless of their beliefs. This principle enables a diverse, pluralistic society to function equitably. A clear line between religious belief and scientific theory must be maintained to ensure that no one set of beliefs is elevated over another.

The current campaign to add intelligent design to public school curricula and classrooms and to denigrate the theory of evolution follows closely on the heels of attempts to add creationism to public school classrooms and textbooks. NCJW opposes this effort to use government funds to subsidize the teaching of religion in our public schools. We firmly believe that the responsibility for religious education is a private matter that belongs in our homes and in our places of worship, not in our public institutions and certainly not in our public schools.

December 6, 2005, New York, NY
NCJW is a volunteer organization, inspired by Jewish values, that works to improve the quality of life for women, children, and families and to ensure individual rights and freedoms for all through its network of 90,000 members, supporters, and volunteers nationwide.
Contact: Rebecca Cole 212 645 4048 ext 182; rcole@ncjw.org

Presbyterian Church (USA), General Assembly

The 214th General Assembly of the Presbyterian Church (USA):

1. Reaffirms that God is Creator, in accordance with the witness of Scripture and The Reformed Confessions.

2. Reaffirms that there is no contradiction between an evolutionary theory of human origins and the doctrine of God as Creator.

3. Encourages State Boards of Education across the nation to establish standards for science education in public schools based on the most reliable content of scientific knowledge as determined by the scientific community.

4. Calls upon Presbyterian scientists and science educators to assist congregations, presbyteries, communities, and the public to understand what constitutes reliable scientific knowledge.

2002

Creation, Evolution, and Intelligent Design:
The View of the Rabbinical Council of America

In response to the public debate over Intelligent Design and Scientific theory, the RCA has issued the following statement clarifying its view on this matter as it relates to Torah Judaism, and the biblical account of creation.

In light of the ongoing public controversy about Evolution, Creationism and Intelligent Design, the RCA notes that significant Jewish authorities have maintained that evolutionary theory, properly understood, is not incompatible with belief in a Divine Creator, nor with the first 2 chapters of Genesis.

There are authentic, respected voices in the Jewish community that take a literalist position with regard to these issues; at the same time, Judaism has a history of diverse approaches to the understanding of the biblical account of creation. As Rabbi Joseph Hertz wrote, "While the fact of creation has to this day remained the first of the articles of the Jewish creed, there is no uniform and binding belief as to the manner of creation, i.e. as to the process whereby the universe came into existence. The manner of the Divine creative activity is presented in varying forms and under differing metaphors by Prophet, Psalmist and Sage; by the Rabbis in Talmudic times, as well as by our medieval Jewish thinkers." Some refer to the Midrash (Koheleth Rabbah 3:13) which speaks of God "developing and destroying many worlds" before our current epoch. Others explain that the word "yom" in Biblical Hebrew, usually translated as "day," can also refer to an undefined period of time, as in Isaiah 11:10-11. Maimonides stated that "what the Torah writes about the Account of Creation is not all to be taken literally, as believed by the masses" (Guide to the Perplexed II:29), and recent Rabbinic leaders who have discussed the topic of creation, such as Rabbi Samson Raphael Hirsch and Rabbi Abraham Isaac Kook, saw no difficulty in explaining Genesis as a theological text rather than a scientific account.

Judaism affirms the idea that God is the Creator of the Universe and the Being responsible for the presence of human beings in this world.

Nonetheless, there have long been different schools of thought within Judaism regarding the extent of divine intervention in natural processes. One respected view was expressed by Maimonides who wrote that "we should endeavor to integrate the Torah with rational thought, affirming that events take place in accordance with the natural order wherever possible." (Letter to the Jews of Yemen) All schools concur that God is the ultimate cause and that humanity was an intended end result of Creation.

For us, these fundamental beliefs do not rest on the purported weaknesses of Evolutionary Theory, and cannot be undermined by the elimination of gaps in scientific knowledge.

Judaism has always preferred to see science and Torah as two aspects of the "Mind of God" (to borrow Stephen Hawking's phrase) that are ultimately unitary in the reality given to us by the Creator. As the Zohar says (Genesis 134a): "istakel be-'oraita u-vara 'alma," God looked into the Torah and used it as His blueprint for creating the Universe.

December 22nd 2005
1 Kislev 5766

For articles and sources on this subject, see Aryeh Carmel and Cyril Domb eds., "Challenge: Torah Views on Science and its Problems," Feldheim, N. Y. 1976; and Rabbi J. H. Hertz, The Pentateuch and Haftorahs (Soncino Press 1960), Additional Notes to Genesis.

Voices for Evolution

Roman Catholic Church (1981)
Pope John Paul II

Cosmogony itself speaks to us of the origins of the universe and its makeup, not in order to provide us with a scientific treatise but in order to state the correct relationship of man with God and with the universe. Sacred Scripture wishes simply to declare that the world was created by God, and in order to teach this truth, it expresses itself in the terms of the cosmology in use at the time of the writer. The sacred book likewise wishes to tell men that the world was not created as the seat of the gods, as was taught by other cosmogonies and cosmologies, but was rather created for the service of man and the glory of God. Any other teaching about the origin and makeup of the universe is alien to the intentions of the Bible, which does not wish to teach how heaven was made but how one goes to heaven.

Address to the Pontifical Academy of Sciences on 3 October 1981.

Roman Catholic Church (1996)

Magisterium Is Concerned with Question of Evolution
For It Involves Conception of Man
Pope John Paul II

Message to Pontifical Academy of Sciences
October 22, 1996
To the Members of the Pontifical Academy of Sciences taking part in the Plenary Assembly

With great pleasure I address cordial greetings to you, Mr President, and to all of you who constitute the Pontifical Academy of Sciences, on the occasion of your plenary assembly. I offer my best wishes in particular to the new academicians, who have come to take part in your work for the first time. I would also like to remember the academicians who died during the past year, whom I commend to the Lord of life.

1. In celebrating the 60th anniversary of the Academy's refoundation, I would like to recall the intentions of my predecessor Pius XI, who wished to surround himself with a select group of scholars, relying on them to inform the Holy See in complete freedom about developments in scientific research, and thereby to assist him in his reflections.

He asked those whom he called the Church's Senatus scientificus to serve the truth. I again extend this same invitation to you today, certain that we will all be able to profit from the fruitfulness of a trustful dialogue between the Church and science (cf.Address to the Academy of Sciences, n. 1, 28 October 1986, L'Osservatore Romano English edition, 24 November 1986, p. 22).

Science at the dawn of the third millennium
2. I am pleased with the first theme you have chosen, that of the origins of life and evolution, an essential subject which deeply interests the Church, since Revelation, for its part, contains teaching concerning the nature and origins of man. How do the conclusions reached by the various scientific disciplines coincide with those contained in the message of Revelation? And if, at first sight, there are apparent contradictions, in what direction do we look for their solution? We know, in fact, that truth cannot contradict truth (cf. Leo XIII, Encyclical Providentissimus Deus).

Moreover, to shed greater light on historical truth, your research on the Church's relations with science between the 16th and 18th centuries is of great importance.

During this plenary session you are undertaking a "reflection on science at the dawn of the third millennium", starting with the identification of the principal problems created by the sciences and which affect humanity's future. With this step you point the way to solutions which will be beneficial to the whole human community. In the domain of inanimate and animate nature, the evolution of science and its applications gives rise to new questions. The better the Church's knowledge is of their essential aspects, the more she will understand their impact. Consequently, in accordance with her specific mission she will be able to offer criteria for discerning the moral conduct required of all human beings in view of their integral salvation.

3. Before offering you several reflections that more specifically concern the subject of the origin of life and its evolution, I would like to remind you that the Magisterium of the Church has already made pronouncements on these matters within the framework of her own competence. I will cite here two interventions.

In his Encyclical Humani generis (1950), my predecessor Pius XII had already stated that there was no opposition between evolution and the doctrine of the faith about man and his vocation, on condition that one did not lose sight of several indisputable points (cf. AAS 42 [1950], pp. 575-576).

For my part, when I received those taking part in your Academy's plenary assembly on 31 October 1992, I had the opportunity, with regard to Galileo, to draw attention to the need of a rigorous hermeneutic for the correct interpretation of the inspired word. It is necessary to determine the proper sense of Scripture, while avoiding any unwarranted interpretations that make it say what it does not intend to say. In order to delineate the field of their own study, the exegete and the theologian must keep informed about the results achieved by the natural sciences (cf. AAS 85 [1993] pp. 764-772; Address to the Pontifical Biblical Commission, 23 April 1993, announcing the document on The interpretation of the Bible in the Church: AAS 86 [1994] pp. 232-243).

Evolution and the Church's Magisterium
4. Taking into account the state of scientific research at the time as well as of the requirements of theology, the Encyclical Humani generis considered the doctrine of "evolutionism" a serious hypothesis, worthy of investigation and in-depth study equal to that of the opposing hypothesis. Pius XII added two methodological conditions: that this opinion should not be adopted as though it were a certain, proven doctrine and as though one could totally prescind from Revelation with regard to the questions it raises. He also spelled out the condition on which this opinion would be compatible with the Christian faith, a point to which I will return.

Today, almost half a century after the publication of the Encyclical, fresh knowledge has led to the recognition that evolution is more than a hypothesis. It is indeed remarkable that this theory has been progressively accepted by researchers, following a series of discoveries in various fields of knowledge. The convergence, neither sought nor fabricated, of the results of work that was conducted independently is in itself a significant argument in favour of this theory.

What is the significance of such a theory? To address this question is to enter the field of epistemology. A theory is a metascientific elaboration, distinct from the results of observation but consistent with them. By means of it a series of independent data and facts can be related and interpreted in a unified explanation. A theory's validity depends on whether or not it can be verified; it is constantly tested against the facts; wherever it can no longer explain the later, it shows its limitations and unsuitability. It must then be rethought.

Furthermore, while the formulation of a theory like that of evolution complies with the need for consistency with the observed data, it borrows certain notions from natural philosophy. And, to tell the truth, rather than the theory of evolution, we should speak of several theories of evolution. On the one hand, this plurality has to do with the different explanations advanced for the mechanism of evolution, and on the other, with the various philosophies on which it is based. Hence the existence of materialist, reductionist and spiritualist interpretations. What is to be decided here is the true role of philosophy and, beyond it, of theology.

5. The Church's Magisterium is directly concerned with the question of evolution, for it involves the conception of man: Revelation teaches us that he was created in the image and likeness of God (cf. Gn 1:27-29). The conciliar Constitution Gaudium et spes has magnificently explained this doctrine, which is pivotal to Christian thought. It recalled that "man is the only creature on earth that God has wanted for its own sake" (n. 24). In other terms, the human individual cannot be subordinated as a pure means or a pure instrument, either to the species or to society; he has value per se. He is a person. With his intellect and his will, he is capable of forming a relationship of communion, solidarity and self-giving with his peers. St Thomas observes that man's likeness to God resides especially in his speculative intellect for his relationship with the object of his knowledge resembles God's relationship with what he has created (Summa Theologica, I-II, q. 3, a. 5, ad 1). But even more, man is called to enter into a relationship of knowledge and love with God himself, a relationship which will find its complete fulfilment beyond time, in eternity. All the depth and grandeur of this vocation are revealed to us in the mystery of the risen Christ (cf. Gaudium et spes, n. 22). It is by virtue of his spiritual soul that the whole person possesses such a dignity even in his body. Pius XII stressed this essential point: if the human body takes its origin from pre-existent living matter the spiritual soul is immediately created by God ("animal enim a Deo immediate creari catholica fides nos retinere inhet"; Encyclical Humani generic, AAS 42 [1950], p. 575).

Consequently, theories of evolution which, in accordance with the philosophies inspiring them, consider the mind as emerging from the forces of living matter, or as a mere epiphenomenon of this matter, are incompatible with the truth about man. Nor are they able to ground the dignity of the person.

6. With man, then, we find ourselves in the presence of an ontological difference, an ontological leap, one could say. However, does not the posing of such ontological discontinuity run counter to that physical continuity which seems to be the main thread of research into evolution in the field of physics and chemistry? Consideration of the method used in the various branches of knowledge makes it possible to reconcile two points of view which would seem irreconcilable. The sciences of observation describe and measure the multiple manifestations of life with increasing precision and correlate them with the time line. The moment of transition into the spiritual cannot be the object of this kind of observation, which nevertheless can discover at the experimental level a series of very valuable signs indicating what is specific to the human being. But the experience of metaphysical knowledge, of self-awareness and self-reflection, of moral conscience, freedom, or again, of aesthetic and religious experience, falls within the competence of philosophical analysis and reflection while theology brings out its ultimate meaning according to the Creator's plans.

We are called to enter eternal life

7. In conclusion, I would like to call to mind a Gospel truth which can shed a higher light on the horizon of your research into the origins and unfolding of living matter. The Bible in fact bears an extraordinary message of life. It gives us a wise vision of life inasmuch as it describes the loftiest forms of existence. This vision guided me in the Encyclical which I dedicated to respect for human life, and which I called precisely Evangelium vitae.

It is significant that in St John's Gospel life refers to the divine light which Christ communicates to us. We are called to enter into eternal life, that is to say, into the eternity of divine beatitude.

To warn us against the serious temptations threatening us, our Lord quotes the great saying of Deuteronomy: "Man shall not live by bread alone, but by every word that proceeds from the mouth of God" (Dt 8:3, cf. Mt 4:4).

Even more, "life" is one of the most beautiful titles which the Bible attributes to God. He is the living God.

I cordially invoke an abundance of divine blessings upon you and upon all who are close to you.

From the Vatican, 22 October 1996.

Official translation published in L'Osservatore Romano, "Weekly Edition in English," 30 October 1996. Reprinted courtesy of Libreria Editrice Vaticana.

Unitarian Universalist Association (1977)

Whereas, currently there are efforts being made to insert the creation story of Genesis into public school science textbooks; and

Whereas, such action would be in direct contradiction with the concept of separation of church and state;

Therefore be it resolved: That the 1977 General Assembly of the Unitarian Universalist Association goes on record as opposing such efforts.

Be it further resolved: That individual societies are urged to immediately provide petitions on the subject to be signed by members and sent to their legislators; and

Be it further resolved: That this resolution be forwarded to the textbook selection committee of each state department of education by the Department of Ministerial and Congregational Services.

Passed at the 1977 General Assembly of the Unitarian Universalist Association.

Unitarian Universalist Association (1982)

Whereas, the constitutional principles of religious liberty and the separation of church and state that safeguards liberty, and the ideal of a pluralistic society are under increasing attack in the Congress of the United States, in state legislatures, and in some sectors of the communications media by a combination of sectarian and secular special interests;

Be it resolved: That the 1982 General Assembly of UUA reaffirms its support for these principles and urges the Board of Trustees and President of the Association, member societies, and Unitarian-Universalists in the United States to: . . . 2. Uphold religious neutrality in public education, oppose all government mandated or sponsored prayers, devotional observances, and religious indoctrination in public schools; and oppose efforts to compromise the integrity of public school teaching by the introduc-

Voices for Evolution

tion of sectarian religious doctrines, such as "scientific creationism," and by exclusion of educational materials on sectarian grounds...

Passed at the 21st annual General Assembly of the UUA in June 1982. The above excerpt omits other articles of the resolution not directly related to creationism.

United Church Board for Homeland Ministries

Creationism, the Church, and the Public School

I. Background On The Creationism Issue

Creationism is a relatively recent development in an older and on-going controversy concerning the relationship between science and religion. In the 1920's the teaching about evolution in public schools (specifically the work of Charles Darwin) was challenged on the basis of perceived conflict with biblical teaching. In Tennessee John Scopes was convicted of violating a law which made it "illegal ... to teach any theory that denies the story of the divine creation of man as taught in the Bible, and to teach instead that man has descended from a lower order of animals." Although the conviction was overturned on a technicality, the Tennessee Supreme Court upheld the constitutionality of the law which was not repealed until 1967.

The central issue in challenges such as this is the apparent conflict between scientific explanations about the origins of life, even the cosmos itself, and biblical accounts of creation. Science and religion often are perceived as being in basic conflict concerning creation.

In more recent decades, the debate has taken a new twist. While still opposing the scientific theories of evolution concerning the origins of life, a number of persons began to suggest that certain scientific data and/or approaches could 'prove' the validity of biblical accounts concerning creation. In the 1960's and early 1970's, several organizations were formed to promote the idea that the creation accounts recorded in the book of Genesis were supported by scientific data. The terms "creation-science," "scientific creationism," and "creationism" are used to describe this interpretation of scripture.

This movement took on more focused activity in 1977 when over twenty state legislatures recorded bills requiring teaching of "creation-science" when evolution was taught. This "balanced treatment" proposition was passed as model legislation by the Arkansas Legislature in 1981.

Opponents of the Act, including religious leaders, educators, and scientists, challenged the constitutionality of the Act in the federal courts (*McLean v Arkansas Board of Education*) and in 1982 the law was declared unconstitutional. A similar law was passed in Louisiana and litigation went all the way to the U.S. Supreme Court. The court in *Edwards v Aguillard* declared the law unconstitutional in 1987. The Supreme Court decision has been applied in subsequent cases involving individual teachers who chose to teach "creation-science" outside the curriculum. Federal courts declared that teaching "creation-science" was a religious advocacy and, therefore, unconstitutional. Courts have taken special care to protect the religious independence of students in the public schools.

Since the Supreme Court decision in *Edwards*, creationists have concentrated their efforts at the level of the local school board, where they pressure educators to teach "creation-science," omit or qualify the teaching of evolution, and/or adopt textbooks that exclude evolution. Additional terms for "creation-science," such as "abrupt appearance theory" or "intelligent design theory" are attempts to avoid the constitutional issue of religious advocacy. However, beyond the notion of "equal time" other issues are emerging. The attempts to use scientific data and methods to prove certain biblical claims are raising concerns among many educators and scientists about the integrity of scientific inquiry itself and what students may be learning about the nature and role of science. Science and scientific methods can be abused by setting out to prove certain assumptions rather than allowing even those assumptions to be open to inquiry and discussion.

The concerns over current activities by creationists touch basic affirmations about the public school made by the United Church Board for Homeland Ministries. The effort to make creationism part of the science curriculum in the public schools tests our commitments to the public school, excellence in education, the integrity of science, and academic freedom. It also tests our interpretation of the Bible and our belief in God's unlimited creative powers.

It is therefore appropriate amidst this controversy for the United Church Board to work with members of the United Church of Christ and others to understand this issue from the perspective of our religious and educational traditions. We mean to assist persons to participate fearlessly in open inquiry, debate, and action concerning the goals of education; to understand the role of science, including an appropriate relationship between science and faith; to help develop consensus in public policy issues affecting the public school; and to support academic freedom at all levels of the educational experience.

II. Affirmations

1) We testify to our belief that the historic Christian doctrine of the Creator God does not depend upon any particular account of the origins of life for its truth and validity. The effort of the creationists to change the book of Genesis into a scientific treatise dangerously obscures what we believe to be the theological purpose of Genesis, viz., to witness to the creation, meaning, and significance of the universe and of human existence under the governance of God. The assumption that the Bible contains scientific data about origins misreads a literature which emerged in a pre-scientific age.

2) We acknowledge modern evolutionary theory as the best present-day scientific explanation of the existence of life on earth; such a conviction is in no way at odds with our belief in a Creator God, or in the revelation and presence of that God in Jesus Christ and the Holy Spirit.

3) We affirm the freedom of conscience and freedom of religion set forth and protected in the U.S. Constitution, including the right of the creationists to their religious beliefs.

4) We believe that the nurturing of faith and religious commitment is the responsibility of the church and home, not of the public school. No person or group should use the school to compel the teaching or acceptance of any creed or to impose conformity to any specific religious belief or practice. Requiring the teaching of the religious beliefs of creationists in the public school violates this basic principle of American democracy. We concur with judicial rulings that the teaching of the religious beliefs of the creationists in the public school science curriculum is unconstitutional.

5) We assert that the public school science curriculum is not the proper arena for the expression of religious doctrine. However, we believe that the public school does have the responsibility to teach about religion, in order to help individuals

formulate an intelligent understanding and appreciation of the role of religion in the life and culture of all people and nations. In this context, it is fully appropriate for the public school to include in its non-science curriculum consideration of the variety of religious literature about the creation and origins of human life.

6) We reaffirm our historic commitment to the public school, and declare that each student has the right to an education which rests firmly on the best understandings of the academic community.

7) We affirm our historic commitment to academic freedom in the public school; in that context, the open and full search for truth about all issues in science including creation must proceed in the light of responsible scholarship and research, subject always to the process of peer review, and of factual and logical verification, and of scientific replication.

8) We reject any modification of science textbooks to include the point of view of the creationists or that weakens scientific teachings, and we support publishers who resist this effort. To do otherwise would abridge both academic freedom and the customary practices of careful scholarship.

9) We affirm the responsibility of professional educators to make final decisions about the public school curriculum. These decisions should be based on sound scholarship, competent teaching practices, and policies of local and state school boards which are accountable to the public and in keeping with judicial decisions upholding Constitutional values.

III. Recommendations
1) That through study and discussion we, as church people, become informed about issues of creation raised by both science and religion, including the "creation-science" controversy.

2) That we urge pastors and teachers to preach and teach about issues of creation, particularly the ways of understanding the first eleven chapters of Genesis, the first chapter of the Gospel of John, and other relevant Scripture passages. We further urge pastors and teachers to teach about the problems of biblical literalism in blocking creative dialogue between the faith community and contemporary educational, scientific, and political communities.

3) That we support the determination of schools, school boards, and textbook publishers to retain their professional integrity in treating the creationism issue, carefully recognizing the distinction between promoting religion and teaching about religion.

4) That we make all efforts to resist any viewpoint which would maintain that belief in both a Creator God and in evolutionary theory are in any way incompatible. Confident in our conviction that God is the ultimate source of all wisdom and truth, we encourage the free development of science and all other forms of intellectual inquiry.

5) That clergy and laity exercise their civic responsibility to monitor the work of state legislatures, taking care that any discussion of proposed "creation-science" legislation include educational and constitutional questions, and affirming that such legislation is a violation of the First and Fourteenth Amendments of the U.S. Constitution.

6) That informed persons, including clergy and laity, in each community monitor the work of local school boards and state departments of education, so that issues of "creation-science" may be discussed fully and openly if and when they come to their agendas. In communities being divided by the creationism controversy, we ask our people to be both a source of reconciliation and a community of support for those who oppose efforts to present creationism as a science.

7) That concerned educators and citizens work with teachers to support their efforts to teach their disciplines with integrity, rather than omit subjects such as evolution as a way of avoiding controversy.

9) That the church renew efforts to understand and relate to science and technology, not only to comprehend and respond to issues of controversy, but also to discover new ways of appreciating and expressing God's creative and redeeming activity.

IV. For Further Reading

Ronald S. Cole Turner, An Unavoidable Challenge: Our Church in an Age of Science and Technology, a Foundation Paper on science and technology as a lifelong issue for education, available from the Division of Education and Publication, UCBHM, Cleveland.

Langdon Gilkey, *Creationism on Trial: Evolution & God at Little Rock*, Harper & Row, 1985.

Betty McCollister, ed., *Voices for Evolution*, The National Center for Science Education, Inc. (P.O. Box 9477, Berkeley, CA 94709)

October 1992

United Methodist Church

Whereas, "Scientific" creationism seeks to prove that natural history conforms absolutely to the Genesis account of origins; and,

Whereas, adherence to immutable theories is fundamentally antithetical to the nature of science; and,

Whereas, "Scientific" creationism seeks covertly to promote a particular religious dogma; and,

Whereas, the promulgation of religious dogma in public schools is contrary to the First Amendment to the United States Constitution; therefore,

Be it resolved that The Iowa Annual Conference opposes efforts to introduce "Scientific" creationism into the science curriculum of the public schools.

Passed June 1984, Iowa Annual Conference of the United Methodist Church.

United Presbyterian Church in the U.S.A. (1982)

Evolution and Creationism

I. Resolution

Whereas, The Program Agency of the United Presbyterian Church in the USA notes with concern a concerted effort to introduce legislation and other means for the adoption of a public school curriculum variously known as "Creationism" or "Creation Science,"

Whereas, over several years, fundamentalist church leadership, resourced by the Creation Science Research Center and the Institute for Creation Research, has prepared legislation for a number of states calling for "balanced treatment" for "creation-science" and "evolution-science," requiring that wherever one is taught the other must be granted a comparable presentation in the classroom;

Whereas, this issue represents a new situation, there are General Assembly policies on Church and State and Public Education which guide us to assert once again that the state cannot legislate the establishment of religion in the public domain;

Whereas, the dispute is not really over biology or faith, but is essentially about Biblical interpretation, particularly over two irreconcilable viewpoints regarding the characteristics of Biblical literature and the nature of Biblical authority:

Therefore, the Program Agency recommends to the 194th General Assembly (1982) the adoption of the following affirmation:

Affirms that, despite efforts to establish "creationism" or "creation-science" as a valid science, it is teaching based upon a particular religious dogma as agreed by the court (*McLean vs Arkansas Board of Education*);

Affirms that, the imposition of a fundamentalist viewpoint about the interpretation of Biblical literature – where every word is taken with uniform literalness and becomes an absolute authority on all matters, whether moral, religious, political, historical or scientific – is in conflict with the perspective on Biblical interpretation characteristically maintained by Biblical scholars and theological schools in the mainstream of Protestantism, Roman Catholicism and Judaism. Such scholars find that the scientific theory of evolution does not conflict with their interpretation of the origins of life found in Biblical literature.

Affirms that, academic freedom of both teachers and students is being further limited by the impositions of the campaign most notably in the modification of textbooks which limits the teaching about evolution but also by the threats to the professional authority and freedom of teachers to teach and students to learn;

Affirms that, required teaching of such a view constitutes an establishment of religion and a violation of the separation of church and state, as provided in the First Amendment to the Constitution and laws of the United States;

Affirms that, exposure to the Genesis account is best sought through the teaching about religion, history, social studies and literature, provinces other than the discipline of natural science, and

Calls upon Presbyterians, and upon legislators and school board members, to resist all efforts to establish any requirements upon teachers and schools to teach "creationism" or "creation science."

Adopted by General Assembly, 1982.

United Presbyterian Church in the U.S.A. (1983)

The Church, the Public School, and Creation Science

Current efforts to legislate the teaching of "creation-science" in the public school challenge and violate basic principles which guide public schools and their responsibility for education of a public that is characterized by its cultural pluralism. These basic principles are grounded both in law (General Welfare Clause of Section 8, Article 1, of U.S. Constitution) and in the Reformed understanding that human response to God's gracious calling is expressed through faithfulness, freedom, and self-determination amidst different claims and alternatives. This Reformed understanding is set forth in the public policy position on public education adopted by the 119th General Assembly:

The biblical impetus toward growth for faith and justice is reaffirmed in the theological stance of the Reformed tradition. This impetus calls for a unique combination of teaching learning experiences: in home, in church, and in public education.

Persons are called "to glorify God and enjoy him forever." Within the Reformed tradition, this calling is God's act of grace. On the Christian's side the act of grace is affirmed through commitment. But commitment is not simply the acceptance of the truth of certain doctrinal statements. It is much more the embodiment of the lifestyle of Jesus. This embodiment takes place in the everyday struggle to make decisions about the common life of God's creatures. Decision-making implies the freedom of self-determination. It calls for consciousness of alternatives and their consequences. Growth in self-determination is thus best achieved in a setting where alternate loyalties are experienced and reflected upon and where the freedom to create new alternatives is not only permitted but encouraged. Pluralism comprises such a setting, and the public school is the context of pluralism which provides an appropriate atmosphere for growth and development toward the maturity of decision-making and commitment.

In addition, Christian love and respect for persons demand that all persons be free to search for the truth wherever they may find it. This free search for truth which is essential to maturity calls for an appreciation and respect for all human efforts toward justice and love. When public education is not restricted by theological positions or secular ideologies, it provides such an arena for free inquiry and appreciation of all efforts toward humanization.

The Reformed tradition seeks, therefore, to sustain and support all efforts toward the removal of ignorance and bigotry and toward the establishment of free institutions as a source of a high degree of social stability. Public education can be such a free institution where ignorance and bigotry are challenged.[1]

The creation-science controversy thus touches basic tenets that are deeply rooted in the nation and in the Reformed tradition. Our primary intent is to contribute to moral discourse, as these issues are debated within the community of faith as well as within the scientific and educational communities. Our purpose is to help people consider how to think rather than to dictate what they are to think.

The goals of this dialogue are to develop public policies which both safeguard individual freedom and contribute to the public good and which strengthen the public school as one of society's most essential institutions, serving all the people. We would mark the discrete functions of the church and the school, while at the same time acknowledging their common commitment to the development of persons and to the formation of a just and humane society.

We accept a responsibility to participate in the education of the public on the issues raised by the creationism controversy and in the continuing formation of public policy affecting the public school. We make these affirmations and offer recommendations for consideration by synods, presbyteries, congregations, and the various publics represented in their membership.

Affirmations

1. As citizens of the United States, we are firmly committed to the right and freedom of conscience and freedom of religion, that is, freedom of each citizen in the determination of his or her religious allegiance, and the freedom of religious groups and institutions in the declaration of their beliefs.

2. As Christians, we believe every individual has the right to an education aimed at the full development of the individual's capacities as a human being created by God, including both intellect and character. We also believe that we have the responsibility to educate and thus will seek maximum educational opportunities for every child of God, that all persons may be prepared for responsible participation in the common life.

3. We affirm that each individual has the right to an education which recognizes rather than obscures the ethnic, racial and religious pluralism of our country and which prepares persons for life in the emerging world culture of the 21st century. Such an education views the individual as a whole person for whom discursive intellect, aesthetic sensitivity and moral perspective are intimately related.

4. We reaffirm our historic commitment to the public school as one of the basic educational institutions of the society. We celebrate its inclusiveness and its role as a major cohesive force, carrying our hopes for a fully democratic and pluralistic society. We further reaffirm the responsibility of public institutions to serve all the population as equitably as possible, neglecting none as expendable or undeserving of educational opportunity.

5. We affirm our faith that God is the author of truth and the Holy Spirit is present in all of our common life, to lead us all into truth. Ours is a journey of faith and of revelation in which the human spirit is fed and led but not coerced.

6. We believe that the nurturing of faith is the responsibility of the home and the church, not the public school. Neither the church nor the state should use the public school to compel acceptance of any creed or conformity to any specific religious belief or practice.

7. We affirm the professional responsibility of educators to make judgments about school curriculum which are based on sound scholarship and sound teaching practices.

8. We affirm that it is inappropriate for the state to mandate the teaching of the specific religious beliefs of the creationists in accord with the Overton ruling (*McLean vs Arkansas Board of Education*). We also affirm the responsibility of the public school to teach about religious beliefs, ideas and values as an integral part of our cultural heritage. We believe the public school has an obligation to help individuals formulate an intelligent understanding and appreciation of the role of religion in the life of people of all cultures. In the context of teaching about religion, it is appropriate to include in the public school curriculum consideration of the variety of religious interpretations of creation and the origins of human life.

9. We affirm our uncompromising commitment to academic freedom, that is, freedom to teach and to learn. Access to ideas and opportunities to consider the broad range of questions and experiences which constitute the proper preparation for a life of responsible citizenship must never be defined by the interests of any single viewpoint or segment of the public.

10. We acknowledge the need to enlarge the public participation in open inquiry, debate and action concerning the goals of education, and in the development of those educational reforms which equip children, youth and adults with equal opportunities to participate fully in the society. This participation must respect the constitutional and intellectual rights guaranteed school personnel and students by our law and tradition.

11. We pledge our continuing efforts to strengthen the public school as the most valuable, open, and accessible institution for formal education for all the people; we assert that educational needs are more important than economic, political and religious ideologies as the basis upon which to formulate educational policies.

12. We affirm anew our faith and oneness in Christ, the way, the truth and the life, as we struggle to make a faithful witness amid the conflict of convictions and conclusions between sisters and brothers who bear a common name.

Recommendations

For Congregations
1. That the General Assembly encourage congregations to study the issues in the creation-science controversy, giving particular attention to:

the historic role of the churches in the founding and developing of the public school.

the diversity of belief about creation and human origin present in our society.

the principles and assumptions which guide the development of the science curriculum in the public school and the use of scientific inquiry within all disciplines and subjects.

the essentials of the church-state issues as they apply to the public school, including a review of the major U.S. Supreme Court decisions and the recent court decisions on the creationism issue (i.e. *McLean vs Arkansas Board of Education*).

the processes of policymaking for the public school including the appropriate roles of the community, the educator, the parent, and the church.

2. That the General Assembly urge congregations to encourage local school boards to discuss issues of creation-science fully and openly, if and when they come onto the board's agenda.

3. That the General Assembly urge congregations to encourage and assist teachers and administrators in becoming sensitive to the religious perspectives of all persons in the schools, without sacrificing their professional commitments and standards regarding the teaching of science and teaching about religion.

4. That the General Assembly encourage congregations in communities divided by the creationism controversy to work for reconciliation and to provide a community of support for those struggling to keep the schools free of ideological indoctrination.

5. That the General Assembly encourage pastors and Christian educators to help their congregations to interpret the biblical passages dealing with creation and the origins of human life in ways that take their message seriously.

6. That the Mission Board provide study resources including the study paper prepared by the United Ministries in Education, "Creationism, the Church, and the Public School." (The paper is available from United Ministries in Education, c/o American Baptist Churches, Valley Forge, PA 19481.)

7. That the General Assembly commend the paper, "The Dialogue Between Theology and Science" (adopted by the 122nd General Assembly), as a study document addressing the basic issues related to the ongoing debate regarding the teaching of evolution and creationism in public schools.

For Synods and Presbyteries
8. That the General Assembly encourage synods and presbyteries to give attention to the work of state legislatures and their committees, taking care that any discussion of proposed creation-science legislation include broader educational, religious, and constitutional questions, and to join with others to have creation-science legislation declared unconstitutional when it is in violation of the First and Fourteenth Amendments to the U.S. Constitution.

9. That the General Assembly urge synods and presbyteries to encourage educators and citizens to examine the textbooks being used now in the public schools for the adequacy of their teaching about creation and evolution and about the differing religious perspective and interpretations of origins, and to resist every effort to purge or discredit data which are held to be part of our common history and heritage.

10. That the General Assembly encourage presbyteries to provide in resource centers information about creation-science, evolution-science and related public school issues.

Footnote in original:

1. Minutes of the 119th General Assembly, p. 526. The paper was adopted by the General Assembly and commended to the Church for study. Passed at the 195th General Assembly of the United Presbyterian Church in the U.S.A., 1983.

PART FOUR

EDUCATIONAL ORGANIZATIONS

Voices for Evolution

American Association of Physics Teachers

The Executive Board of the American Association of Physics Teachers is dismayed at organized actions to weaken and even to eliminate significant portions of evolution and cosmology from the educational objectives of states and school districts.

Evolution and cosmology represent two of the unifying concepts of modern science. There are few scientific theories more firmly supported by observations than these: Biological evolution has occurred and new species have arisen over time, life on Earth originated more than a billion years ago, and most stars are at least several billion years old. Overwhelming evidence comes from diverse sources – the structure and function of DNA, geological analysis of rocks, paleontological studies of fossils, telescopic observations of distant stars and galaxies – and no serious scientist questions these claims. We do our children a grave disservice if we remove from their education an exposure to firm scientific evidence supporting principles that significantly shape our understanding of the world in which we live.

No scientific theory, no matter how strongly supported by available evidence, is final and unchallengeable; any good theory is always exposed to the possibility of being modified or even overthrown by new evidence. That is at the very heart of the process of science. However, biological and cosmological evolution are theories as strongly supported and interwoven into the fabric of science as any other essential underpinnings of modern science and technology. To deny children exposure to the evidence in support of biological and cosmological evolution is akin to allowing them to believe that atoms do not exist or that the Sun goes around the Earth.

We believe in teaching that science is a process that examines all of the evidence relevant to an issue and tests alternative hypotheses. For this reason, we do not endorse teaching the "evidence against evolution," because currently no such scientific evidence exists. Nor can we condone teaching "scientific creationism," "intelligent design," or other non-scientific viewpoints as valid scientific theories. These beliefs ignore the important connections among empirical data and fail to provide testable hypotheses. They should not be a part of the science curriculum.

School boards, teachers, parents, and lawmakers have a responsibility to ensure that all children receive a good education in science. The American Association of Physics Teachers opposes all efforts to require or promote teaching creationism or any other non-scientific viewpoints in a science course. AAPT supports the National Science Education Standards, which incorporate the process of science and well-established scientific theories including cosmological and biological evolution.

This statement was adopted by the Executive Board of the American Association of Physics Teachers on April 24, 2005.

American Association of University Professors

The theory of evolution is all but universally accepted in the community of scholars and has contributed immeasurably to our understanding of the natural world. The Ninety-first Annual Meeting of the American Association of University Professors deplores efforts in local communities and by some state legislators to require teachers in public schools to treat evolution as merely a hypothesis or speculation, untested and unsubstantiated by the methods of science, and to require them to make students aware of an "intelligent-design hypothesis" to account for the origins of life. These initiatives not only violate the academic freedom of public school teachers, but can deny students an understanding of the overwhelming scientific consensus regarding evolution.

The implications of these efforts for higher education are particularly troubling to this Meeting. To the degree that college and university faculty in the field of biology would be required to offer instruction about evolution and the origins of life that complied with these restrictions and was at variance with their own understanding of scientific evidence, their freedom to determine what may be taught and how would be seriously abridged.

This Meeting calls on local communities and state officials to reject proposals that seek to suppress discussion of evolution in our public schools as inimical to principles of academic freedom.

Adopted June 11, 2005

American Association of University Women

The American Association of University Women is committed to the pursuit of knowledge and access to that knowledge by all citizens. AAUW is also committed as a national organization to the doctrine of separation of church and state. We are concerned that the inclusion in the public schools of information on the creationist theory will open the door to rightful requests for equal time by the many individual faiths, thus creating an unmanageable situation. Decisions need to be made relating to questions such as:

Who is qualified to relay this information to students?

Who will decide what texts to recommend for further reading?

Which theories will be included for presentation?

AAUW recognizes that theory will not be taught in the classroom, but we have reservations as to how it will be presented. Is it not better to leave the responsibility of religious thought to individual churches? All knowledge is not gained in the public classroom. AAUW believes citizens have a protected right to avail themselves of education through many sources, and the primary source for religious education must be the church.

Arkansas Science Teachers Association

Position Statement on Science Education

Arkansas Science Teachers Association (ASTA) members hold various personal views concerning the origin of the universe and of life. As a professional organization, ASTA is opposed to any religious view, such as creationism or intelligent design, being taught in the public schools as science.

ASTA finds science and religion to be complementary rather than contradictory. Science strives to explain the nature of the cosmos while religion seeks to give the cosmos and the life within it a purpose. Human existence is enriched by a knowledge and understanding of both science and religion.

Religious explanations of the origin of the universe and of life are based on faith. Because these explanations vary among different religions, the views are best taught in the home or within the context of religious institutions.

Scientific explanations regarding the origin of the universe and of life are based on experimentation and may change, as new evidence is uncovered. The goal of science is to discover and investigate universally accepted natural explanations. This process of discovery and description of natural phenomena should be taught in public schools. Therefore, both curriculum and selection of instructional materials for public schools must reflect established scientific evidence.

2006

Association of College and University Biology Educators

Evolution is good science. Understanding evolution and the nature of science is essential to a well-educated society. Thus, ACUBE supports the teaching of evolution.

Statement modified from that drafted by the National Conference on the Teaching of Evolution and adopted by ACUBE at the 44th Annual Meeting held 12-14 October 2000 at Indiana State University.

Association of Pennsylvania State College and University Biologists

Throughout the United States, "Scientific Creationism," a religious doctrine based upon the literal interpretation of the Bible, is being proposed as a valid scientific alternative to the Theory of Evolution. Creationists who represent this fundamentalist Christian religious movement are seeking "equal time" in science classrooms and science textbooks.

The Creationists' movement is an attempt to persuade, mislead, and pressure legislators, public school officials and the general public that since evolution is "only" a theory, implying opinion or conjecture, it is therefore open to any alternative. They propose that their alternative, the "Theory of Special Creation," is scientific and therefore is just as valid as the Theory of Evolution. Creationists reject the evolution of life from a single line of ancestors through chance mutation and natural selection and hold that the universe and all living things were divinely created beginning six to ten thousand years ago. They cite as their "scientific evidence" the biblical story of Genesis as written in the King James version of the Bible. Although Creationists are attempting to equate "Special Creation" as a scientific theory, they in fact claim absolute truth for their belief. Science, which does not deal with beliefs based on faith and does not claim absolute truth for its findings, utilizes an organized method of problem solving in an attempt to explain phenomena of our universe.

The Association of Pennsylvania State College and University Biologists together with other scientific associations such as the National Association of Biology Teachers, the National Academy of Science, the American Association for the Advancement of Science and the American Institute for Biological Sciences agrees that "Scientific Creationism" does not meet the criteria of science and cannot be considered a scientific theory. Scientists of these associations agree that Creationism can be neither verified nor refuted through scientific investigation, and the models or beliefs which involve the supernatural are not within the domain of science. However, to support the Theory of Evolution is not to be "antireligious" as Creationists propose. The majority of religions in America find no basic conflict between religion and science, and most accept the Theory of Evolution and reject Creationism. Throughout the U.S. scientists as well as clergy have opposed the Creationists' attempt to legislate the teaching of "Scientific Creationism" in science classrooms. During the December 1981 trial in Arkansas, in which a Creationist "equal time"

Voices for Evolution

law was contested and overturned, a great majority of witnesses in support of the Theory of Evolution were clergy of the Catholic, Protestant, and Jewish faiths.

The Theory of Evolution meets the criteria of science and the criteria of a scientific theory and is not based on faith, mere speculation or dogma. Evolution as a scientific theory is supported by a vast body of scientifically scrutinizable evidence coming from such sources as anatomy and physiology, biochemistry, genetics and the fossil record. To state, as Creationists do, that the Theory of Evolution is "only" a theory illustrates ignorance of science and the scientific method. The Theory of Evolution will be accepted and supported by the scientific community unless another theory which is based on science and the scientific method takes its place.

The Association of Pennsylvania State College and University Biologists recognizes that the move to equate a non-scientific belief with science is a threat to the very integrity of science. APSCUB respects the religious beliefs held by Creationists and others pertaining to the origin and diversity of life and does not oppose the teaching of those concepts as religion or philosophy. However, APSCUB members as scientists and educators are in opposition to any attempt to introduce Creationism or any other non-scientific or pseudoscientific belief as science in the public school system in the Commonwealth of Pennsylvania. APSCUB further recommends the following:

1. All public school science teachers in the Commonwealth should reject science textbooks which treat Creationism as science. The inclusion of non-scientific material as science in a science textbook reflects on the credibility of the teacher who uses it. Textbooks which deal with the diversity of life but do not mention the Theory of Evolution or restrict its discussion should also be rejected.

2. Biology teachers in the public school system of Pennsylvania should teach the Theory of Evolution not as absolute truth but as the most widely accepted scientific theory on the diversity of life. Biology teachers of the Commonwealth should not be intimidated by pressures of the Creationists and simply avoid the issue by not teaching the Theory of Evolution. Avoiding established concepts in science is pseudoscience which also threatens the integrity and credibility of science. Avoiding the teaching of evolution is a victory for the Creationists.

Members of APSCUB will, when possible, give advice and support to teachers, legislators, public school officials, and the general public where matters of "Scientific Creationism" or other nonscientific beliefs concerning the diversity of life arise in their local community within the Commonwealth of Pennsylvania.

Undated; 1982 or later.

Auburn University Faculty Senate (1981)

We understand that the Alabama legislature is considering a requirement that "Scientific Creationism" be included as an alternative to evolutionary theory during discussions in Alabama public schools of the origin and development of life; and

We consider the theory of scientific creationism to be neither scientifically based nor capable of performing the roles required of a scientific theory; and

We agree with the statement of the National Academy of Sciences that "religion and science are separate and mutually exclusive realms of human thought whose presentation in the same context leads to misunderstanding of both scientific theory and religious belief"; and

The proposed action would impair the proper segregation of teaching of science and religion to the detriment of both; and

We favor the continued observance of the First Amendment to the U.S. Constitution guaranteeing freedom of religion by assuming separation of Church and State; and

The inclusion of the theory of creation represents dictation by a lay body of what shall be included within science;

Therefore, let it be resolved that the Auburn University Senate go on record in strenuous opposition to any legislative attempt to determine or to direct what is taught as science in Alabama's public schools.

A variation of the University of Alabama, Huntsville, faculty senate resolution adapted and ratified by voice vote, without dissent, by the Auburn University faculty senate on 10 March 1981. Wording is inferred from the Hunstville resolution and a memorandum attached to it from John Kuykendall to Delos McKown spelling out the changes made at Auburn.

Auburn University Faculty Senate (1983)

To: Members of the Science Work Group who developed the 1982 revision of the Science Course of Study

We, the undersigned members of the Auburn University faculty in the sciences, are writing to express our dismay at the action of your committee in removing references to standard topics and concepts in the fields of biological and earth sciences from the Alabama Course of Study of Science.

Recent reports from study groups have emphasized the great deficiencies in science education across the nation. We who teach the graduates of Alabama high schools are particularly aware that our state is no exception. Lawmakers and civic and business leaders alike agree that Alabama must develop "high-tech" industries if we are to prosper or even keep up with our neighbors economically. Yet we are seeing the undermining of teaching of science in the public school to such an extent that few of our best and brightest students are likely to be directed toward careers in science and engineering. Those who are will enter college woefully unprepared to think scientifically and lacking the basic acquaintance with current ideas and facts in science on which a college teacher expects to build.

The signers of this letter represent a wide spectrum of religious beliefs as well as a wide variety of scientific disciplines. Our concern is not with the beliefs of individuals, but with what is genuine science, and that Alabama students be exposed to the scientific information and ideas on which the modern technological world is based. The Course of Study as currently stated gives so much leeway that a course called "biology" or "earth science" could be taught with no scientific content at all. We must not handicap Alabama students with that possibility!

We do not know how you voted on the question of removing terms relating to evolution, the history of the earth, and the age of the universe from the Course of Study. We do know that standard parliamentary procedure allows one who voted for a motion to move for its reconsideration. We urge you to take this or whatever other means lie at your disposal to reconsider the damaging position previously taken – for the sake of Alabama young people and the welfare of our State as a whole.

Passed by the University Senate.

Authors of Biology Textbooks

Statement on Evolution in Textbooks

Evolution and Science

The coverage of evolution in biology textbooks we have written reflects the broad consensus in the scientific community. As noted in a booklet issued by the National Academy of Sciences, "Evolution pervades all biological phenomena. To ignore that it occurred or to classify it as a form of dogma is to deprive the student of the most fundamental organizational concept in the biological sciences" (Science and Creationism, National Academy Press, 1985, p. 22).

Our textbooks are written from this point of view. Evolution occupies a prominent position, and is covered explicitly. Many sections use evolutionary concepts to explain the diversity of living and fossil organisms, the adaptations of organisms to their environments, and similarities of structure and function shared by related organisms. In this way, we present students with the understanding of biology shared by the overwhelming majority of working scientists in the United States and throughout the world.

What Do States Require of Biology Textbooks?

Although state requirements vary, the majority require that biology curricula must include extensive coverage of evolution. The few states where standards or curriculum guidelines do not mention evolution by name nonetheless require the coverage of evolutionary topics. If we omitted proper coverage of evolutionary facts and theories, we would not be in compliance with these and other curricula that require complete, accurate, up-to-date, and conceptually-based educational materials.

Our Message to Textbook Adopters

As scientists and teachers, we find it unacceptable that school districts considering our books for adoption would be encouraged to choose one book over another based on the perception that teachers should avoid the topic of evolution. We encourage school districts deciding among our books to use genuine scientific and educational criteria.

We also deplore the efforts made in some states and districts to require that evolution be disclaimed. Such disclaimers single out evolution from all other scientific ideas as somehow less reliable or less accepted by scientists, or as "only a theory." Evolution is a normal part of science, and should be treated the same way as all other scientific ideas. It does a disservice to students to mislead them about the important position that evolution holds in biological and other sciences.

Those who have joined in this statement do so as individuals. We do not speak on behalf of our publishers, but for ourselves, as biologists, authors, and educators.
(In alphabetical order; institutions are listed for purposes of identification only)

Bruce Alberts, National Academy of Sciences
Sandra Alters, Montreal, Quebec, Canada
Gerald Audesirk, University of Colorado, Denver
Teresa Audesirk, University of Colorado, Denver
Alton Biggs, Biggs Educational Consulting, Allen TX
Neil Campbell, University of California, Riverside
Helena Curtis, Sag Harbor NY
Michael Dougherty, Hampton-Sydney College
Jennie Dusheck, Santa Cruz CA

Carol Gontang, Mountain View High School, Mountain View CA
H. Craig Heller, Stanford University
Paul Hummer, Hood College
Alexander Johnson, University of California, San Francisco
George Johnson, Washington University
David Krogh, Kensington CA
William Leonard, Clemson University
Joseph Levine, Concord MA
Ricki Lewis, Scotia NY
Marilyn Lisowski, Eastern Illinois University
Linda Lundgren, Bear Creek High School, Lakewood CO
James McLaren, Newton South High School, Newton Center MA
Joseph McInerney, National Coalition for Health Professional Education in Genetics
Kenneth Miller, Brown University
Raymond Oram, Peddie School, Hightstown NJ
Gordon H. Orians, University of Washington
John Penick, North Carolina State University
William K. Purves, Harvey Mudd College
Peter Raven, Missouri Botanical Garden
Joseph Raver, Three Rivers Local Schools, Cleves OH
David Sadara, Claremont McKenna College
Gerald Skoog, Texas Tech University
Cecie Starr, Belmont CA
Eric Strauss, Boston College
Ralph Taggart, Michigan State University
Albert Towle, Auburn CA
Peter Walter, University of California, San Francisco

March 26, 1999; updated in 2003 and 2005.

Biological Sciences Curriculum Study (1971)

Position on the Teaching of Biology

Dr. Addison E. Lee, Professor of Science Education and Biology, and Director of the Science Education Center, The University of Texas at Austin, serves as Chairman of the Board of Directors of the Biological Sciences Curriculum Study. His distinguished accomplishments as science educator and biologist enable him to write with authority in support of the BSCS position on the teaching of evolution. Dr. Lee's many publications as author or editor include Laboratory Studies in Biology and a monograph series entitled Research and Curriculum Development in Science Education.

The BSCS program began in 1959 amid considerable debate about the approach to be taken in the teaching of biology. Should it be molecular, organismal, developmental, ecological, or other? Should it include one textbook or several? How much and what kind of attention to laboratory work should be given? Amidst all these debates, however, it was an early consensus that certain themes should be included in all biology programs, no matter what approach is selected, and whatever attention may be given to various details. These themes were identified and have consistently pervaded the several approaches and different materials developed by the BSCS during the past twelve years. They are:

1. Change of living things through time: evolution

2. Diversity of type and unity of pattern in living things

3. The genetic continuity of life

4. The complementarity of organism and environment

5. The biological roots of behavior

6. The complementarity of structure and function

7. Regulation and homeostasis: preservation of life in the face of change

8. Science as inquiry

9. The history of biological conceptions

It should be noted that these unifying themes were identified and accepted by a large group of distinguished scientists, science teachers, and other educators. And although members of this group represented many interests, specialties, and points of view, there was and has continued to be general agreement concerning the importance, use, and nature of these themes.

It should also be noted that evolution is not only one of the major themes but is, in fact, central among the other themes; they are inter-related, and each is particularly related to evolution.

The position of the BSCS on the importance of evolution in teaching biology has been clearly stated in both the first (1963) and second (1970) editions of the Biology Teachers' Handbook:

> *It is no longer possible to give a complete or even a coherent account of living things without the story of evolution. On the other hand, many of the most striking characteristics of living things are "products" of the evolutionary process. We can make good sense and order of the similarities and differences among living things to the particular environments in which they live, their distribution over the surface of the earth, the comings and goings of their parts during development, even the chemistry by which they obtain energy and exchange it among their parts - all such matters find illumination and explanation, in whole or in part, from the history of life on earth.*
>
> *On the other hand, another great group of characteristics of living things can be fully understood only as the means and mechanisms by which evolution takes place. There are first, and conspicuously, the events of meiosis and fertilization, universal in sexual reproduction. It is only in terms of the contribution of these processes to the enhancement and sorting out of a vast store of heritable variations that we make sense of them. The same point applies to the complex processes that go under the name of mutation. Similarly, we see everywhere the action and consequences of natural selection, of reproductive isolation of populations, of the effects of size and change on intrabreeding groups.*
>
> *Evolution, then, forms the warp and woof of modern biology...* *

Evolution is a scientific theory in the sense that it is based on scientific data accumulated over many years and organized into a unifying idea widely accepted by modern biologists. The BSCS is concerned with any scientific theory relevant to the biological sciences that can be dealt with in terms of scientific data accumulated and organized. It is not, on the other hand, concerned with religious doctrines that are based only on faith or beliefs, nor does it consider them relevant to the teaching of biological science.

The BSCS program was carried through an extensive tryout period during its early development; feedback and input from hundreds of scientist and science teachers were used in the initial edition that was made available to biology teachers in the United States. A revised second edition of the three major textbooks produced has been published, and a revised third edition is nearing completion. In spite of efforts of various groups to force changes in the content of the texts by exerting pressures on textbook selection committees and on local and state governments, throughout the last twelve years the BSCS position on using the unifying themes of biology remains unchanged.

Footnote in original: * BSCS, Biology Teachers' Handbook, Joseph J. Schwab (supervisor), John Wiley and Sons, New York, 1963. BSCS, Biology Teachers' Handbook, Second Edition, Evelyn Klinckmann (supervisor), John Wiley and Sons, New York, 1970.

Biological Sciences Curriculum Study (1995)

Position on the Teaching of Evolution for Voices for Evolution

BSCS, founded in 1958, was largely responsible for reintroducing evolution into the high school biology curriculum, following a four-decade period during which evolution virtually disappeared from high school biology textbooks. From its inception, BSCS has treated evolution as the central organizing theme of biology, listing it first, for example, among the biological principles that guided the development of all early BSCS programs.

The Biology Teachers' Handbook, published by BSCS in 1963, stressed the importance of concentrating on major principles in biology and gave special attention to evolution, stating: "It is no longer possible to give a complete or even a coherent account of living things without the story of evolution." The intervening three decades have affirmed that assertion, with progress in genetics, molecular biology, behavior, development, neuroscience, and other sub-disciplines reinforcing and expanding evolutionary perspectives originally based on gross morphological data.

The recent and rapid growth of knowledge in all areas of biology makes it ever more important - and difficult - to focus curriculum and teaching on major principles. To that end, BSCS recently published Developing Biological Literacy: A Guide to Developing Secondary and Post-secondary Biology Curricula (1993). This document identifies six unifying principles of biology that should pervade the teaching of biology, and it states the BSCS position on evolution quite clearly:

How can one simultaneously account of the extraordinary diversity and observable unity of living systems in the world today? The answer, in a word, is evolution. Evolution is the unifying theory of biology because it has played a role in the history and lives of all living organisms on Earth today - and of those that are now extinct. Evolution is the major conceptual scheme of biology because it helps us understand relationships between organisms, past and present, and the many ways organisms have succeeded in different habitats.

We recognize that there are other ways of knowing, but ours is the scientific pursuit of knowledge. As BSCS approaches its fortieth anniversary of service to science education, it remains committed to the accurate and thorough representation of evolution as the conceptual keystone to our understanding of life on Earth. Furthermore, BSCS will continue to defend scientific integrity and will resist all attempts to influence its materials in ways that portray non-scientific explanations of life on Earth as scientifically valid.

Approved by the BSCS Board of Directors
January 1995

Voices for Evolution

California Science Teachers Association

Policy Statement on the Teaching of Evolution

Our planet is billions of years old, and life has existed on it for a large part of that time. Through the eons, the Earth and its life have changed in an unending procession of new forms and vistas. This history and the mechanisms that bring about these changes are what is known as evolution.

Evolution occurred in the past and is still occurring today. To fully appreciate and acquire an understanding of life on Earth, one must know a great deal about present-day forms and their history. For this reason, evolution is a necessary part of everyone's education. It makes as little sense for a biology teacher to present life on Earth as a collection of static entities as it would for a social studies teacher to present civics and geography without their historical contexts.

Biological evolution refers to the scientific understanding that living things share ancestors from which they have diverged – descent with modification. It is the consensus of the scientific community that evolutionary theory best explains the history of life and accounts for the similarities among living things, as well as life's diversity. As living communities profoundly affect the composition of Earth's atmosphere, weather, soils, and temperature, evolutionary theory also explains many features of the physical world in which we live. Evolutionary biology also contributes to society in more practical ways, including increased understanding of drug resistance by human pathogens, alternatives to pest controls, use of fossil fuels, and conservation.

Teaching evolution in our science classrooms is essential. As noted in *Teaching About Evolution and the Nature of Science*, issued by the National Academy of Sciences, "Evolution pervades all biological phenomena. To ignore that it occurred or to classify it as a form of dogma is to deprive the student of the most fundamental organizational concept in the biological sciences." Evolution is identified as a unifying principle in the National Science Education Standards and is integral to the California Science Content Standards.

The California Science Teachers Association endorses the teaching of evolution at all levels of our students' education. Furthermore, we do not endorse teaching the "evidence against evolution," as there is no scientific evidence that evolution has not occurred. Nor can we condone teaching "scientific creationism," "intelligent design," or other non-scientific explanations as valid scientific theories. These beliefs ignore empirical data and fail to provide testable hypotheses. They should not be a part of the science curriculum.

Adopted December 7, 2002

Empire State Association of Two Year College Biologists

Resolution of the Teaching of Evolution

Whereas A popular movement to compromise the teaching of Evolution exists, and

Whereas any compromise in the teaching of evolution weakens the teaching of biology in general, and

Whereas efforts on the part of textbook publishers to accommodate special interest groups, such as the popular anti-evolution movement, contributes to the weakening of biology instruction, and

Whereas this practice is most pronounced at the pre-college level, be it

Resolved that the E.S.A.T.Y.C.B. opposes anything less than the full textbook presentation of evolution as it is currently accepted by the biological community, and be it further

Resolved that the E.S.A.T.Y.C.B. opposes the introduction of non-biological ideas as alternatives to evolution, and be it further

Resolved that the E.S.A.T.Y.C.B. recommends that its members become aware of the publishers' policies concerning exclusion of sound scientific information to accommodate special interest groups and that these policies be considered when selecting a text.

Spring 1998

Georgia Citizens' Educational Coalition

Statement on the Teaching of Creationism in Georgia Public High School Science Classes

There is grandeur in this view of life, with its several powers, having been originally breathed by the Creator into a few forms or into one... and from so simple a beginning endless forms most beautiful and most wonderful have been, and are being evolved.

– Charles Darwin
The Origin of Species

We oppose the teaching of "creationism" as science in Georgia's public schools. Creationism is based on the religious belief in biblical literalism, or biblical inerrancy, and not on scientific theory. It includes belief in six 24-hour days of creation which occurred less than 10,000 years ago.

The First Amendment specifically forbids the State to force its citizens to profess a belief, or disbelief, in any religion. Creationism is a particular sectarian doctrine held only by those who believe in biblical literalism.

We have no objection to the belief in biblical literalism by those who are obliged by their religion to do so, but object strongly to injecting this religious belief, in the form of creationism, into the science classroom.

However, we recognize the right of parents to uphold their deep religious convictions by withdrawing their children from the study of the scientific theory of evolution.

Many of us believe there is no contradiction between the acts of the Creator God in the Bible and the theory of evolution, and in fact see the evolutionary process as one of God's greatest works.

It is no longer possible to teach biology without the study of the scientific theory of evolution, which has been universally accepted into mankind's general body of knowledge, and stands today as the organizing principle of biology and the general theory of life. There is no competing theory that is taken seriously.

We therefore strongly oppose the teaching of creationism in Georgia's public high school science classrooms because

1. it is not science, and

2. it would impose a particular religious belief on our students.

1980; written by Charles C. Brooks, President.

Voices for Evolution

The Teaching of Evolution

Evolution, in the broadest sense, can be defined as the idea that the universe has a history: that change through time has taken place. If we look today at the galaxies, stars, the planet Earth, and the life on planet Earth, we see that things today are different from what they were in the past: galaxies, stars, planets, and life forms have evolved. Biological evolution refers to the scientific theory that living things share ancestors from which they have diverged; it is called "descent with modification". There is abundant and consistent evidence from astronomy, physics, biochemistry, geochronology, geology, biology, anthropology, and other sciences that evolution has taken place.

As such, evolution is a unifying concept for science. The National Science Education Standards recognizes that conceptual schemes such as evolution "unify science disciplines and provide students with powerful ideas to help them understand the natural world" (p. 104) and recommends evolution as one such scheme. In addition, Benchmarks for Science Literacy from AAAS's Project 2061, as well as other national calls for science reform, all name evolution as a unifying concept because of its importance across the disciplines of science. Scientific disciplines with a historical component, such as astronomy, geology, biology, and anthropology, cannot be taught with integrity if evolution is not emphasized.

There is no longer a debate among scientists about whether evolution has taken place. There is considerable debate about how evolution has taken place: What are the processes and mechanisms producing change, and what has happened specifically during the history of the universe? Scientists often disagree about their explanations. In any science, disagreements are subject to rules of evaluation. Scientific conclusions are tested by experiment and observation, and evolution, as with any aspect of theoretical science, is continually open to and subject to experimental and observational testing.

The importance of evolution is summarized as follows in the National Academy of Sciences publication Teaching about Evolution and the Nature of Science: "Few other ideas in science have had such a far-reaching impact on our thinking about ourselves and how we relate to the world" (p. 21).

The National Science Education Standards note that, "[e]xplanations of how the natural world changes based on myths, personal beliefs, religious values, mystical inspiration, superstition, or authority may be personally useful and socially relevant, but they are not scientific" (p. 201). Because science limits itself to natural explanations and not religious or ultimate ones, science teachers should neither advocate any religious interpretation of nature nor assert that religious interpretations of nature are not possible.

Some policy makers continue attempts to distort the teaching of evolution through mandates that would require teachers to teach evolution as "only a theory" or that require a textbook or lesson on evolution to be preceded by a disclaimer. Regardless of the legal status of these mandates, they are bad educational policy. Such policies have the effect of intimidating teachers, which may result in the de-emphasis or omission of evolution. As a consequence, the public will only be further confused about the nature of scientific theories. Furthermore, if students learn less about evolution, science literacy itself will suffer.

The Idaho Science Teachers Association (ISTA) strongly supports the position that evolution is a major unifying concept in science and should be included in the K-12 science education curricula. Furthermore, if evolution is not taught, students will not achieve the level of scientific literacy they need. This position is consistent with that of the National Academies, the American Association for the Advancement of Science (AAAS), and many other scientific and educational organizations.

ISTA also recognizes that evolution has not been emphasized in science curricula in many locations in a manner commensurate to its importance because of official policies, intimidation of science teachers, the general public's misunderstanding of evolutionary theory, and a century of controversy. In addition, some teachers are being pressured to introduce creationism, "creation science," intelligent design and other nonscientific views, which are intended to weaken or eliminate the teaching of evolution.

Within this context, ISTA recommends that:

- all teacher certification institutions require courses in the nature of science and evolution.

- evolution be taught as an essential unifying concept in science that should be included in the K-12 curricula.Teachers of science should be supported in the teaching of evolution and the strong body of scientific evidence supporting it, and not be pressured to present nonscientific views.

- science curricula, Idaho state science standards, and teachers should empha- size evolution in a manner commensurate with its importance as a unifying concept in science and its overall explanatory power.

- science teachers should not advocate any religious interpretations of nature and should be nonjudgmental about the personal beliefs of students.

- policy makers and administrators should not mandate policies requiring the teaching of "creation science" or related concepts, such as so-called "intelligent design," "abrupt appearance," and "arguments against evolution." Administra- tors also should support teachers against pressure to promote nonscientific views or to diminish or eliminate the study of evolution.

- Administrators and school boards should provide support to teachers as they review, adopt, and implement curricula that emphasize evolution.This should include professional development to assist teachers in teaching evolution in a comprehensive and professional manner.

- Parental and community involvement in establishing the goals of science edu- cation and the curriculum development process should be encouraged and nurtured in our democratic society. However, the professional responsibility of science teachers and curriculum specialists to provide students with qual- ity science education should not be compromised by censorship, pseudosci- ence, inconsistencies, faulty scholarship, or unconstitutional mandates.

Adopted by the ISTA Board 2/24/2007

References:

NSTA Position Statement - The Teaching of Evolution: National Congress on Science Education - 8/05CNG9, 8/05CNG10.

Illinois Community College Faculty Association

A Resolution on the Teaching of Evolution

WHEREAS it is the responsibility of the academic community to preserve the integrity of science, and

WHEREAS science is a systematic method of investigation based on continuous experimentation, observation, and measurement leading to evolving explanations of natural phenomena, explanations which are continuously open to further testing, and

WHEREAS evolution fully satisfies these criteria, irrespective of remaining debates concerning its detailed mechanisms, and

WHEREAS we the faculty respect the right of people to hold diverse beliefs about creation that do not come within the definitions of science, and

WHEREAS specific references to evolutionary biology have been omitted from the public schools science standards, and

THEREFORE BE IT RESOLVED the Illinois Community College Faculty Association urges citizens, educational authorities, and legislators to encourage the Illinois State Board of Education to include specific reference to evolutionary biology in the public school science standards.

Adopted by the Illinois Community College Faculty Association Delegate Assembly, October 29, 1999 Springfield.

Inter-University Council of Ohio

Members of the Ohio State Board of Education
c/o Susan Tave Zelman, Board Secretary
25 South Front Street, 7th Floor
Columbus, Ohio 43215-4183

Dear Members of the Ohio State Board of Education:

We, the presidents of the Inter-University Council of Ohio, request that you adopt elementary through high school science standards that indicate students' understanding of the explanatory and predictive power of science. Such understanding is required for completing a degree at all of our institutions and for functioning as a member of a scientifically literate work force and electorate.

While we recognize the great value of spirituality and faith in today's society, we urge you to reject the concept of intelligent design creationism as a part of the science curriculum. We also request that you establish the foundation for a preeminent science curriculum in Ohio dedicated to rigorous testing and experimentation, strengthened with thorough teaching of evolution in our science requirements.

We have entered a remarkable new era in genetics and biotechnology, one in which we have the opportunity to benefit from the greatest wave of scientific achievement in human history. As Ohio strives to become a leader in this knowledge-based economy, Governor Taft is promoting a multi-billion-dollar "Third Frontier

Project" to rejuvenate Ohio's economy through advances in biotechnology and other areas of science and technology. The federal government and private industry are investing heavily in research and development, and our state is dedicating hundreds of millions of dollars to improve science and math education in public schools. Such initiatives rely on the application of basic scientific knowledge and fact-based inquiry to fields as diverse as agriculture, health care, and environmental protection. To adopt intelligent design creationism in our state science standards - or to imply that evolution and intelligent design are equally valid as scientific theories - will sabotage these educational and economic development efforts at the very time when our children and state need them most.

Evolution is the single unifying scientific theory of life and an essential element of scientific literacy. As noted scientist Theodosius Dobzhansky observed, "Nothing in biology makes sense except in the light of evolution."

The proposed science standards that the State Board of Education received in December made substantial advances by making evolution a central subject in the curriculum. Now, however, instead of building upon this important step, we risk pushing science education in Ohio back to the 19th century. House Bill 481 and other curriculum recommendations being debated would require public schools to teach concepts such as intelligent design creationism when they teach evolution, or would provide little guidance on the issue, leaving decisions up to local schools. Because no data support the belief of intelligent design, such policies could, in essence, bring creationism into science class and equate supernatural beliefs with scientific theory, which by its very nature is based on testing and rigorous observation of nature. This misrepresents both science and religion and is a disservice to both.

Ohio's young people who are denied a basic understanding of evolution or who are taught the "scientific" validity of non-scientific "theories" will enter college far behind students from other states. A new generation of K-12 teachers that we are now training - and that must pass certification exams - will have significant misconceptions about basic science and scientific methods. Furthermore, if Ohio is perceived as one of the nation's intellectual backwaters, our universities - as well as private industry - will be severely handicapped in trying to recruit and retain top researchers in the biological sciences, as well as other fields. As a result, Ohio will be ill equipped to develop the innovative businesses that will help create the "Third Frontier" envisioned by Governor Taft.

Perhaps most important, in a world in which rapid technological advancement affects nearly every aspect of our lives, Ohio's citizens must possess a solid scientific literacy in order to make intelligent decisions ranging from whether to buy a genetically engineered vegetable at the grocery store to how to determine national policy issues related to human genetics. Understanding the primacy of evolution in the development of such options and the decision to exercise them is fundamental.

Clearly, we must acknowledge and respect the faiths of students and other citizens. Parents and clerics play a crucial role in teaching matters of religious philosophy, and education plays a role in teaching about the history of these ideas. The role of diverse faiths likely belongs in our K-12 curricula in courses on comparative religions and the history of science. However, our public schools and science teachers owe it to our children to pass on to them the very best scientific knowledge available and to instill in them a method of learning based on close observation, thorough testing, and impartial analysis.

For the future well being of Ohio and its citizens, we strongly urge the Ohio

State Board of Education to adopt rigorous science curriculum that makes evolution an integral part of our biological science requirements and that limits scientific endeavors to observable and definable phenomena subject to thorough scientific testing and experimentation.

Sincerely,
Robert Glidden
President, Ohio University
Chair, Inter-University Council

On behalf of IUC presidents:
Luis Proenza, University of Akron
Sidney Ribeau, Bowling Green State University
John Garland, Central State University
Joseph Steger, University of Cincinnati
Michael Schwartz, Cleveland State University
Carol Cartwright, Kent State University
Frank McCullough, Medical College of Ohio
James Garland, Miami University
Robert Blacklow, Northeastern Ohio Universities College of Medicine
William Kirwan, Ohio State University
Michael Field, Shawnee State University
Daniel Johnson, University of Toledo
Kim Goldenberg, Wright State University
Daniel Sweet, Youngstown State University

March 15, 2002

Iowa Council of Science Supervisors

Because of the insistence that special creation be taught in Iowa science courses as an alternative concept to evolution, we, the Iowa Council of Science Supervisors, as representatives of the science educators in Iowa, make the following statement:

Science educators are responsible for interpreting the spirit and substance of science to their students. Teachers are bound to promote a scientific rationale based upon carefully defined and objective judgments of scientific endeavors. When conflicts arise between competing paradigms in science, they must be resolved by the scientific community rather than by the educators of science.

Based upon court decisions in Indiana and Tennessee, and in the creationists' own statements of beliefs, the Creation Research Society is premised upon the full belief in the Biblical record of special creation.

"The Bible is the Written Word of God, and because it is inspired throughout, all its assertions are historically and scientifically true in all original autographs. To the student of nature this means that the account of origins in Genesis is a factual presentation of simple historical truths."[1]

Science is tentative and denies an ultimate or perfect truth as claimed by scientific creationism. We suggest that creationists submit their creation theories and models to recognized science organizations such as the American Association for the Advancement of Science (AAAS) or their affiliated scientific societies. The claims of these paradigms should be substantiated with validated objective evidence. The scientific organizations would assume responsibility for analyzing the materials, making their findings available for national review through AAAS scientific journals.

Until "scientific creation" receives substantial support from such organizations as AAAS, American Anthropological Association, state academies of science, National Academy of Science, and national paleontological and geological associations, it is recommended that this organization and the science teachers of Iowa reject further consideration of scientific creationism as an alternative approach to established science teaching practices.

[1] Membership application forms for the Creation Research Society. Corrections of spelling and punctuation by editors.

Iowa Department of Public Instruction

Creation, Evolution and Public Education: The Position of the Iowa Department of Public Instruction

The Controversy

In Iowa and other states, "creationism" has recently been advanced as an alternative to the theory of evolution. Attempts have been made to legislatively mandate "equal time" for creationist concepts in science classrooms, materials, and textbooks.

Interviews and surveys conducted by the Iowa Department of Public Instruction show that most Iowa religious leaders, science educators, scientists and philosophers contacted support the present patterns of teaching science in Iowa's schools. In addition, due to the nature of scientific and theological concepts, these authorities feel that the specifics of each discipline should be confined to their respective houses.

The National Academy of Science has stated that religion and science are "separate and mutually exclusive realms of human thought whose presentation in the same context leads to misunderstanding of both scientific theories and religious beliefs." [1]

Creationism

In America, religion is usually defined as the expression of man's belief in, and reverence for, a metaphysical power governing all activities of the universe. Where there is not belief in metaphysical power, religion is a concern for that which is ultimate. Generally, creationism is a religious concept. It proposes that all living things were created by a Creator. According to the creation model, "all living things originated from basic kinds of life, each of which was separately created." [2]

There are many versions of creation. Generally, creationists advocate that all permanent, basic life forms originated thousands of years ago through directive acts of a Creator - independent of the natural universe. Plants and animals were created separately with their full genetic potentiality provided by the Creator. Any variation, or speciation, which has occurred since creation has been within the original prescribed boundaries. Since each species contains its full potentiality, nature is viewed as static, reliable and predictable. Based on alleged gaps in the geologic record, creationists reject the theory of the descent of plants and animals from a single line of ancestors arising through random mutation and successively evolving over billions of years. It is further alleged that, through analysis of geologic strata, the earth has experienced at least one great flood or other natural global disaster accounting for the mass extinction of many biological organisms. Following such extinctions there followed sudden increases in the number, variety and complexity of organisms.

Having all Biblical accounts of creationism placed in comparative theology courses with other religious accounts of origins will not placate ardent creationists. They require that creationism be presented as a viable scientific alternative to evolution.[3] More zealous creationists argue that "it is only in the Bible that we can possibly obtain any information about the methods of creation, the order of creation, the duration of creation, or any other details of creation."[4]

Science
Science is an attempt to help explain the world of which we are a part. It is both an *investigatory process* and a *body of knowledge* readily subjected to investigation and verification. By a generally accepted definition, science is not an indoctrination process, but rather an objective method for problem solving. Science is an important part of the foundation upon which rest our technology, our agriculture, our economy, our intellectual life, our national defense, and our ventures into space.

The formulation of theories is a basic part of scientific method. Theories are generalizations, based on substantial evidence, which explain many diverse phenomena. A theory is always tentative. It is subject to test through the uncovering of new data, through new experiments, through repetition and refinements of old experiments, or through new interpretations. Should a significant body of contrary evidence appear, the theory is either revised or it is replaced by a new and better theory. The strength of a scientific theory lies in the fact that it is the most logical explanation of known facts, principles, and concepts dealing with an idea which does not currently have a conclusive test.

Evolution
The *theory* of evolution meets the criteria of a scientific theory. It can explain much of the past and help predict many future scientific phenomena. Basically, the theory states that modern biologic organisms descended, with modification, from pre-existing forms which in turn had ancestors. Those organisms best adapted, through anatomical and physiological modification to their environment, left more offspring than did non-adapted organisms. The increased diversity of organisms enhanced their ability to survive in various environments and enabled them to leave more progeny.

The theory of evolution is designed to answer the "how" questions of science and biological development; it cannot deal effectively with the "who" or "why" of man's origin and development. It is, however, an effective means of integrating and clarifying many otherwise isolated scientific facts, principles and concepts.

There have been alternatives proposed to the theory of evolution (i.e., creationism, exo-biology, spontaneous generation); however, none are supported by the amount of scientific evidence that presently supports the theory of evolution.

It is evident that the process of evolution occurs. Successful species of living organisms change with time when exposed to environmental pressures. Such changes in species have been documented in the past, and it can be confidently predicted that they will continue to change in the future. Evolution helps explain many other scientific phenomena: variations in disease, drug resistance in microbes, anatomical anomalies which appear in surgery, and successful methods for breeding better crops and farm animals. Modern biological science and its applications on the farm, in medicine, and elsewhere are not completely understandable without many of the basic concepts of evolution.

There are many things that evolution is not. It is not dogma. Although there is intense dispute among scientists concerning the details of evolution, most scientists accept its validity on the ground of its strong supporting evidence.

Department of Public Instruction Decision
Teaching religious doctrine is not the science teacher's responsibility. Teachers

should recognize the personal validity of alternative beliefs, but should then direct student inquiries to the appropriate institution for counseling and/or further explanation. Giving equal emphasis in science classes to non-scientific theories that are presented as alternatives to evolution would be in direct opposition to understanding the nature and purpose of science.

Each group is fully entitled to its point of view with respect to the Bible and evolution; but the American doctrine of religious freedom and the Establishment Clause in the First Amendment to the U.S. Constitution forbid either group – or any other religious group – from pressing its point of view on the public schools. An Indiana court decision declared: "The prospect of biology teachers and students alike forced to answer and respond to continued demand for 'correct' Fundamentalist Christian doctrines has no place in public schools."[5]

The science curriculum should emphasize the theory of evolution as a well-supported scientific theory – not a fact – that is taught as such by certified science teachers. Students should be advised that it is their responsibility, as informed citizens, to have creationism explained to them by theological experts. They must then decide for themselves the merits of each discipline and its relevance to their lives.

The Iowa Department of Public Instruction feels that public schools cannot be surrogate family, church and all other necessary social institutions for students, and for them to attempt to do so would be a great disservice to citizens and appropriate institutions.

Footnotes in original:

1 Resolution adopted by the National Academy of Science and the Commission of Science Education of the American Academy [sic] for the Advancement of Science (Washington, D.C. 17 October 1972).

2 Bliss, R. B., *Origins: Two Models: Evolution, Creation* (San Diego: Creation Life Publishers, 1976), p. 31.

3 Morris, Henry M., *The Remarkable Birth of Planet Earth* (San Diego: Creation Life Publishers, 1972).

4 National Association of Biology Teachers, *A Compendium of Information on the Theory of Evolution and the Evolution-Creationism Controversy* (June 1977).

5 Hendren vs Campbell, Supreme [sic] Court No. 5, Marion County, Indiana (1977), p. 20

Released by the Iowa DPI in March 1980.

Maryland Association of Science Teachers

Statement by the Maryland Association of Science Teachers and the Maryland Science Supervisors Association in Support of the Teaching of Evolution in Science Classes in Maryland

Position Statement:

The Maryland Association of Science Teachers and the Maryland Science Supervisors Association hereby affirm that biological evolution and scientific concepts of earth history should be taught in Maryland science classes. We support the position that evolution is, and should remain, a cornerstone concept in the science content standards adopted by the state of Maryland. We also support and agree with the positions stated by the National Science Teachers Association in its position paper *The Teaching of Evolution*, which is attached herewith, and with the expectations on this subject found in the National Science Education Standards by the National Research Council.

Supporting statements:

1. Evolution is a well documented and well-established scientific explanation that unifies many pieces of evidence gathered by earth scientists and biologists. Though evidence which continues to accumulate through scientific study will refine our understanding of the mechanisms and the changes that have come about through evolution, the scientific community has no doubts that it has occurred, is occurring now, and will continue to occur.

2. Evolution meets the definition of a theory in science, which is an integrated understanding of a concept supported by numerous lines of evidence; it should not be confused with the more common definition of a theory as a guess or hypothesis. Other scientific theories such as atomic theory, or the theory of plate tectonics, are examples of other validated conceptualizations of how the world works, similar in nature to the status of the theory of evolution.

3. Throughout the science education community, evolution is seen as an important, required topic. If students are to understand the larger themes of how the world works, and indeed if they are to understand how science works, evolution is at once a critical unifying concept and a classic example of the scientific process.

4. Other doctrines that have been proposed to be taught instead of or in addition to evolution, variously called "creationism," "intelligent design," and other terms, have repeatedly been found by the U.S. Supreme Court and other courts to be unconstitutional for public schools because these ideas are based on religious doctrines, and so violate church-state separation. Scientists and science educators recognize that these ideas fall outside the realm of science, which requires evidence for all understandings, and so have no place in the subject matter of a science class.

5. Science as a discipline neither supports nor refutes religious doctrines or beliefs, because such beliefs are not proper topics of study for science. Science and religion are not opposites or mutually exclusive, instead they concentrate on different facets of existence and so have different matters within their purview. For more information, readers may examine statements by religious organizations for the opinions of those organizations on the place of evolution in classroom education.

6. Evolution is a part of Maryland's and other states' education standards, and is expected to be part of all students' learning. NSTA and many other organizations

have stated their support for the teaching of evolution. This support comes from scientific organizations such as the National Academy of Sciences, the American Association for the Advancement of Science, and many other state science organizations. It also includes many education organizations such as the National Association of Biology Teachers, various state Departments of Education, and national and state associations of science supervisors and science teachers. These statements of support may be examined by contacting these organizations.

Adopted December 2002

Michigan Science Teachers Association (1981)

Creation, Evolution, and Science Education

Scientific creation, special creation, and creation-science are terms used synonymously when referring to the thesis that the universe and all forms of life were brought into existence by sudden acts of a Divine Creator. Supporters of this thesis are creationists, some of whom are campaigning vigorously in favor of the inclusion of creation-science in the science classrooms of the nation's public schools. In effect, such inclusion would constitute a two-model approach to questions of origins. One of these models is the *theory of evolution;* the second model is *creation-science.*

The theory of evolution is the theory or model presented in the life sciences curricula of public school science classrooms. Evolution theory is taught because its existence as a developing network of observations, hypotheses, predictions, facts, principles, and sub-theories is the result of scientific inquiry free of any a priori design.

In comparison, the creation-science model is not an observation-hypothesis-prediction-fact-principle-accessory theory sequence. It does not encourage open-ended questioning because any raising of questions must produce answers that converge on the Divine Creator thesis. As a result, the creation-science model cannot generate information and ideas useful in the development of new areas of scientific investigation. Thus, creation-science is not acceptable as a scientific theory. Even so, the necessity exists for public school science educators to consider certain causal concerns of creationists. A major concern is that students from creationist backgrounds are exposed to theories regarding questions of origins not consonant with their religious training; a second concern is that many science teachers teach the theory of evolution as fact.

Therefore, in consequence of the creationists' concerns and in consequence of the need to maintain the integrity of science education, the Michigan Science Teachers Association adopts the following position with respect to the evolution/creation issue:

1. The Michigan Science Teachers Association affirms the necessity of rejecting the teaching of non-scientific theories in the science classrooms of Michigan's public schools.

2. The Michigan Science Teachers Association recommends that its professional development committee be responsible for the design of an inservice model for helping science teachers learn how to work sensitively and objectively with the evolution/creation concerns expressed by students, parents, and boards of education.

3. The Michigan Science Teachers Association reaffirms its goals of (a) helping students acquire useful science knowledge and skills (b) helping students progress in the understanding and use of processes of scientific inquiry, and (c) helping students separate scientific thought and activity from thought rightfully the province of humankind's diverse ways of spiritual expression and responsiveness to the need for authoritarian guidance.

4. The Michigan Science Teachers Association recommends the establishment of procedures for the dissemination of the position expressed herein to Michigan Science teachers, to the Michigan Department of Education through its science specialist, and to Michigan Boards of Education and to science specialists of other states on request.

Approved on November 21, 1981, by the Board of Directors of the Michigan Science Teachers Association on behalf of the Michigan Science Teachers Association.

Michigan Science Teachers Association (2003)

The Teaching of Evolution and Michigan House of Representatives Bill #4946

Bill sponsors – Bradstreet, Palmer, Stahl, Hummel, Voorhees, Vander Veen, Moolenaar, Newell, Hager, Kooiman, Ehardt, Caswell, Casperson, Garfield, Tabor, Richardville, Hart, Reeves, Drolet, Hoogendyk, Nitz, Van Regenmorter, Emmons, Murphy, McConico.

In adopting the position statement of the National Science Teachers Association (NSTA http://www.nsta.org/159&psid=10) (1997) regarding the teaching of evolution, The Michigan Science Teachers Association (MSTA) supports the position that evolution is a major unifying concept of science and should be included as part of K-College science frameworks and curricula. The MSTA recognizes that evolution has not been emphasized in science curricula in a manner commensurate to its importance because of official policies, intimidation of science teachers, the general public's misunderstanding of evolutionary theory and a century of controversy. Furthermore, teachers are being pressured to introduce creationism, creation "science", and other nonscientific views, which are intended to weaken or eliminate the teaching of evolution.

In accordance of the Michigan State Board of Education's March 10, 1982 resolution regarding the "Teaching of Religion and Creationism in Michigan Public Schools", the MSTA agrees with the position that the "...State Board of Education oppose the teaching, in public educational institutions, of any course in religion which is outside of the realm of a secular program of education and be it further resolved that the State Board of Education recommend that any school district currently teaching creationism or any course in religion in an attempt to indoctrinate toward any particular belief or disbelief cease and desist such teaching."

In recognition of the Michigan State Board of Education's resolution on the teaching of evolution and the MSTA adoption of the NSTA position statement on teaching evolution, the Michigan Science Teachers Association advocates that HB 4946 & HB 5005 be removed from any further consideration by the House of Representatives.

Approved August 5, 2003

The Teaching of Evolution and Global Warming Michigan House of Representatives Bill #5251

Michigan House of Representatives Bill #5251 (2005) would require the amendment of "The Revised School Code" (PA 451, 1976; Sect. 1278 (MCL 380.1278)) in order to "...*revise the recommended model core academic curriculum content standards in science to ensure that pupils will be able to do the following: a) use the scientific method to critically evaluate scientific theories including, but not limited to, the theories of global warming and evolution b) use relevant scientific data to assess the validity of those theories and to formulate arguments for or against those theories.*"

Whereas the Michigan Department of Education's (MDOE) "Content Standards and Benchmarks for Science Education" (1995, 2002) already require students to "*use scientific knowledge to make decisions about real-world problems*" and to be "*able to make informed judgments on statements and debates claiming to have a scientific basis*", the Michigan Science Teachers Association (MSTA) can identify no valid reason for legislative intervention that would modify the existing standards as developed and adopted by the MDOE working in collaboration with Michigan's professional science education community.

Whereas global warming and evolution are the only two theories selected for mandatory "critical evaluation" in HB 5251, it is the position of the MSTA that this requirement is inappropriate both pedagogically and scientifically. If the true academic and pedagogical intent of HB 5251 is to teach the critical evaluation of scientific theory, it is the position of the MSTA that global warming and evolution should not be isolated for mandatory student review. A legislative mandate that includes only evolution and global warming in such an evaluation may suggest to students and the public that these theories are somehow less robust or less scientific than are other scientific theories that were not selected for mandatory evaluation e.g., plate tectonics, atomic theory, cell theory, relativity. Such inference would be in clear contrast to the preponderance of scientific evidence supporting both of these theories and would represent a dishonest and unprofessional approach to the sciences and science education in Michigan.

In adopting the position statement of the National Science Teachers Association (1997) regarding the teaching of evolution, The Michigan Science Teachers Association supports the position that evolution is a major unifying concept of science and should be included as part of K-College science frameworks and curricula. The MSTA recognizes that evolution has not been emphasized in science curricula in a manner commensurate to its importance because of official policies, intimidation of science teachers and the general public's misunderstanding of evolutionary theory and the nature of science in general. Furthermore, the MSTA recognizes that science teachers may feel pressured to modify or eliminate their presentation of scientific topics that may have socio-political or economic implications e.g., evolution, global warming, stem-cell research and cloning.

In recognition of the aforementioned, it is the position of the Michigan Science Teachers Association that HB 5251 be removed from any further consideration by the Michigan House of Representatives.

HB 5251 Sponsors: John Moolenaar (Primary Sponsor), Brian Palmer, Jim Plakas, Scott Hummel, Judy Emmons, Joel Sheltrown, John Stahl, John Gleason, Rick Baxter, Roger Kahn, Gary Newell, Richard Ball, Fulton Sheen, Shelley Taub, Michael Sak, David Farhat, Robert Gosselin, Jacob Hoogendyk, Howard Walker, Tom Pearce.

October 2005

Michigan Science Teachers Association (2007)

Evolution Education & the Nature of Science

It is the mission of the Michigan Science Teachers Association (MSTA) to support and provide leadership for the improvement of science education throughout Michigan. In fulfillment of this mission, the MSTA recognizes that it is essential that students be introduced to the most contemporary scientific scholarship available. The MSTA recognizes that evolutionary theory is representative of this contemporary scientific scholarship as is evident by the scientific community's resounding consensus on the validity and robustness of evolutionary theory.

However, in spite of the scientific community's repeated validation of evolutionary theory, there continues to be socio-political pressure to eliminate, mitigate or weaken the instruction of evolution theory and/or to introduce non-scientific ideologies into the science classroom. Opponents of evolution education have suggested that evolutionary theory does not represent an empirically (tested) derived body of knowledge. This assertion demonstrates a profound misunderstanding of the nature and process of science.

Scientists view and seek to explain the natural world through the empirical lens of science. The nature of scientific investigation is to ask a question and then to work to find the answer. While philosophy and theology are valuable forms of human inquiry that also seek to explain our world, science is unique in its approach by relying exclusively upon empirical natural law (e.g., the laws of physics, chemistry, geology, etc.) in its explanation and not upon supernatural intervention or untestable conjecture. It is this testability that is a hallmark of the nature and process of science. Scientific hypotheses and theory must be testable against the natural world and therefore at least potentially falsifiable. Furthermore, any conclusions formulated from these tests are tentative pending new data to the contrary. As our scientific knowledge expands and provides us with better insights into the natural world, science is able to modify previous conclusions and theory to incorporate this new knowledge. Like all scientific theories, evolutionary theory is dynamic and will be modified as new information becomes available.

It is these properties of the nature of science that separates scientific inquiry from theology or philosophy and therefore excludes such non-scientific ideologies as "creation science", "creationism", "intelligent design" or other non-scientific "alternatives to evolution" from the science classroom as they do not meet the characteristics and rigor of scientific empiricism.

Although scientists continue to discuss and even disagree on some of the finer details of natural selection, the process that governs evolution, there is an overwhelming consensus in the scientific community that evolution has happened in the past and is occurring today and that furthermore, evolutionary theory is the best and only scientific explanation for the diversification of life on Earth. By the very nature of science, there will always be questions that remain unanswered because in the process of answering a question or solving a problem, more questions arise; an admirable quality of science.

The scientific community's strong advocacy for evolution theory is a result of the preponderance of corroborating empirical data originating from virtually all disciplines of the physical and biological sciences. The scientific community regards evolutionary theory as one of the most robust and well-substantiated scientific theories to date as evolutionary theory represents the convergence of corroborating evidence from independent lines of scientific investigation.

The goal of science is the establishment of scientific theory which is then employed as a predictive tool. In colloquial usage, theory implies a guess or a hunch. However; in science, theory represents the complete opposite. The National Academy of Sciences defines theory as a "...well substantiated explanation of some aspect of the natural world that incorporates facts, laws, inferences and tested hypotheses". Scientific theory and therefore evolutionary theory is the antithesis of a guess.

It is the position of the Michigan Science Teachers Association that evolutionary theory is an integral, validated and therefore essential component of modern scientific inquiry and should therefore be taught in a manner commensurate with this importance. Furthermore, it is the position of the MSTA that teachers should teach only evolutionary theory as a scientific explanation of the development and diversification of life on Earth. Evolution should be taught unaccompanied by non-scientific ideologies offered as "alternatives" to evolution. Teaching theological or philosophical explanations alongside or in place of evolution theory would not make the classroom presentation "fair or equal" but would result in the offering of false scientific alternatives to our students which would be a violation of academic honesty and our professional responsibilities as trustees of our student's academic development and science literacy.

Approved Unanimously by the MSTA Board of Directors on February 3, 2007

Michigan State Board of Education

Whereas, the United States Constitution provides for the separation of church and state; and

Whereas, the Constitution of the State of Michigan establishes the same doctrine of separation of church and state; and

Whereas, the State Board of Education is concerned that the laws pertaining to this subject matter be vigorously enforced with regard to the public schools of this state; and

Whereas, the Michigan Attorney General has opined on this matter in Michigan Attorney General Opinion 4405; now, therefore, be it

Resolved, that the State Board of Education oppose the teaching of any course in religion in any public institution which is outside of the realm of a secular program of education.

Resolved, further that the State Board of Education recommend that any school district currently teaching creationism or any course in religion in an attempt to indoctrinate toward any particular belief or disbelief cease and desist such teaching.

Resolved, that the State Board of Education recommend to the Michigan Attorney General that the full force and effect of the Constitutions of the United States and Michigan and the Attorney General Opinion No. 4405 be vigorously supported and enforced with regard to the separation of church and state in all respects.

Unanimously approved by the Michigan State Board of Education
at its meeting on 10 March 1982.

Voices for Evolution

National Association of Biology Teachers (1980)

The procedures and processes of science are well defined within the discipline. The facts and theories of science have been established through experiment and synthesis of subject, peer review, and acceptance for validity within the scientific community. Materials that do not meet the test of science or are not directly derivative from the accepted norms for the discipline should not be a part of the science curriculum.

Science deals with material things and the consequences of their application. As such, it is not in conflict with other means of knowing about the universe. There are those who see the facts and theories of science as a threat either to their belief systems or to their interpretations which may be at variance with scientific data. While science is moot on these issues, attempts are made to intercalate into the scientific enterprise conclusions neither based on scientific data nor verified by the scientific process. These conclusions, arising outside the field of science and resulting from ignoring or misinterpreting scientific data, have no place in the science classroom as a part of the body of scientific knowledge.

The NABT, through its obligation to biological education, will make every effort to educate the public as to the unscientific nature of efforts to equate non-science with the scientific enterprise. NABT will resist attempts to place non-scientific dogma into the classroom as science. Wherever such efforts are attempted, NABT should correct the record and provide adequate scientific evidence designed to allow decision-makers full access to the facts by means of which to judge the efforts to intercalate non-scientific material into science classrooms or to remove or change the data of science to accommodate a given set of conclusions derived from outside the scientific enterprise.

The credibility and usability of science depends on maintenance of the integrity of science as a discipline. While no feature in this policy is to be construed as preventing the full range of applications of science and the elucidation of its social and humanistic implications, there is an obligation to insure that the scientific data thus used is both accurate and derived within the accepted procedures of the discipline. Without the maintenance of the integrity of the initial data with which one works, any subsequent applications or derivations may be ill-conceived and of little service to the human enterprise.

NABT has an obligation to maintain the integrity of biology as a scientific discipline. To this end it must act to resist efforts to include in the science classroom materials derived outside the scientific process. It must insist that the data and concepts of science as presented to students meet the accepted standards of the discipline, and data which can best be described as para-scientific (creationism, astrology, anti-germ theory, etc.) cannot be condoned as science within classrooms.

Adopted 23 October 1980. Published in The American Biology Teacher 14:445
(October 1982).

National Association of Biology Teachers (1995)

Scientific Integrity

The ongoing procedures and processes of science are well defined within each scientific discipline, including biology. The principles and theories of science have been established through repeated experimentation and observation and have been refereed through peer review before general acceptance by the scientific community. Acceptance does not imply rigidity or constraint, or denote dogma. Instead, as new data become available, scientific explanations are revised and improved, or rejected and replaced. Materials, methods, and explanations that fail to meet these ongoing tests of science are not legitimate components of the discipline and must not be part of a science curriculum.

Science may appear to conflict with other ways of knowing about the universe, unfortunately leading some groups to see selected theories of science as a threat to their belief systems. This is not the case; science does not, in fact cannot, study, explain, or judge, non-scientific issues or supernatural belief systems.

Science is but one way of making sense of the world, with internally-consistent methods and principles that are well described. Among these principles is the notion that proposed causes and explanations must be naturalistic. Any attempt to mix or contrast supernatural beliefs and naturalistic theories within science misrepresents the scientific enterprise and debases other, non-scientific, ways of knowing. These attempts, which commonly result from a misunderstanding of the nature of science itself, have no place in science, or in the science classroom or laboratory.

The credibility and utility of science, and therefore biology, depend on maintaining its integrity. NABT has a special obligation, to promote this integrity in life science education. The data, concepts, and theories of science presented to students must meet the accepted standards of the discipline. To this end, NABT will not support efforts to include in the science classroom materials or theories derived outside of the scientific processes. Nonscientific notions such as geocentricism, flat earth, creationism, young earth, astrology, psychic healing and vitalistic theory, therefore, cannot legitimately be taught, promoted, or condoned as science in the classroom.

Revision adopted by the Board of NABT, 3/15/95

National Association of Biology Teachers (2000)

Statement on Teaching Evolution

As stated in *The American Biology Teacher* by the eminent scientist Theodosius Dobzhansky (1973), "Nothing in biology makes sense except in the light of evolution." This often-quoted assertion accurately illuminates the central, unifying role of evolution in nature, and therefore in biology. Teaching biology in an effective and scientifically-honest manner requires classroom discussions and laboratory experiences on evolution.

Modern biologists constantly study, ponder and deliberate the patterns, mechanisms and pace of evolution, but they do not debate evolution's occurrence. The fossil record and the diversity of extant organisms, combined with modern techniques of molecular biology, taxonomy and geology, provide exhaustive examples and powerful evidence for genetic variation, natural selection, speciation, extinction and other well-established components of current evolutionary theory. Scientific deliberations and modifications of these components clearly demonstrate the vitality and scientific integrity of evolution and the theory that explains it.

This same examination, pondering and possible revision have firmly established evolution as an important natural process explained by valid scientific principles, and clearly differentiate and separate science from various kinds of nonscientific ways of knowing, including those with a supernatural basis such as creationism. Whether called "creation science," "scientific creationism," "intelligent-design theory," "young-earth theory" or some other synonym, creation beliefs have no place in the science classroom. Explanations employing nonnaturalistic or supernatural events, whether or not explicit reference is made to a supernatural being, are outside the realm of science and not part of a valid science curriculum. Evolutionary theory, indeed all of science, is necessarily silent on religion and neither refutes nor supports the existence of a deity or deities.

Accordingly, the National Association of Biology Teachers, an organization of science teachers, endorses the following tenets of science, evolution and biology education:

- The diversity of life on earth is the outcome of evolution: an unpredictable and natural process of temporal descent with genetic modification that is affected by natural selection, chance, historical contingencies and changing environments.

- Biological evolution refers to changes in populations, not individuals. Changes must be successfully passed on to the next generation. This means evolution results in heritable changes in a population spread over many generations. In fact, evolution can be defined as any change in the frequency of alleles within a gene pool from one generation to the next.

- Evolutionary theory is significant in biology, among other reasons, for its unifying properties and predictive features, the clear empirical testability of its integral models and the richness of new scientific research it fosters.

- The fossil record, which includes abundant transitional forms in diverse taxonomic groups, establishes extensive and comprehensive evidence for organic evolution.

- Natural selection, the primary mechanism for evolutionary changes, can be demonstrated with numerous, convincing examples, both extant and extinct.

- Natural selection – a differential, greater survival and reproduction of some genetic variants within a population under an existing environmental state – has no specific direction or goal, including survival of a species.

- Adaptations do not always provide an obvious selective advantage. Furthermore, there is no indication that adaptations – molecular to organismal – must be perfect: adaptations providing a selective advantage must simply be good enough for survival and increased reproductive fitness.

- The model of punctuated equilibrium provides another account of the tempo of speciation in the fossil record of many lineages: it does not refute or overturn evolutionary theory, but instead adds to its scientific richness.

- Evolution does not violate the second law of thermodynamics: producing order from disorder is possible with the addition of energy, such as from the sun.

- Although comprehending deep time is difficult, the earth is about 4.5 billion years old. *Homo sapiens* has occupied only a minuscule moment of that immense duration of time.

- When compared with earlier periods, the Cambrian explosion evident in the fossil record reflects at least three phenomena: the evolution of animals with readily-fossilized hard body parts; Cambrian environment (sedimentary rock) more conducive to preserving fossils; and the evolution from pre-Cambrian forms of an increased diversity of body patterns in animals.

- Radiometric and other dating techniques, when used properly, are highly accurate means of establishing dates in the history of the planet and in the history of life.

- Recent findings from the advancing field of molecular genetics, combined with the large body of evidence from other disciplines, collectively provide indisputable demonstration of the theory of evolution.

- In science, a theory is not a guess or an approximation but an extensive explanation developed from well-documented, reproducible sets of experimentally-derived data from repeated observations of natural processes.

- The models and the subsequent outcomes of a scientific theory are not decided in advance, but can be, and often are, modified and improved as new empirical evidence is uncovered. Thus, science is a constantly self-correcting endeavor to understand nature and natural phenomena.

- Science is not teleological: the accepted processes do not start with a conclusion, then refuse to change it, or acknowledge as valid only those data that support an unyielding conclusion. Science does not base theories on an untestable collection of dogmatic proposals. Instead, the processes of science are characterized by asking questions, proposing hypotheses, and designing empirical models and conceptual frameworks for research about natural events.

- Providing a rational, coherent and scientific account of the taxonomic history and diversity of organisms requires inclusion of the mechanisms and principles of evolution.

- Similarly, effective teaching of cellular and molecular biology requires inclusion of evolution.

- Specific textbook chapters on evolution should be included in biology curricula, and evolution should be a recurrent theme throughout biology textbooks and courses.

- Students can maintain their religious beliefs and learn the scientific foundations of evolution.

- Teachers should respect diverse beliefs, but contrasting science with religion, such as belief in creationism, is not a role of science. Science teachers can, and often do, hold devout religious beliefs, accept evolution as a valid scientific theory, and teach the theory's mechanisms and principles.

Voices for Evolution

- Science and religion differ in significant ways that make it inappropriate to teach any of the different religious beliefs in the science classroom.

Opposition to teaching evolution reflects confusion about the nature and processes of science. Teachers can, and should, stand firm and teach good science with the acknowledged support of the courts. In *Epperson v. Arkansas* (1968), the U.S. Supreme Court struck down a 1928 Arkansas law prohibiting the teaching of evolution in state schools. In *McLean v. Arkansas* (1982), the federal district court invalidated a state statute requiring equal classroom time for evolution and creationism.

Edwards v. Aguillard (1987) led to another Supreme Court ruling against so-called "balanced treatment" of creation science and evolution in public schools. In this landmark case, the Court called the Louisiana equal-time statute "facially invalid as violative of the Establishment Clause of the First Amendment, because it lacks a clear secular purpose." This decision – "the Edwards restriction" – is now the controlling legal position on attempts to mandate the teaching of creationism: the nation's highest court has said that such mandates are unconstitutional. Subsequent district court decisions in Illinois and California have applied "the Edwards restriction" to teachers who advocate creation science, and to the right of a district to prohibit an individual teacher from promoting creation science, in the classroom.

Courts have thus restricted school districts from requiring creation science in the science curriculum and have restricted individual instructors from teaching it. All teachers and administrators should be mindful of these court cases, remembering that the law, science and NABT support them as they appropriately include the teaching of evolution in the science curriculum.

References and Suggested Reading

Aguillard, D. (1999). Evolution education in Louisiana public schools: a decade following *Edwards V. Aguillard. The American Biology Teacher, 61*, pp. 182-188.

Brack, A. (Ed.).(1999). *The Molecular Origins of Life: Assembling Pieces of the Puzzle.* Cambridge: Cambridge University Press.

Futuyma, D. (1986). *Evolutionary biology*, 2nd ed. Sunderland, MA: Sinauer Associates, Inc.

Futuyma, D. (1995). *Science on Trial.* Sunderland, MA: Sinauer Associates, Inc.

Gillis, A. (1994). Keeping creationism out of the classroom. *Bioscience, 44*, pp. 650-656.

Gould, S. (1994, October). The evolution of life on earth. *Scientific American, 271*, pp. 85-91.

Gould, S. (1995). *Dinosaur in a Haystack. Reflections in Natural History.* New York: Harmony Books.

Kiklas, K. (1997). *The Evolutionary Biology of Plants.* Chicago: The University of Chicago Press.

Matsumura, M. (Ed.). (1995). *Voices for Evolution.* Berkeley, CA: The National Center for Science Education.

Mayr, E. (1991). *One Long Argument: Charles Darwin and the Genesis of Modern Evolutionary Thought.* Cambridge, MA: Harvard University Press.

Moore, J. (1993). *Science as a Way of Knowing - The Foundations of Modern Biology.* Cambridge, MA: Harvard University Press.

Moore, R. (1999). Creationism in the United States: VII. The Lingering Threat. *The American Biology Teacher*, 61, pp.330-340. See also references therein to earlier articles in the series.

National Academy of Sciences. (1998). *Teaching About Evolution and the Nature of Science.* Washington, DC: National Academy Press.

National Academy of Sciences. (1999). *Science and creationism-A View from the National Academy of Sciences.* Washington, DC: National Academy Press.

National Center for Science Education. P.O. Box 9477, Berkeley, CA 94709. Numerous publications such as Bartelt, K. (1999), *A Scientist Responds to Behe's Black Box*.

National Research Council. (1996). *National Science Education Standards*. Washington, DC: National Academy Press.

Pennock, R.T. (1999). *Tower of Babel: The Evidence Against the New Creationism*. Cambridge, MA: MIT Press.

Weiner, J. (1994). *Beak of the Finch - A Story of Evolution in our Time*. New York: Alfred A. Knopf.

Wilson, E. (1992). *The Diversity of Life*. New York: W.W. Norton & Co.

Adopted by the Board of Directors March 15, 1995. Revised October 1997 and August 2000. Endorsed by: The Society for the Study of Evolution, June 1998, The American Association of Physical Anthropologists, July 1998.

National Council for the Social Studies (1981)

Resolution Regarding Pressure Groups, submitted by Religion in Schools Committee and supported by Science and Society Committee

Whereas public schools and legislatures nationwide are being pressured to give "equal time" to the scientific creationism interpretation of creation in science and social studies courses; and

Whereas the pressures are perceived as part of a much larger problem;

Be it resolved that the NCSS affirms that, although community values should be an integral consideration in the establishment of the goals of education, curriculum decision-making regarding instructional method and specific content ultimately should be the responsibility of certificated personnel; and

Be it further resolved that NCSS affirms that throughout the curriculum, educators should make explicit the foundations from which conclusions about the world are drawn, including religious, philosophical, and other ideological systems, as well as the basic assumption underlying the academic disciplines themselves; and

Be it further resolved that the NCSS reaffirms that social studies is a logical curricular area in which to examine the societal issues which arise when persons have different world views and sets of assumptions about life; and

Be it further resolved that NCSS commit itself to use existing programming and publishing vehicles to provide professional development opportunities to better enable social studies educators to deal with these issues.

November 1981

Voices for Evolution

Intelligent Design

Introduction

There have been efforts for many decades to introduce religious beliefs about the beginning of life on Earth into the science curriculum of the public schools. Most recently, these efforts have included "creation science" and "intelligent design." Following a number of court decisions finding the teaching of creationism and intelligent design in the public school science curriculum to be unconstitutional, there have been efforts to introduce these beliefs into the social studies curriculum. Although the National Council for the Social Studies believes in the open and thoughtful discussion of ideas, public school classrooms are not the place for the teaching of religious beliefs. Social studies is the forum for open analysis and discussion of historical, social, economic, geographic, political and global issues. Thus our recommendations seek to include the study of intelligent design within that framework.

Background

The American Heritage Dictionary (2007) defines intelligent design as the "belief that physical and biological systems observed in the universe result from purposeful design by an intelligent being rather than from chance or undirected forces." Attempts to introduce this doctrine, originally termed "creationism," then "creation science," and most recently, "intelligent design," into public school curricula have been found unconstitutional in state and federal courts. The first Supreme Court decision regarding the issue came in *Epperson v. Arkansas* in 1968, when the Court ruled that an Arkansas anti-evolution law was unconstitutional. Twenty years later in *Edwards v. Aguillard*, the Court held that a Louisiana law which required equal time for the teaching of "creation science" along with the teaching of evolution, was unconstitutional. Most recently, a district court in Pennsylvania struck down an intelligent design policy adopted by the Dover Area School Board in Dover, Pennsylvania (*Kitzmiller v. Dover Area School District*).

These decisions have struck down state attempts to interfere with the teaching of evolution in the public school science curriculum. In the *Kitzmiller* decision, for instance, the judge found that the policy of the Dover school board, which called for teachers to discuss problems with the theory of evolution and make students aware of intelligent design, failed the test of the Establishment Clause of the First Amendment, since the policy's primary purpose was to advance a religious belief.

Because federal courts, to date, have ruled against the teaching of creationism and intelligent design in the science curriculum, an approach called "critical analysis" has been introduced to get around these decisions. This approach seeks to incorporate what the courts have ruled to be religious belief into the public school curriculum by contending that public schools should take a critical view of the theory of evolution. In this critical view, particular attention is to be focused on any uncertainties in the fossil record as well as what are contended to be examples of "irreducible complexity." This view then introduces intelligent design as an explanation addressing these uncertainties.

This "critical analysis" approach to teaching intelligent design has attracted political support in several states and districts. It was a motivating force behind former Senator Rick Santorum's unsuccessful attempt to include a statement that evolution was a controversial scientific theory into the original *No Child Left Behind* legislation. It has also figured prominently in the much-publicized battle over the treatment of evolution in the Kansas science standards. In Ohio, the state board of education has suggested that although a critical analysis of the theory of evolution with the teaching of intelligent design should not be put into the science curriculum, "social studies appears to be a good fit" (Columbus Dispatch, September 2002).

Rationale for Recommendations

Social studies may, at first glance, seem to be a better fit for this approach to teaching intelligent design, but the same constitutional issues arise whether religious beliefs are taught in science or in the social studies curriculum. While the social studies classroom is the proper forum for the discussion of controversial issues, educators should be wary of being used to promote a religious belief in the public schools. This unintended outcome can be the result of teaching students that a scientific controversy exists between intelligent design and the theory of evolution when, in fact, no such controversy exists.

Teaching about religion in human society is an important component of many social studies courses (see the NCSS position statement "Study about Religions in the Social Studies Curriculum," revised and approved by the Board of Directors in 1998). However, teaching religious beliefs as the equivalent of scientific theory is not consistent with the social studies nor is it allowed under the First Amendment. Evolution is a scientific theory subject to testing by the scientific method. In contrast, religious teaching based on the existence of a supreme being does not allow for the scientific processes of hypothesizing, gathering evidence or questioning as they are based on faith, not scientific observations or experimentation.

Nonetheless, social studies may have to contend with these issues because of local or state mandates. The curricular recommendations that follow allow for substantive discussion of the issues surrounding intelligent design, while avoiding First Amendment problems. Most significantly, these recommendations prevent the social studies curriculum from being a repository for intelligent design instruction in the public schools, while still allowing students to analyze the political, legal, and historical issues involved.

Teaching Recommendations

Prior to teaching about intelligent design, social studies teachers should check their district's policies related to teaching controversial issues and teaching about religion. There are a number of ways in which social studies teachers might introduce the issues surrounding intelligent design in their curriculum. The following recommendations examine the issues from a social studies, rather than a religious, perspective.

- Constitutional perspective: A teacher using this approach would focus on court cases that consider policies requiring the teaching of intelligent design in public schools and the Establishment Clause of the First Amendment.

- Historical perspective: A teacher adopting this perspective would focus on the historical conflict between science and religion since the Middle Ages, with particular attention to public debates over the teaching of evolution in the United States in the past century.

- Sociological perspective: A teacher using this lens would focus on competing organizations and social forces involved in the attempts to teach about intelligent design in the schools.

Voices for Evolution

- Anthropological perspective: A teacher choosing this perspective would have students analyze creation stories and beliefs of many cultures as well as scientific theories dealing with the origin and development of human life.

- Public issues perspectives: A teacher using this approach would encourage students to research intelligent design and debate whether intelligent design should be taught in the public schools.

Concluding Statement

The National Council for the Social Studies believes that a free and open discussion of ideas is essential to a healthy democracy. However, the social studies classroom should not and cannot be used for teaching any specific religious belief, as this is antithetical to the First Amendment. The National Council for the Social Studies recommends analysis, and thoughtful discussion, not indoctrination.

This position statement, which was prepared by the NCSS Task Force on Intelligent Design, was approved by the NCSS Board of Directors in May 2007.

National Education Association

Statement in Support of the Teaching of Evolution

The National Education Association (NEA) was founded in 1857, two years before Charles Darwin published *The Origin of Species*. Although these two events remain unrelated, Darwinism and evolution came to play prominent roles over the next fifty years in the science curricula in our nation's public schools.

But like so many scientific theories that challenge established orthodoxy, evolution is still being contested. The issue of evolution versus creationism, unresolved by the weight of case law, is still the subject of debate.

NEA's position in this debate has been firm. Most recently, our 1982 Representative Assembly made clear that NEA opposes all efforts to alter the science curricula in any way that would place the teaching of scientific creationism on an equal footing with the teaching of evolution.

While the National Education Association believes that educational materials should accurately portray the influence of religion in our nation and throughout the world, we also believe that for American education to flourish, religious dogma must neither guide nor hamper the pursuit of knowledge by students and teachers in our public schools.

1994

National Science Education Leadership Association

The Teaching of Creationism in the Science Curriculum

The National Science Supervisors Association is opposed to the teaching of "creationism" in the science curricula of the nation's schools. Creationism, and other pseudo-sciences, are premised upon supernatural explanations of natural phenomena and therefore are outside the realm of science.

We therefore stand with such organizations as the National Association of Biology Teachers, the Council of State Science Supervisors, the National Science Teachers Association, the National Academy of Sciences, and the American Association for the Advancement of Science in opposing the inclusion of such pseudo-sciences in the science curricula of the schools of the nation.

Adopted 5 April, 1990. Originally published by the National Science Supervisors Association, which has since changed its name to the National Science Education Leadership Association. Permission to print the National Science Education Leadership Association's position paper, "The Teaching of Creationism in the Science Curriculum," is given with the expressed written consent of NSELA.

National Science Teachers Association (1973, 1982)

Inclusion of Nonscience Theories in Science Instruction

Throughout recorded history, man has been vitally concerned in finding out all that he can about his universe. He has explored it in many ways, raised questions about it, designed methods by which he could increase and organize his knowledge, and developed systems to aid him in understanding and explaining his origin, and nature, and his place in the universe. Among these systems are philosophy, religion, folklore, the arts, and science.

Science is the system of knowing the universe through data collected by observation and controlled experimentation. As data are collected, theories are advanced to explain and account for what has been observed. The true test of a theory in science is threefold: (1) its ability to explain what has been observed; (2) its ability to predict what has not yet been observed; and (3) its ability to be tested by further experimentation and to be modified as required by the acquisition of new data.

The National Science Teachers Association upholds the right and recognizes the obligation of each individual to become informed about man's many endeavors, to understand and explain what each endeavor has contributed to mankind, and to draw his own conclusions in each area.

The National Science Teachers Association also recognizes its great obligation to that area of education dealing with science. Science education cannot treat, as science, those things not in the domain of science. It cannot deal with, as science, concepts that have been developed in other than scientific ways. Moreover, the National Science Teachers Association vigorously opposes all actions that would legislate, mandate, or coerce the inclusion in the corpus of science, including textbooks, of any theories that do not meet the threefold criteria given above.

National Science Teachers Association (1985)

Inclusion of Nonscience Tenets in Science Instruction

People have always been curious about the universe and their place in it. They have questioned, explored, probed, and conjectured. In an effort to organize their understandings, people have developed various systems that help them explain their origin, e.g., philosophy, religion, folklore, the arts, and science.

Science is the system of exploring the universe through data collected and controlled by experimentation. As data are collected, theories are advanced to explain and account for what has been observed. Before a theory can be included in the system of science, it must meet all of the following criteria: (1) its ability to explain what has been observed, (2) its ability to predict what has not yet been observed, and (3) its ability to be tested by further experimentation and to be modified as required by the acquisition of new data.

NSTA recognizes that only certain tenets are appropriate to science education. Specific guidelines must be followed to determine what does belong in science education. NSTA endorses the following tenets:

1. Respect the right of any person to learn the history and content of all systems and to decide what can contribute to an individual understanding of our universe and our place in it.

2. In explaining natural phenomena, science instruction should only include those theories that can properly be called science.

3. To ascertain whether a particular theory is properly in the realm of science education, apply the criteria stated above, i.e., (1) the theory can explain what has been observed, (2) the theory can predict that which has not yet been observed, (3) the theory can be tested by further experimentation and be modified as new data are acquired.

4. Oppose any action that attempts to legislate, mandate, or coerce the inclusion in the body of science education, including textbooks, of any tenets which cannot meet the above stated criteria.

National Science Teachers Association (2003)

NSTA Position Statement: The Teaching of Evolution

Introduction

The National Science Teachers Association (NSTA) strongly supports the position that evolution is a major unifying concept in science and should be included in the K-12 science education frameworks and curricula. Furthermore, if evolution is not taught, students will not achieve the level of scientific literacy they need. This position is consistent with that of the National Academies, the American Association for the Advancement of Science (AAAS), and many other scientific and educational organizations.

NSTA also recognizes that evolution has not been emphasized in science curricula in a manner commensurate to its importance because of official policies, intimidation of science teachers, the general public's misunderstanding of evolutionary theory, and a century of controversy. In addition, teachers are being pressured to introduce creationism, creation "science," and other nonscientific views, which are intended to weaken or eliminate the teaching of evolution.

Declarations

Within this context, NSTA recommends that

- Science curricula and teachers should emphasize evolution in a manner commensurate with its importance as a unifying concept in science and its overall explanatory power.

- Science teachers should not advocate any religious interpretations of nature and should be nonjudgmental about the personal beliefs of students.

- Policy makers and administrators should not mandate policies requiring the teaching of creation science or related concepts, such as so-called "intelligent design," "abrupt appearance," and "arguments against evolution." Administrators also should support teachers against pressure to promote nonscientific views or to diminish or eliminate the study of evolution.

- Administrators and school boards should provide support to teachers as they review, adopt, and implement curricula that emphasize evolution. This should include professional development to assist teachers in teaching evolution in a comprehensive and professional manner.

- Parental and community involvement in establishing the goals of science education and the curriculum development process should be encouraged and nurtured in our democratic society. However, the professional responsibility of science teachers and curriculum specialists to provide students with quality science education should not be compromised by censorship, pseudoscience, inconsistencies, faulty scholarship, or unconstitutional mandates.

- Science textbooks shall emphasize evolution as a unifying concept. Publishers should not be required or volunteer to include disclaimers in textbooks that distort or misrepresent the methodology of science and the current body of knowledge concerning the nature and study of evolution.

Adopted by the NSTA Board of Directors July 2003

NSTA offers the following background information:

The Nature of Science and Scientific Theories

Science is a method of explaining the natural world. It assumes that anything that can be observed or measured is amenable to scientific investigation. Science also assumes that the universe operates according to regularities that can be discovered and understood through scientific investigations. The testing of various explanations of natural phenomena for their consistency with empirical data is an essential part of the methodology of science. Explanations that are not consistent with empirical evidence or cannot be tested empirically are not a part of science. As a result, explanations of natural phenomena that are not based on evidence but on myths, personal beliefs, religious values, and superstitions are not scientific. Furthermore, because science is limited to explaining natural phenomena through the use of empirical evidence, it cannot provide religious or ultimate explanations.

The most important scientific explanations are called "theories." In ordinary speech, "theory" is often used to mean "guess" or "hunch," whereas in scientific terminology, a theory is a set of universal statements that explain some aspect of the natural world. Theories are powerful tools. Scientists seek to develop theories that

- are firmly grounded in and based upon evidence;

- are logically consistent with other well-established principles;

- explain more than rival theories; and

- have the potential to lead to new knowledge.

The body of scientific knowledge changes as new observations and discoveries are made. Theories and other explanations change. New theories emerge, and other theories are modified or discarded. Throughout this process, theories are formulated and tested on the basis of evidence, internal consistency, and their explanatory power.

Voices for Evolution

Evolution as a Unifying Concept

Evolution in the broadest sense can be defined as the idea that the universe has a history: that change through time has taken place. If we look today at the galaxies, stars, the planet Earth, and the life on planet Earth, we see that things today are different from what they were in the past: galaxies, stars, planets, and life forms have evolved. Biological evolution refers to the scientific theory that living things share ancestors from which they have diverged; it is called "descent with modification." There is abundant and consistent evidence from astronomy, physics, biochemistry, geochronology, geology, biology, anthropology, and other sciences that evolution has taken place.

As such, evolution is a unifying concept for science. *The National Science Education Standards* recognizes that conceptual schemes such as evolution "unify science disciplines and provide students with powerful ideas to help them understand the natural world" (p. 104) and recommends evolution as one such scheme. In addition, *Benchmarks for Science Literacy* from AAAS's Project 2061, as well as other national calls for science reform, all name evolution as a unifying concept because of its importance across the disciplines of science. Scientific disciplines with a historical component, such as astronomy, geology, biology, and anthropology, cannot be taught with integrity if evolution is not emphasized.

There is no longer a debate among scientists about whether evolution has taken place. There is considerable debate about how evolution has taken place: What are the processes and mechanisms producing change, and what has happened specifically during the history of the universe? Scientists often disagree about their explanations. In any science, disagreements are subject to rules of evaluation. Scientific conclusions are tested by experiment and observation, and evolution, as with any aspect of theoretical science, is continually open to and subject to experimental and observational testing.

The importance of evolution is summarized as follows in the National Academy of Sciences publication *Teaching about Evolution and the Nature of Science*: "Few other ideas in science have had such a far-reaching impact on our thinking about ourselves and how we relate to the world" (p. 21).

Creationism and Other Non-Scientific Views

The *National Science Education Standards* note that, "explanations of how the natural world changed based on myths, personal beliefs, religious values, mystical inspiration, superstition, or authority may be personally useful and socially relevant, but they are not scientific" (p. X). Because science limits itself to natural explanations and not religious or ultimate ones, science teachers should neither advocate any religious interpretation of nature nor assert that religious interpretations of nature are not possible.

The word "creationism" has many meanings. In its broadest meaning, creationism is the idea that the universe is the consequence of something transcendent. Thus to Christians, Jews, and Muslims, God created; to the Navajo, the Hero Twins created; for Hindu Shaivites, the universe comes to exist as Shiva dances. In a narrower sense, "creationism" has come to mean "special creation": the doctrine that the universe and all that is in it was created by God in essentially its present form, at one time. The most common variety of special creationism asserts that

- the Earth is very young;

- life was created by God;

- life appeared suddenly;

- kinds of organisms have not changed since the creation; and

- different life forms were designed to function in particular settings.

This version of special creation is derived from a literal interpretation of Biblical Genesis. It is a specific, sectarian religious belief that is not held by all religious people. Many Christians and Jews believe that God created through the process of evolution. Pope John Paul II, for example, issued a statement in 1996 that reiterated the Catholic position that God created and affirmed that the evidence for evolution from many scientific fields is very strong.

"Creation science" is a religious effort to support special creationism through methods of science. Teachers are often pressured to include it or other related nonscientific views such as "abrupt appearance theory," "initial complexity theory," "arguments against evolution," or "intelligent design theory" when they teach evolution. Scientific creationist claims have been discredited by the available scientific evidence. They have no empirical power to explain the natural world and its diverse phenomena. Instead, creationists seek out supposed anomalies among many existing theories and accepted facts. Furthermore, creation science claims do not lead to new discoveries of scientific knowledge

Legal Issues

Several judicial decisions have ruled on issues associated with the teaching of evolution and the imposition of mandates that creation science be taught when evolution is taught. The First Amendment of the Constitution requires that public institutions such as schools be religiously neutral; because creation science asserts a specific, sectarian religious view, it cannot be advocated in the public schools.

When Arkansas passed a law requiring "equal time" for creation science and evolution, the law was challenged in Federal District Court. Opponents of the bill included the religious leaders of the United Methodist, Episcopalian, Roman Catholic, African Methodist Episcopal, Presbyterian, and Southern Baptist churches, along with several educational organizations. After a full trial, the judge ruled that creation science did not qualify as a scientific theory (*McLean v. Arkansas Board of Education*, 529 F. Supp. 1255 [ED Ark. 1982]).

Louisiana's equal time law was challenged in court, and eventually reached the Supreme Court. In *Edwards v. Aguillard* [482 U.S. 578 (1987)], the court determined that creation science was inherently a religious idea and to mandate or advocate it in the public schools would be unconstitutional. Other court decisions have upheld the right of a district to require that a teacher teach evolution and not teach creation science (*Webster v. New Lenox School District #122*, 917 F.2d 1003 [7th Cir. 1990]; *Peloza v. Capistrano Unified School District*, 37 F.3d 517 [9th Cir. 1994]).

Some legislators and policy makers continue attempts to distort the teaching of evolution through mandates that would require teachers to teach evolution as "only a theory" or that require a textbook or lesson on evolution to be preceded by a disclaimer. Regardless of the legal status of these mandates, they are bad educational policy. Such policies have the effect of intimidating teachers, which may result in the de-emphasis or omission of evolution. As a consequence, the public will only be further confused about the nature of scientific theories. Furthermore, if students learn less about evolution, science literacy itself will suffer.

References

American Association for the Advancement of Science (AAAS), Project 2061. (1993). *Benchmarks for science literacy.* New York: Oxford University Press.

Edwards v. Aguillard, 482 U.S. 578 (1987).

McLean v. Arkansas Board of Education, 529 F. Supp. 1255 (ED Ark. 1982).

National Academy of Sciences (NAS). (1998). *Teaching about evolution and the nature of science.* Washington, DC: Steering Committee on Science and Creationism, National Academy Press.

National Research Council. (1996). *National science education standards.* Washington, DC: National Academy Press.

Peloza v. Capistrano Unified School District, 37 F.3d 517 (9th Cir. 1994).

Webster v. New Lenox School District #122, 917 F.2d 1003 (7th Cir. 1990).

Additional Resources

Laudan, Larry. (1996). *Beyond positivism and relativism: Theory, method, and evidence.* Boulder, CO: Westview Press.

National Academy of Sciences (NAS). (1999). *Science and creationism: A view from the National Academy of Sciences,* Second Edition. Washington, DC: National Academy Press.

Skehan, James W., S.J., and Nelson, Craig E. (1993). *The creation controversy & the science classroom.* Arlington, VA: National Science Teachers Association.

Ruse, Michael. (1996). *But is it science: The philosophical question in the creation/evolution controversy.* Amherst, NY: Prometheus.

This position statement reprinted courtesy of the National Science Teachers Association, Arlington, VA, http://www.nsta.org/positionstatement&psid=10

New Mexico Coalition for Excellence in Science and Math Education

The Coalition for Excellence in Science and Math Education (CESE) has been directly involved in the promotion of the teaching of the Theory of Evolution since 1997. CESE encourages and supports all efforts to promote sound science teaching and curriculum in American Public schools while opposing any attempt to undermine that purpose.

CESE recognizes that the United States of America is severely underperforming compared with the rest of the industrialized nations of the world in science, math and engineering education and literacy. The scientific literacy of the general American population is being further eroded by the attempts of a small, but highly motivated and relatively well financed group of mostly religiously driven people. These people denounce the Theory of Evolution and would substitute a non-scientific, supernatural explanation of the origins of life forms on earth. This explanation is called creationism. Other forms of creationism include creation science or a recent variant called intelligent design that is intended to bypass the Establishment Clause of the First Amendment to the US Constitution. All forms of creationism are an attempt to redefine or eliminate evolution, which is one of the central theories of all science. Such attacks on scientific theory impact all major fields of science, including biology, physics, geology, astrophysics, chemistry, etc.

The creationist goal is to allow supernatural explanations into science in order to change the very basis of science. Science deals with natural explanations for natural phenomena. Creationism or intelligent design, if allowed, would change this to promote supernatural explanations for natural phenomena – a contradiction in terms with regard to science. Intelligent design is also sterile as far as science is concerned. To be considered as real science, it must be able to explain and predict natural phenomena. Intelligent design proponents simply say that life is too complex to have arisen naturally. Therefore, an intelligent being (God) must have directly intervened whenever it chose to cause the diversity of the species. This explains everything and it explains nothing; it is not science.

The creationist groups attempt to masquerade their ideas as science simply by calling the concept "intelligent design theory". No testable hypotheses or any form of scientific research has been presented to support their attempts to insert religion into science. Furthermore, it is suspected that the aim of these religiously motivated people is to redefine the meaning of science; if they were successful, science would become useless as a method for learning about the natural world. CESE decries the very usage of science terminology where there is no sound use of science. CESE also decries any political attempt to discredit the Theory of Evolution. Creationists present false statements concerning the validity of observed evidence for evolution such as: "there is no fossil evidence for evolution," "it is impossible to obtain higher complexity systems from lower complexity systems," etc. They call into question the motives and beliefs of scientists with claims such as, "if you believe in evolution, you are an atheist," etc. They have even invented an imaginary scientific "controversy" to argue their agenda.

The Coalition for Excellence in Science and Math Education respectfully asks that the citizens of this country and, in particular, those public officials responsible for educational policy be aware of the fact that these creationist groups do not represent mainstream science or religion and that their actions are contrary to the facts and to the welfare of the country. We also understand that no one should be forced to believe in something that his specific religious doctrine forbids. We ask that this group not be allowed to force their religious beliefs into public education science classrooms.

New York State Education Department

There are several views regarding origins and changes that have occurred on the earth over time. Six-day creation, gap creation, progressive creation, theistic evolution, creationism, evolution, and planetary seeding are terms used to describe some of these views. The contrasts among these ideas, especially between creationism and evolution, have been discussed publicly.

During the process of revising the Regents Biology Syllabus, suggestions for including creationism as part of this course of study were forwarded to the New York State Education Department. It was suggested that the topic Modern Evolution be replaced by a two-model approach involving creationism and evolution.

The State Education Department requested expert scientific examination of this suggestion in terms of its bases in modern science and its appropriateness for the state high school biology curriculum. The American Association for the Advancement of Science, the American Institute for Biological Sciences, the National Association of Biology Teachers, and the New York Academy of Sciences reviewed the creationism materials and made recommendations as to their inclusion in the science curriculum. Department staff members met with representatives from these scientific associations to review their expert opinion concerning the use of creationism materials in high school science courses.

Their opinion was that creationism does not qualify as information generated by scientific processes and is not part of the body of scientific knowledge accepted by most scientists. Also expressed was the view that creationism can neither be verified nor refuted through scientific investigation and that models or theories which involve the supernatural are not within the domain of science. Accordingly, the following are recommended:

1. Contrasting religion with scientific theories is not the role of the science teacher. Students should be informed, however, that there are supernatural accounts of origins outside the domain of science. These accounts are derived mainly from scripture and religious authority and are beyond the scope of scientific investigation. The personal religious beliefs of an individual are safeguarded by the Constitution, and should be respected.

2. It should be understood that "scientific creationism" is not accepted as science by the majority of experts working in those fields of science related to origins. It is considered by these experts to be a field of study more closely related to religion than to science.

3. Evolution should be taught, not as a fact, but as a scientific theory which has substantial support from the scientific community. The concept of modern evolution incorporates the work of many scientists. Current dialogues among scientists are indicative of possible modifications in evolutionary theory.

4. Teachers should respect the personal beliefs of students and recognize that in a pluralistic society, the personal beliefs of some may not be compatible with all aspects of evolutionary theory.

The teaching of supernatural accounts of origins by science teachers in science classrooms as part of the science curriculum is not a recommended procedure. Science teachers should acknowledge the personal validity of their students' beliefs and direct the student to the most appropriate counsel for assistance in questions outside the scope of the science classroom. Technical questions beyond the training and background of the science teacher about the fossil record, homology, biochemistry, etc., should be directed to specialists in those fields. Questions related to scripture, revelation and the supernatural should be directed to the religious authorities on those topics.

1980
Ratified also by the Parent-Teachers Association of Ithaca, NY,
and by the Parent-Teacher Students Association of Syosset High School, Syosset, NY.

New York State Science Supervisors Association

Position Statement

The New York State Science Supervisors Association concurs with the position taken by the Science Bureau of the State Education Department concerning the teaching of evolution. The study of supernatural accounts of origins by science teachers in science classrooms as part of the science curriculum is not a recommended procedure. Questions related to scripture, revelation and the supernatural should be directed to the religious authorities.

Published in the NYSSSA Newsletter, VI:3, Summer 1981.

North Carolina Science Teachers Association

The North Carolina Science Teachers Association stands for and supports the cause of science education. It opposes attempts by individuals or groups to offer, advocate, or require non-scientific explanations of natural phenomena in science classes in North Carolina Public Schools.

The primary goal of science teaching is to produce scientifically literate citizens. Science is both a process and a body of knowledge. It is pragmatic, observational, experimental and replicable. To be acceptable as science, explanations, statements, and theories must be capable of test by observation and experiment. Science is used in an attempt to explain the world about us. Courses in science should be concerned only with scientific knowledge and theories.

Attempts are being made by individuals and groups to have included in the public school science curriculum non-scientific explanations of the origin and development of living organisms. Efforts are being made to have special creation (Biblical accounts) presented in science classes as scientific accounts of creation. These efforts are an attempt to counteract or replace the teaching of the evolutionary theory of the origin and development of living organisms.

In general, creationism is a religious concept. Religion is based on one's belief or faith, not on scientific evidence. Evolution is a scientific theory based on scientific data accumulated over many years and organized, by logic and reason, into a unifying idea. The theory of evolution is, as all theories are, tentative in that it cannot produce a conclusive answer.

Religion and science are two important and exclusive realms of human thought. Efforts to present both in the same context lead to misunderstanding of both. Therefore, science instruction and materials in our public schools should be limited to matters of science.

The NCSTA recommends that the theory of evolution be taught as a scientific theory - not a fact - in our public schools by teachers certified in science. The NCSTA is sensitive to, and understanding of, the various religious beliefs of students and in no way wishes to change their religious beliefs. The theory of evolution should be taught, primarily, for awareness and understanding and for use in further scientific study - not for acceptance.

September 1981

Oklahoma Science Teachers Association

The scientific content of science courses should be determined by scientists and science educators and not by political directives. In particular, science teachers should not be required to teach, as science, ideas, models and theories that are clearly extra-scientific. An extra-scientific hypothesis, as such, might legitimately be discussed in a science class when examination of its logical construction and criteria for acceptance would illuminate the corresponding features of a scientific hypothesis and scientific method. Any requirement for equal time for such hypotheses is not justifiable.

Scientific hypotheses have a number of distinguishing properties, the foremost of which is that one should be able to deduce, from the basic postulates, logical consequences that can be tested against observation. Attention should be paid to the possible kinds of evidence that would falsify the hypothesis, rather than just the evidence that might confirm it. Other properties include:

1. The hypothesis should have more general consequences than those observations which initially suggested it. Thus it should be independently testable and not ad hoc.

2. It should be fruitful, suggesting new lines of research to pursue, raise new questions to be investigated by future research.

3. It should be logically consistent.

4. It should be consistent with the general scientific philosophy that the observed phenomena of the universe are real and that nature is consistent and understandable, that is, describable and explainable in terms of laws and theories.

Hypotheses that postulate miracles or supernatural events are falsified scientifically because they explicitly admit they cannot explain phenomena within their sphere of application. Furthermore, they are extra-scientific and non-explanatory because those phenomena are declared to be beyond human understanding. Thus they can not be considered alternate explanations to any scientific hypothesis because, by their very nature, they are anti-explanatory, seeking only to establish and perpetuate a mystery or mysteries.

All such hypotheses, models and theories that claim to be scientific should be required to meet the same criteria as do those hypotheses commonly considered to be scientific by the scientific community at large.

Adopted October 15, 1981 (later adopted by the Oklahoma Academy of Sciences)

Oklahoma State University Department of Zoology

Statement on Evolution

Evolution has nearly 150 years of empirical support from diverse disciplines of scientific inquiry, ranging from biogeography and paleontology to genetics and molecular biology. This rigorously tested and overwhelmingly supported scientific theory is the central unifying principle in biology, and understanding evolution is thus a critical component of any sound education in a scientific discipline.

In spite of the vast consensus view among trained scientists and science educators, there continue to be political attempts in numerous states including Oklahoma to force a so-called alternative to evolution – "Intelligent Design" (ID) – into the science curriculum of public schools. ID is not a scientific theory and its claims cannot be addressed by scientific means. These political actions severely undermine the accurate and thorough understanding of the nature of science. Furthermore, they threaten to put our state at a competitive disadvantage in attracting and retaining jobs in an increasingly technologically-oriented society.

Therefore, the Department of Zoology at Oklahoma State University joins with numerous other organizations devoted to science education and research in affirming the centrality of evolution to biology and in opposing attempts to introduce the teaching of ID into any science curriculum.

Adopted 10 February 2006

Science Museum of Minnesota (1995)

As an institution whose mission is to invite learners of all ages and backgrounds to experience the world through science, this museum must be consistent in the meaning given to "science". By definition, science is knowledge derived from observation, study, and experimentation. Science encompasses a wide variety of disciplines. Each discipline has a characteristic focus but all are united by use of the scientific method, and all are affected by censorship.

There are few areas of life in which one will not encounter a degree of censorship. But since each of the various disciplines of science is bound indissolubly to the others, if one topic is omitted through censorship, the ability to study any of them is inhibited. While the study of biology focuses on organisms, it is forever dependent on chemistry, chemistry on physics, physics on mathematics, and so on. All scientific disciplines are united in demonstrating the evolution of life on this planet.

In every area of scientific research and education, one strives to remain consistent in vocabulary. "Theory" is just one of many words that has a different meaning in the world of science from the meaning it has in daily life. In daily life, one definition of "theory" is, "a mere guess at something." However, a scientific theory reflects an enormous amount of study that has gone into accounting for some natural phenomenon, and in science the word "theory" is not used lightly. As for the theory of evolution, it is widely accepted within the scientific community that evolution itself is fact. It is theory about the mechanisms of evolution that continues to be refined.

The Science Museum of Minnesota is currently undergoing the process of developing internal policies concerning discussion of evolution. Appropriate information is provided for staff in order to educate them and allow them to conduct informed discussions on the topic. In instances where creationists visit the museum, they are not discouraged providing they are not disruptive to the staff or other visitors. Leafleting of any kind is not allowed within this institution. Following is a list of critical issues scientific institutions must decide upon when striving to fulfill their missions in research, practice and education.

The Age of the Earth
In order to carry on consistent conversations on a variety of topics, scientists must agree on the age of the earth. An educational institution cannot seriously discuss topics such as geology, biodiversity, human biology, embryology, ecology, paleontology, anthropology, and so forth, without first establishing a timeline of events. Since creationist doctrine provides a myriad of options as to the age of the earth, it does not lend itself to this process and therefore cannot be used. Based on current research, scientists generally agree that the age of the earth is approximately 4.5 billion years. An institution of scientists and science educators are obliged to use this date until further study finds otherwise.

Educational Objectives
Being true to educational objectives requires honesty. If science educators are to compare the enormous variety of life forms which have inhabited the planet, they must account for both the similarities and differences in those animals. Evolution is the framework within which these topics can be discussed. In addition, evolution applies to all life forms, not just some. It is the scientific institution's responsibility to the public not to negate pertinent information on the basis that it may not be acceptable to all.

Speaking Freely about Science

If an institution is bound by censorship of topics fundamental to its work, it is of little use in either the educational or the scientific arena. If instead, the bounds of censorship are lifted, the quality of information that can be provided to the public becomes unlimited. Evolution is fundamental in the scientific discussion of life on earth and of the earth itself.

Providing Clear Guidelines to Staff

An institution owes its staff clear guidelines on controversial topics so that they may convey the institution's position. However, it must also respect the rights of its staff to live by whatever ideology or doctrine they choose. An institutional policy statement does not prevent controversy, but since front line staff are the ones most likely to encounter difficulties, institutional support will aid in their handling of situations that arise. Staff are not required to agree with evolution, but they are expected to be able to provide direct answers to the public as to why the institution supports evolution. Staff should not be expected to defend their personal beliefs to visitors.

Being Honest with Visitors

An institution has a responsibility to its visitors to provide a simple, concise and unbiased explanation as to why it accepts the evidence for evolution. While some visitors may disagree, they will not be led astray or told untruths. In an institution of science, visitors should expect to see all aspects of science within that institution's programs. The institution should be free to discuss science without regret or apology.

1995

Editor's note: Official position statements of the Science Museum of Minnesota are not public documents; other, similar institutions should direct requests for further information to Patty Forber, Manager, Paleontology Science Hall, Science Museum of Minnesota, 30 East 10th Street, Saint Paul, MN 55101. We are grateful to the Museum for submitting this essay specifically for publication in Voices for Evolution.

Science Teachers Association of New York State (1980)

Move that we reject the proposal made by the Scientific Creationist movement that creationism be taught in our schools as a scientific alternative to Darwinian evolution. This clearly oversteps the separation of church and state as outlined in the Constitution of the United States. Another reason we must reject this proposal is that creationism is not science and therefore has no place in the science classroom.

The Science Teachers Association of New York State supports the theory of evolution as outlined in the New York State Biology Syllabus (September 1968, pages 86-90: Unit 6, Parts II B and C), and the evidence for evolution as outlined in the New York State Biology Syllabus (September 1968, pages 84-85; Unit 6, Part I A, B, C, D, and E).

May, 1980

Society for College Science Teachers

Position Statement on the Teaching of Evolution

The Society for College Science Teachers (SCST) recognizes the centrality of evolutionary theory to modern science, and encourages the teaching of evolution at an appropriate level throughout primary, secondary, and higher education science curricula. Along with many other scientific and science education societies (e.g., AAAS, NRC, NABT, and NSTA), SCST strongly endorses the position that no science curriculum, especially at the high school and college level, is complete unless it acknowledges evolutionary theory as the core scientific explanation for the diversity of life on Earth and, wherever possible, educates students about the processes and patterns of evolution. While such discussions will most often be a part of life science courses, evolution is also often an appropriate topic in disciplines such as astronomy, chemistry, geology, and physics.

In the nearly 150 years since Darwin first suggested that living things share a common ancestry, a voluminous and robust body of evidence in support of evolutionary theory has accumulated. That living things on Earth have descended with modification from a common ancestry is not a point of scientific dispute. Science teachers are therefore obligated to present the topic in an accurate and thorough fashion as part of their classes. Indeed, because of the fundamental role that evolution plays in tying together scientific disciplines, teachers do their students a great disservice by not making evolution a key component of their teaching. The obligation to include evolution in the science classroom requires that accurate and complete information be taught, and also that non-scientific "alternatives" to evolution such as creation science and intelligent design not be presented as legitimate science or a valid replacement for evolutionary theory. Suggesting to students that such non-scientific ideas qualify as legitimate alternatives to evolution undermines science, prevents students from understanding one of the most important ideas in human history, and constitutes inappropriate educational practice. If teachers encounter situations where colleagues are teaching inaccurate content about evolution or promoting non-scientific explanations in its place, or experiencing pressure to do so, SCST encourages those teachers to seek advice from local, state, and national organizations (e.g., the National Center for Science Education) about how best to address the situation and to elevate the overall quality of science education at their institution.

SCST advises science teachers at all levels, but especially those involved with developing and delivering high school and college curricula, to be well versed in evolutionary theory and to include it as a core theme within their science courses. To do otherwise is to deprive students of essential scientific knowledge that they will need to be thoughtful, productive citizens, and to successfully compete for jobs in the increasingly scientific workplace of the 21st century.

Adopted March 2007

To find out more about SCST, please visit www.scst.org.

For further information about evolutionary theory, the role of evolution in science education, and the problems with non-scientific "alternatives" to evolution, SCST recommends the following print and online resources:

- Alters B. J. & Nelson C. E. (2002). Teaching evolution in higher education. *Evolution* 56 (10): 1891–1901.
- American Physical Society (http://aps.org/policy/statements/81_1.cfm)
- Freeman, S. & J. C. Herron (2004). *Evolutionary Analysis* (3rd ed.). Pearson/Prentice Hall.

- National Academies of Science (http://www.nationalacademies.org/evolution/)
- National Center for Science Education (http://www.ncseweb.org/)
- National Science Education Standards (http://www.nap.edu/readingroom/books/nses/)
- National Science Teachers Association (http://www.nsta.org/220)
- Scott, E. C. (2005). *Evolution vs. Creationism: An Introduction.* Univ. of California Press.
- Talk.Origins Archive (http://www.talkorigins.org/)
- Understanding Evolution (http://evolution.berkeley.edu)

Syracuse Parent-Teacher Association

Whereas minimum standards for curriculum in the public school system are set by the New York State Board of Regents; and

Whereas the board of education or such body or officer as performs the functions of such boards shall designate textbooks to be used; and

Whereas textbook publishers are under continuous pressure by special interest groups to alter textbooks to specific beliefs and/or religious points of view; and

Whereas such pressure has led to a remarkable reduction in the amount of information on evolution, biology, and related sciences in the textbooks; and

Whereas some groups have organized a sophisticated propaganda campaign to influence school boards and textbook publishers that scientific creationism should be included in the science curriculum of the public school system; and

Whereas creationism is a belief and not a science and will blur the distinction between science and religious beliefs; and

Whereas the teaching of creationism amounts to establishing the practices and beliefs of particular religious groups under the aegis of the government which is a violation of the First Amendment; therefore be it

Resolved that the Syracuse Parent-Teacher Association agrees with the New York State Board of Regents Biology Syllabus that evolution should be taught not as fact, but as a scientific theory which has substantial support from the scientific community, and be it further

Resolved that the Syracuse Parent-Teacher Association strongly opposes any attempts to insert in the science curriculum any philosophical theories not substantiated by scientific data, and be it further

Resolved that the Syracuse Parent-Teacher Association recommends that Districts, Councils, and Local Units urge School Boards and teachers' organizations to discourage any such materials in a science curriculum, and redirect it to its appropriate discipline, thereby maintaining freedom of information in textbooks; and be it further

Resolved that the Syracuse Parent-Teacher Association urge Boards of Education to establish procedures for dealing with challenges to curriculum and content of school textbooks, and be it further

Resolved that this resolution be forwarded to the New York State Congress of Parents and Teachers for consideration at its next convention.

1984

University of Alabama at Huntsville Faculty Senate

Whereas we understand that the Alabama legislature is considering a requirement that "Scientific Creationism" be included as an alternative to evolutionary theory during discussions in Alabama public schools of the origin and development of life; and

Whereas we consider the theory of scientific creationism to be neither scientifically based nor capable of performing the roles required of a scientific theory; and

Whereas we agree with the statement of the National Academy of Sciences that "religion and science are separate and mutually exclusive realms of human thought whose presentation in the same context leads to misunderstanding of both scientific theory and religious belief"; and

Whereas the proposed action would impair the proper segregation of teaching of science and religion to the detriment of both; and

Whereas we favor the continued observance of the First Amendment to the U.S. Constitution guaranteeing freedom of religion by assuming separation of Church and State; and

Whereas the inclusion of the theory of creation represents dictation by a lay body of what shall be included within science;

Therefore, The University of Alabama in Huntsville Faculty Senate resolves both that:

1. It is opposed to the requirement of teaching of special creation in Alabama public schools and to its presentation as a scientific theory; and

2. It is opposed to the passage of the scientific creationism bills (H-526 and S-353) before the Alabama legislature.

1981

University of California Academic Council of the Academic Senate

It is our understanding that within the next few months the California State Board of Education will be approving many science textbooks for use in California public schools, grades K through 8. The text of the Science Framework for California Schools, prepared in 1969, suggests that one criterion for the board's approval of a text may be the extent to which, in the discussion of the origins of life, a "special theory of creation" is treated as a scientific theory in a manner parallel to an account of evolution. We believe that a description of special creation as a scientific theory is a gross misunderstanding of the nature of scientific inquiry.

To provide the basis of a scientific theory, an hypothesis must make testable predictions. Our ideas of biological evolution are continually being tested in the process of an enormous amount of investigation by thousands of professional biological scientists throughout the world. As in all sciences, there are many facets of the evolution picture that are not yet thoroughly understood, and researchers at the frontier of knowledge, often in disagreement with each other concerning details, continually revise their thinking. Thus, evolutionary theory itself has evolved considerably since the time of Darwin. But virtually all biological scientists are agreed on the broad features of the theory of evolution of life forms, the evidence for which is completely overwhelming.

Approved by the Academic Council of the
University of California Academic Senate on October 27, 1972

University of New Mexico History Department

Resolution

The faculty of the History Department at the University of New Mexico objects to the new Content Standards in Science for New Mexico's public schools (K-12), adopted by the State Board of Education (SBE) in August 1996. Our objection centers on

- The Standard's deletion of all specific references to biological evolution

- The Standard's encouragement to teach alternative theories through "critical scientific analysis of theories of biological origin based on direct observations, investigations, or historical data that accounts for the present form and function of objects, organisms, and natural systems."

We urge the SBE to reconsider the Content Standards in Science, to restore the specific references to biological evolution, and to refrain from encouraging teachers to include non-scientific theories of biological origin in science classes.

Discussion

While the Standards adopted by the State Board of Education in August 1996 do not explicitly encourage the inclusion of "scientific creationism" in New Mexico's public school science classes, this is clearly the intent of the last-minute revisions to the Standards. Boardmember Roger X. Lenard, one of the architects of the new Standards and a self-described anti-evolutionist, has written that the Standards provide "a rigorous, principled environment where various theories about the age of the earth and the universe and biological origins will be studied" (*Albuquerque Journal,* 21 September 1996, p. A9). State schools Superintendent Alan Morgan, a supporter of the new Standards, has stated that they are designed to affect "schools that are focusing on one view, one theory, and one set of facts ... because those systems aren't helping students develop critical analytical skills. So if science classes discuss only the theory of evolution, there may be trouble." (*Albuquerque Journal,* 31 August 1996, pp. A1-A2).

Superintendent Morgan also stated that many people believe that there is a "modicum, if not more, of scientific evidence to support creationism" (Ibid.).

There are many good reasons not to allow, much less encourage, the teaching of non-scientific theories like creationism in public school science classes. The technical and practical arguments against the practice have been articulated very well by scientists and scientific organizations around the state since the SBE adopted the new Standards.

However, rather than repeat the many scientific objections to the Standards, we, as a faculty in the humanities, would like to offer a different argument against them. We oppose these Standards for reasons that are based not on the technical issues involved, but on our belief in the value of liberal arts education and its ability to illuminate diverse and distinct ways of studying and understanding the world. Our argument is two-fold.

First, to include creationist ideas within a science curriculum is a serious and detrimental distortion of the historical definition of science in the western world. As it has evolved since Greek antiquity, and especially since the scientific revolution of the 17th century, science has come to refer to a method of articulating certain kinds of explanations about natural phenomena. Historically, scientific explanations have exhibited several characteristics. They tend to be mechanical in nature. They often tend to include descriptions that can be articulated using mathematics. And, they have always been devoid of supernatural agents. In this regard, all forms of creationism, with their implicit reliance on a supernatural creator, are non-scientific by definition, regardless of any appropriation of scientific or science-like language. Calling one form of creationism "scientific" does not make it so, because it still entails the action of a supernatural deity or deities.

It is important to realize that our desire to protect the integrity of science as a distinct intellectual discipline is not an attempt to elevate science above all other intellectual endeavors; quite the contrary. Science is one way of knowing the world; it is not the only way of knowing, and it is certainly not the only way of knowing everything. Indeed, in the grand scheme of human thought and action, the domain of science is modest – the realm of natural phenomena. Science, as it has developed historically, will not and can never tell us anything about the nature of beauty, or the attributes of justice, or the qualities of goodness. There are many ideas and many truths (like the belief that all people are created equal, or that they have the right to life, liberty, and the pursuit of happiness) upon which science must remain mute. Supernatural creation stories may, in fact, be true; but science, as only one way of knowing, will never tell us this. Science is simply not equipped to speak on supernatural issues, and it would be a mistake to try to force it to do so.

The second part of our argument addresses why it would be a mistake to try to change the definition of science to include supernatural entities. To insist that religious creation stories be considered scientific (and included in science classes) would reinforce the dangerous myth that science is the only way of knowing. Other ways of knowing the world – through art, or literature, or philosophy, or religion – are valuable and meaningful in their own right; treating them all merely as science would diminish their status as important and alternative methods of understanding by forcing them to surrender to the criteria of one particular intellectual discipline. It is precisely because we should not subsume all other ways of knowing under science that we should keep religious or literary stories distinct from it.

In short, we should actively keep non-scientific or religious creation stories out of the public school science curriculum in order to maintain the intellectual integrity of science as well as the intellectual integrity of all other disciplines. Such ideas can and should be examined critically, with value and honor, in humanities or social science classes that focus on the disciplines of history, philosophy, comparative religion, or literature.

On these grounds, in addition to the many others being voiced by the scientific community, we urge the State Board of Education to reconsider and revise the new Content Standards for Science.

University of Oklahoma Department of Zoology

Statement on Evolution

Biological evolution, defined as genetic change in species over time, is an observable fact. It is a fact that insects evolve resistance to pesticides, that new diseases arise when viruses evolve the ability to invade new hosts, and that humans have created new species using the same mechanisms that produce species naturally. Furthermore, the evidence based on facts from molecular biology and geology (i.e. gene sequences, dated fossils) clearly indicates that all living species, including our own, share a common ancestor, which is over 3 billion years old.

Voices for Evolution

The theory of evolution explains the mechanisms (e.g. non-random natural selection acting on random mutation) by which organisms change over time (microevolution), become more complex, and diversify into new species (macroevolution). Evolution is the central unifying theory of biology, supported by independent evidence from paleontology, geology, genetics, molecular biology and genomics, developmental biology, biogeography and behavioral ecology. Even though new information from nearly every field of science has been applied, attempts to falsify evolutionary theory using the scientific method have failed. As is true for any active science, the details of the theory are continually debated as new data are collected. However, there is no controversy in the scientific community about the fact of evolution.

Although in popular speech the word 'theory' means 'a guess', in science 'theory' refers to an explanation so well supported by facts that it is as close to the truth as science can come. Although even the most successful theory can never be proven, any scientific theory can be refuted by facts that are at odds with its predictions. In fact, the most useful theories are those that generate many testable predictions and thus leave themselves particularly susceptible to being proven wrong. It is this quality that most distinguishes a scientific concept from a non-scientific one.

In science, not all explanations are equal. By the rigorous criteria of science, supernatural mechanisms, including Intelligent Design creationism, are not scientific because they do not generate testable predictions about how species change or diversify. To argue that supernatural explanations merit discussion in science classrooms so that 'both sides' of the issue are taught is to advocate that non-science be legitimized as science. In an era where scientific solutions to complex problems are of first priority, this is dangerous logic.

We thus oppose any attempt to weaken scientific standards with respect to evolution, or to broaden the science curriculum to include the supernatural. In this, we stand with our colleagues in the National Academy of Sciences, the American Association for the Advancement of Science, and other scientific organizations. We urge all citizens to learn about science and work to assure that our children receive a first-class science education.

Passed 4/19/2006

The University of Queensland (Australia)
Board of the Faculty of Science

...I fully support the decision of the Board of Secondary School Studies and its Science Advisory Committee to include the teaching of evolution as a component of the core syllabus for Senior Biology, and the decision not to include "Creation Science" as a compulsory component of Senior Biology. Indeed "Creation Science" as it is espoused by its supporters has no place in the syllabus of any science subject....

On May 6, 1984, the Board of the Faculty of Science at the University of Queensland resolved to endorse their Dean's letter to the Minister for Education, supporting teaching evolution in the secondary schools. The above statement is excerpted from that letter, recorded as a resolution in the minutes of the Board meeting.

University System of Georgia Biology
Academic Advisory Committee

Statement on Evolution

Biological evolution is a major unifying concept in modern biology and provides a conceptual framework that helps make biology a unified science. The centrality of evolution to modern biology has been acknowledged by a number of major scientific organizations including the American Association for the Advancement of Science and the National Academy of Sciences. As the appointed representatives of college and university biology professors from around the state, we expect that all students entering our colleges and universities have a clear and accurate understanding of the basic tenets of biological evolution so that they will be prepared for college-level biology classes.

Furthermore, we oppose attempts to have creationism (or its variants such as "scientific creationism" or "intelligent design") taught as science because these ideas are outside the scope of science. In order to properly prepare scientifically literate citizens/students, it is necessary for schools to teach biological evolution.

As professional scientists and educators, we offer our services to any faculty, administrator or school board who needs advice about how to best teach biological evolution.

Adopted on 07 November 2003 by the USG Biology Academic Advisory Committee represented by:

Ray Barber, Ph.D. - Abraham Baldwin Agricultural College
Kenneth Relyea, Ph.D. - Armstrong Atlantic State University
Emil K. Urban, Ph.D. - Augusta State University
Greg Hampikian, Ph.D. - Clayton College & State University
Eugene Keferl, Ph.D. - Coastal Georgia Community College
William S. Birkhead, Ph.D. - Columbus State University
John Lugthart, Ph.D. - Dalton State College
Steve Schenk, M.S. - Darton College
Jimmy Wedincamp, Ph.D. - East Georgia College
Donna Daugherty, Ph.D. - Floyd College
Bill Wall, Ph.D. - Georgia College & State University
Jung H. Choi, Ph.D. - Georgia Institute of Technology
Sheryl Shanholtzer, Ph.D. - Georgia Perimeter College
Stephen Vives, Ph.D. - Georgia Southern University
Steven Kudravi, Ph.D. - Georgia State University
Theresa L. Stanley, Ph.D. - Gordon College
Ronald H. Matson, Ph.D. - Kennesaw State University
Eric L. Sun, Ph.D. - Macon State College
John Pasto, Ph.D. - Middle Georgia College
Terry Schwaner, Ph.D. - North Georgia College & State University
Gene Mesco, Ph.D. - Savannah State University
Carl Quertermus, Ph.D. - State University of West Georgia
Timothy Rhoads, Ph.D. - South Georgia College
Bill Burnett, Ph.D. - Southern Polytechnic State University
William Barstow, Ph.D. - University of Georgia
David L. Bechler, Ph.D. - Valdosta State University

Voices for Evolution

Utah Science Teachers Association

Whereas, the science teachers of the State of Utah are being subjected to increasing pressure to teach non-science material in their science classrooms, and,

Whereas, the Utah Science Teachers Association supports the wisdom and constitutionality of the separation of church and state,

The Utah Science Teachers Association hereby affirms that the science teachers of the State of Utah should[1]

1. Teach science and related disciplines (technology, societal implications of science and technology, etc.) in their science classrooms, and not teach religion as science.

2. Teach students that science is a dynamic, self-correcting discipline based on empirical data and reasonable analyses thereof.

3. Teach the theory of evolution as the major organizing theory in the discipline of the biological and geological sciences.

4. Teach the students to distinguish between various types of evidence; to distinguish "fact," "theory," "hypothesis," "inference," etc.; and to recognize that in its strict sense, "theory" (as a generalization organizing massive amounts of diverse and repeatedly-tested data), is the most useful statement that life science can make.

5. Help students understand that accepting the theory of evolution by natural selection, and other biological phenomena, is not equating science with atheism and that the theory of evolution by natural selection does not rule out the possibility of the involvement of a divine Creator.

6. Help students understand that accepting the theory of evolution by natural selection need not compromise their religious beliefs, whatever their religion may be, since science and religion are based on separate premises and use different methodologies.

7. Help students understand that creationism, as taught by prominent creationist organizations of the day, is pseudoscience and not science.

8. Help students understand that religion is a belief system based on faith and religious experience, and that religious principles can still be followed without conflict while accepting the premises and methodology of science.

9. Help students understand that both science and religion, as two among several human endeavors, have strengths and limits in pursuing human knowledge and action; that neither alone is a sufficient guide for either individual or group conduct. It has never been an endeavor of science, nor is it appropriate for individual scientists, to falsely apply the methodology of science to undermine matters of religious faith.

Resolution adopted January 27, 1990

1 Statements 1 through 4 refer to actual classroom teaching recommendations. Statements 5 though 9 refer to suggestions teachers may want to consider in helping students outside of class.

Utah State Board of Education

Position Statement on Teaching Evolution

The Theory of Evolution is a major unifying concept in science and appropriately included in Utah's K-12 Science Core Curriculum.

This position is consistent with that taken by the National Academy of Sciences, the American Association for the Advancement of Science (AAAS), and most other scientific and educational organizations. The Utah State Board of Education and these organizations affirm science as an essential way of understanding for all students and the importance of evolution as a unifying concept in science.

Science: A Way of Knowing

Science is a distinctive way of understanding the natural world. Science seeks to increase our understanding through empirical evidence. As a way of knowing, science assumes that anything that can be observed or measured is amenable to scientific investigation.

By the very nature of scientific inquiry, there are infinite possibilities for further refinement of current knowledge and understanding.

Understanding may be derived from sources and perspectives other than science such as historical and logical analyses, art, religion and philosophy. These sources rely upon other ways of knowing, such as emotion and faith. While these ways of understanding and creating meaning are important to individuals and society, they are not amenable to scientific investigation and thus not appropriate for inclusion in the science curriculum.

Science relies nearly exclusively on observation and empirical evidence. Since progress in the modern world is tied so closely to this way of knowing, scientific literacy is essential for a society to be competitively engaged in a global economy.

Evolution: A Unifying Concept

Evolution in the broadest sense can be defined as the idea that the universe has a history and has changed over time. Observation of the galaxies, stars, planet Earth, and life on Earth clearly demonstrates that significant changes have occurred. There is abundant and consistent evidence from astronomy, physics, biochemistry, geochronology, geology, biology, anthropology, and other sciences that evolution has taken place. This evidence is found in widely divergent areas, from the geologic fossil record to DNA analysis.

Evolution is an ongoing process with crucial implications for disciplines such as medicine, agriculture, and conservation biology. The Theory of Evolution provides a unifying basis upon which the elements of life are understood and upon which predictions can be made. Moreover, viewing present-day organisms as products of evolution provides the most productive framework for investigating and understanding their structure and function. As such, evolution is a unifying concept for science and provides the foundation for understanding nature. The *National Science Education Standards* from the National Academies of Science and *Benchmarks for Science Literacy* from the American Association for the Advancement of Science identify evolution as a unifying concept across the major disciplines of science. Scientific disciplines with strong historical components – such as astronomy, geology, biology, and anthropology – rely upon the concepts of evolution to understand the nature of changes that have occurred or can be predicted.

There is little or no debate among credible scientists about *whether* evolution has taken place. However, since our understanding is still incomplete, there is considerable and productive debate about processes of evolution. Research questions remain, and scientists often disagree about their explanations, as they should. The nature of science encourages ongoing and meaningful investigation of all assertions made by science. Scientific conclusions are tested by experiment and observation as all scientific theories are subject to continued evaluation.

While some describe the principle of evolution as "just a theory," the scientific definition of a theory is far more rigorous than may be commonly understood. In science, a theory is a systematic explanation of observed phenomena. It must be consistent with all natural laws and withstand the scrutiny and inquiry of the scientific community. The National Academy of Sciences has stated, "Evolution is one of the strongest and most useful scientific theories we have." As a fundamental scientific concept, evolution is a necessary part of science classroom instruction, and it will continue to be taught and progressively refined as a key scientific principle.

Student Beliefs and Teaching Evolution
Teachers should be aware that students bring with them a set of beliefs. Teachers and students should respect and be nonjudgmental about students' beliefs, and teachers should help students understand that science is an essential way of knowing. Teachers should encourage students to discuss any seeming conflicts with their parents or religious leaders. Science teachers should make available to interested parents their planned instruction and the context for that instruction.

Wisconsin Department of Public Instruction

Evolution, Creation and the Science Curriculum
The incorporation of creation science within the science curriculum raises serious legal issues in light of the constitutional doctrine requiring separation of the church and state and sec. 115.28(2), Wis. Stats. This statute requires the State Superintendent to exclude all sectarian instruction and materials from the public schools of this state. In the context of science teaching, the only federal court to consider the question has ruled that the creation science view is inherently religious in character and, accordingly, cannot constitutionally be presented as a scientific explanation of origins in public schools. Under the circumstances, the rationale behind the Arkansas Creation Science Case (*McLean vs Arkansas Board of Education*) cannot be ignored in approaching science curriculum development and organization at the local school district level.

The primary goal of the public schools is the transmission of knowledge from one generation to the next through disciplined study. On the specific issue of science teaching and its relation to creation science and evolution, it should be recognized that science and religion have different theoretical bases; that is, that they are two different areas of knowledge which address different questions in different ways.

Science
Science is concerned with studying nature and the world of which we are a part and yields testable hypotheses. It is both an investigatory process and a body of knowledge which can be subjected to verification by investigation, observation and logical analysis. Science is fundamentally non-dogmatic and is self-correcting. The process is ongoing and developmental. Science is also calculated to encourage the

development of new propositions and ideas about nature and to lead ad infinitum toward new vistas and frontiers of further scientific inquiry.

The formulation of theories, or generalizations based upon substantial evidence which explain phenomena occurring in the natural world, is a fundamental component of scientific inquiry. The "answers" to questions which scientists address must be confirmed by evidence, and these answers are always tentative, awaiting new interpretations which can better explain the evidence. Where a significant body of contrary evidence appears as a result of this process, a scientific theory is subject to revision or replacement by a new theory which offers a better explanation of that evidence. The strength of science is that it is a systematic process for developing the most logical and plausible explanations of known facts, principles, concepts and probabilities relating to any phenomenon. For these reasons, no scientific theory, including evolution, should be presented to students as absolute and unchanging fact. Indeed, dogma and indoctrination are incompatible with an understanding of science; accordingly, the tentative and theoretical nature of the subject matter must be stressed by science instructors. Proper teaching requires presentation of science as open-ended and without preset conclusions.

Religion

Religion is based upon knowledge and wisdom believed to be revealed by a divine creator or through a supernatural order. Unlike tentative scientific knowledge, religious knowledge remains customarily unchallengeable by observable evidence. Religion deals with meanings of life and death and is based ultimately upon faith. Faith precedes prediction and explanation. Because science and religion have different structural bases, one cannot replace the other, for they serve different functions. Due to the fundamental differences in these areas of knowledge, the presentation of religious concepts is inappropriate to the science curriculum. While science instructors should respect and recognize the personal validity of alternative religious beliefs, their responsibility in this regard should be limited to directing student inquiries to the appropriate institutions, including church and family, for further explanation and clarification of religious alternatives. The exclusion of religious explanations from the science class does not amount to telling students that they should not maintain those beliefs – only that those beliefs are not acceptable as science. Giving comparable emphasis in science, which are advanced as alternatives to evolution would be in direct opposition to understanding the nature and purpose of science.

Position of the Department of Public Instruction

1. Alternate scientific theories may be compared in the science classroom, but only those that best explain evidence which has been validated by repeated scientific testing should be accepted, and that only tentatively.

2. Years of intensive geological, biological and other scientific studies have provided the most acceptable explanations of the origin and development of the earth and life on the earth. The theory of evolution has the general consensus of the scientific community because it integrates and clarifies many otherwise isolated scientific facts, principles and concepts in a manner which is consistent with known evidence and

3. Like any scientific theory, evolution remains subject to modification and revision as new evidence is discovered. Therefore, evolution should never be presented to students as absolute fact. Good teaching dictates that students be reminded of the tentative nature of conclusions resulting from scientific inquiry.

Voices for Evolution

Science can only answer certain kinds of questions. If questions are posed outside of the scientific domain, then other disciplines must be employed but not in the guise of science. Science is not superior in explanatory power to religion . . . only different. Educators should be certain that science is not asked to deal with ideas which are beyond its domain and processes. If attempts are made to force all knowledge, including religious doctrine, into a scientific mode, a great part of our cultural heritage may be lost.

Religious beliefs and writings, including accounts of creation, comprise a body of human knowledge and may properly be addressed in their own right in other areas of the public school curriculum. There is no legal prohibition against the non-sectarian academic study of such matters where appropriate to locally established curricular goals in such disciplines as literature, philosophy, history or religious studies.

In Wisconsin, the decisions regarding the goals of the science curriculum and its more specific teaching objectives, as well as the goals and objectives for religious studies in the curriculum, are legally and properly a responsibility of local boards of education. However, local districts dealing with these decisions may wish to consult the Department of Public Instruction for technical assistance relative to both legal and curricular problems and issues.

1982

PART FIVE

CIVIL LIBERTIES ORGANIZATIONS

Voices for Evolution

American Civil Liberties Union

Position Statement On Creationism And Public Schools

For seventy-five years, the American Civil Liberties Union has been dedicated to upholding First Amendment protections of civil liberties. Consistent with the requirements of the Establishment Clause, the ACLU policy on religion in public schools states that "...any program of religious indoctrination – direct or indirect – in the public schools or by use of public resources is a violation of the constitutional principle of separation of church and state and must be opposed...." In 1980, the Board of Directors further clarified this policy by stating, "ACLU also opposes the inculcation of religious doctrines even if they are presented as alternatives to scientific theories." "Creation science" in all its guises, for example "abrupt appearance theory" or "intelligent design theory", is just such religious doctrine.

Among the problems "creation-science" creates in the academic environment is the foreclosure of scientific inquiry. The unifying principle of "creationism" is not the law of nature, but divinity. A divine explanation of natural data is not subject to experiment, it cannot be proved untrue, it cannot be disputed by any human means. Creationism necessarily rests on the unobservable; it can exist only in the ambiance of faith. Faith – belief that does not rest on logic or on evidence – has no role in scientific inquiry.

The constitutional defect of any law or policy requiring the teaching of creationism, or of "evidence against evolution," is not that it requires instruction about facts which coincide with a religious belief, but that it requires instruction in one religious belief as the unifying explanation of facts. This unifying concept is not a secular topic such as biology, chemistry, art, phonics, or literature which is familiar to the elementary and secondary school curricula. Instead, teachers are required to identify, organize, or teach facts and inferences supporting a specific belief – "special creation". To require public schools to marshal "evidences" and "inferences" in service of one religious belief, or to impose an embargo on a scientific theory that Fundamentalists dislike, is not to use religious works "for the teaching of secular subjects," (*Abington School Dist. v. Schempp*), but to place "the power, prestige and financial support of government...behind a particular religious belief" (*Engel v. Vitale*) The year-by-year, school-by-school, and teacher-by-teacher decision-making on whether and how to imbue "creationism" into the sciences and humanities promises continuing anguish in the educational community and assures inordinate involvement of religious groups in the affairs of government.

In our society, government is not permitted to instruct a child in religion, because it is not the government's job to promote a religious form of truth. No provision of the Constitution so firmly assures the essential freedom of the individual as does the Establishment Clause. The provision recognizes that choices about the ultimate meaning of life must be made in the private recesses of the conscience and not in the earthly controversies of political power. Were every person in this country of the same faith, the Establishment Clause would serve as a powerful expression that humans must decide their relationship to God, not at the bidding of the state, but at the calling of the soul. That we are a nation of many religions does not alter this basic function of the Clause; it only enhances the need for vigilance against state manipulation of belief.

Vigilance requires firm and consistent opposition to every effort to use the nation's schools to teach any biblical text, including Genesis, as literal truth, either directly or disguised as "alternative" science. To reject creationism as science is to defend the most basic principles of academic integrity and religious liberty.

1994

American Civil Liberties Union of Ohio

ACLU Expresses Concern and Caution Over Intelligent Design: Science Curriculum Initiative Threatens Church State Separation

The American Civil Liberties Union of Ohio Foundation is deeply concerned by efforts to include "intelligent design theory" in the proposed science curriculum of Ohio public schools. Intelligent design theory posits that living things are too complex to have developed through the operation of evolution over time, and thus must be the work of an unnamed Creator.

Proponents of intelligent design theory are frequent critics of evolution, and their theory, which has typically been rejected by mainstream science, is closely associated with Biblical creationism. In a number of cases decided in the nineteen-eighties, the United States Supreme Court held that states cannot require that creationism be taught in public schools alongside, or instead of, scientific evolution.

In doing so, the Court has held that creationism cannot be separated from its Biblical roots, and remains an essentially religious doctrine. Foes of Darwinian evolution have adapted their tactics accordingly: "This is a perennial battle," said Christine Link, Executive Director of the ACLU of Ohio. "Advocates of Biblical Creationism have been trying for years to get their doctrine into the public schools, and this is just their latest way of doing so."

Efforts to interject religious critiques of evolution into public school science curricula have come in many guises. Some proponents of creationism have portrayed their efforts as an attempt to teach a more diverse set of beliefs. Others have claimed that teaching creationism alongside evolution promotes critical thinking skills. Still others have claimed the right to teach creationism under the doctrine of academic freedom. Courts have consistently rejected these arguments as fig leaves designed to conceal attempts to teach religious doctrine.

ACLU of Ohio Legal Director Jeffrey Gamso said, "Intelligent design has been proven to be nothing more than a thin cover for those who wish to teach creationism, an idea of human origins endorsed by certain Christian denominations, in science classes."

Gamso went on, "Proponents of intelligent design have been unable to provide any credible scientific evidence to support their theories. The scientific community has, time and again, largely refuted purported evidence supporting intelligent design. By continuing to allow teachers to implement intelligent design into the science curriculum, educators are misinforming Ohio's children on the fundamental principles of science."

Compiled from 2002 and 2006 statements

American Civil Liberties Union of Utah

The Teaching of Creationism, Intelligent Design, and Divine Design in Public Schools

There have been three distinct movements to establish the teaching of the Biblical interpretation of creation in American public schools. The first was made popular by the Scopes "Monkey Trial" after the State of Tennessee prohibited the teaching of evolution in public schools. The second movement attempted to mandate that public schools give equal time to the theory of evolution and Creation Science. And today, the third movement seeks to introduce creationism into the public school science curriculum through either the mandatory teaching of Intelligent Design or Divine Design, or mandatory disclaimers as to the factual nature of the theory of evolution.

All three movements share the idea that all living species in their present form can be attributed to a creator or designer that is supernatural or not knowable by scientific means. All three also share a common goal of undermining or opposing the scientific theory of evolution – that all living species are the result of physical changes over vast periods of time through natural processes knowable through scientific means.

The first movement sought to prohibit the teaching of evolution in public schools altogether, and often mandated the teaching of creationism. This movement is best exemplified by the 1925 Scopes "Monkey Trial" in *Scopes v. State*, 289 S.W. 363 (Tenn. 1927). The ACLU assisted in the defense of public school teacher John Scopes, charged under a Tennessee state statute prohibiting the teaching of evolution. Mr. Scopes lost his case and the issue wasn't resolved until the 1968 U.S. Supreme Court case, *Epperson v. State of Arkansas*, 393 U.S. 97 (1968), which struck down a similar Arkansas prohibition of the teaching of evolution. In *Epperson*, the Court held the Arkansas law unconstitutional under the Establishment Clause of the First Amendment of the U.S. Constitution because its purpose was the advancement of a religious belief in the creation account found in the Book of Genesis, and the protection of such religious belief against a contrary scientific theory.

As the *Epperson* Court stated, the Establishment Clause of the Constitution draws an "absolute" prohibition against government aiding religion, preferring a religious doctrine, or protecting religious doctrine from an antagonistic theory. Government must remain neutral towards religion and non-religion alike. So while teaching religion in public schools as part of a "literary or historic viewpoint, presented objectively as part of a secular program of education" is acceptable, teaching for the purposes of furthering a religious doctrine or protecting such a doctrine from another theory is constitutionally forbidden. The second movement attempted to avoid violating the Establishment Clause by mandating the teaching of Creation Science as an alternative theory to evolution. Creation scientists sought to sidestep creationism being classified as a promotion of religion by avoiding reference to a literal interpretation of Genesis and by providing scientific explanations of divine creation. The creation scientists retained the premise that the universe was created by God and creationism's opposition to the theory of evolution in public school science class. Rather than trying to ban the teaching of evolution in favor of creationism, creationists attempted to formulate an alternative scientific theory.

In 1987, the U.S. Supreme Court held that a Louisiana law mandating the equal-time teaching of creationism was unconstitutional (*Edwards v. Aguillard*, 482 U.S. 578 (1987)). The Court noted that parents entrust their children to the schools "on the understanding that the classroom will not purposely be used to advance religious views that may conflict with the private beliefs of the student and his or her family." Further, the court noted that because children are impressionable and public school attendance is mandatory, the courts are especially vigilant of Establishment Clause violations. The Louisiana law purported to protect academic freedom by requiring the teaching of creation science in addition to evolution, but the Court found this to be a "sham" secular purpose. Teachers already had the flexibility and freedom to teach any scientific theory. The Court decided that the purpose of the law was the invalid furtherance of a religious doctrine that a supernatural being created humankind, and the prohibition of a theory perceived to be antagonistic to that religious doctrine. The religious nature of Creation Science was unavoidable because of the ties between creationists and creation scientists, the inescapably religious nature of a supernatural creator, and the inherent conflict between creationism and mainstream science. Of particular importance is the Court's statement in *Edwards* that the Establishment Clause bars any theory predicated on supernatural or divine creation because such theories are inherently and inescapably religious, regardless of whether "they are presented as a philosophy or as a science." Today, proponents of creationism are attempting to introduce creationism into the public school curriculum in two ways: 1) disclaimers from either teachers or stickers on books telling students that advocates of creationism dispute the scientific theory of evolution; and 2) advocating equal time for the teaching of Intelligent Design or Divine Design. The disclaimer approach has been struck down as unconstitutional in *Freiler v. Tangipahoa Parish Bd. of Education*, 185 F.3d 337 (5th Cir. 1999) and *Selman v. Cobb County School District*, 2005 WL 83829. Most recently, parents represented by the ACLU successfully challenged a Dover Pennsylvania School District policy that required high school science teachers to read a statement questioning the theory of evolution and presenting Intelligent Design as an alternative (see Kitzmiller et al v. Dover Area School District).

Divine Design disassociates itself from traditional creationism by theorizing that a non-sectarian supernatural creator designed the universe. Intelligent Design proponents go further and seek to avoid the unconstitutionality of the Creation Science equal-time approaches by not mentioning the nature of the intelligent designer or the Bible altogether. But these approaches are semantic glosses on the underlying creationist concept of a supernatural designer unknowable by science, the creation of all living species by non-natural processes, and opposition to the scientific theory of evolution.

The mandatory inclusion of Intelligent or Divine Design theory in public school science curriculum is thus likely to be held unconstitutional for reasons similar to those articulated in the *Edwards v. Aguillard* equal-time decision. Just as in *Edwards*, Intelligent or Divine Design advances an inherently religious belief in an unknowable creator and it opposes the scientific theory of evolution. The conflict between Intelligent or Divine Design and mainstream science, the inherently religious nature of a universal designer, and the historical link between proponents of Intelligent Design and creationism is likely just as fatal today as it was when *Edwards* was decided in 1987. The religious nature of Intelligent or Divine Design proposals cannot be avoided, as the U.S. Supreme Court noted in *Edwards*, "merely because they are presented as a philosophy or as a science."

January 2006

Americans for Religious Liberty

A free and secular democratic state values education in science. It recognizes that a strong country needs citizens who are trained in the methods of science and makes it available through public institutions. Since it protects the integrity of science and free inquiry it refuses to allow public school classrooms to be used for religious indoctrination. It especially defends the integrity of modern biology. The evolution of life is science. It is more than speculation. It is an established truth, which over one hundred years of biological research has confirmed.

Approved by the Board of Directors, 1982

Americans United for Separation of Church and State (1994)

In recent years, a great deal of conflict has erupted over the issue of religion in public education. Although some individuals and organizations have worked to interject sectarian dogma into the schools, the Supreme Court has repeatedly ruled that public education must remain neutral on religious matters.

One area of especially sharp conflict has been creationism. While all religious denominations espouse a particular theology regarding the origins of the universe and humankind, these theological beliefs vary widely among faith groups. "Creationism" as a term commonly used by Christian fundamentalists in this country refers specifically to the belief that the creation story found in Genesis 1 and 2 is literally true and that the universe and humankind were created by God 6,000 years ago. This view, which is at odds with modern scientific understanding, is not shared by all American Christians.

As such, the teaching of creationism as science in the public schools would promote a particular religious viewpoint and would discount the theologies of other faith groups, thus amounting to an establishment of religion and a violation of the First Amendment.

The Supreme Court has dealt with the issue twice. The Court ruled that public schools may not forbid the teaching of evolution just because some religious groups find it offensive (Epperson v. Arkansas, 1968) and that the teaching of creationism as science in public schools violates church-state separation since it is a theological concept (Edwards v. Aguillard, 1987).

Ideas concerning the origins of humans and the universe that are based on religion are appropriate when used within the context of religious education, such as sabbath schools and private church school instruction. These ideas are not appropriate for use in public schools, where students of many different religious faiths gather. Public school curricula – including science classes – must be kept free of sectarian dogma.

Public school educators and administrators should resist pressures to introduce creationism into science classes. While creationism could be discussed objectively in comparative religion courses or classes on the history of science, it has no place as a viable theory in science classes because it amounts to the introduction of sectarian dogma into the curriculum and violates the separation of church and state.

1994

Science, Religion And Public Education: An Evolving Controversy

Around the country, disputes have arisen over the teaching of creationism, or its closely aligned cousin, "intelligent design" (ID), in public schools. Aggressive Religious Right activists are working feverishly to undercut the teaching of evolution by insisting that students be exposed to "both theories."

This approach threatens the separation of church and state and sound science education. Creationism and its variants are religious doctrines, not science. While some religious believers accept the validity of these ideas, many others do not. In addition, the scientific community is in overwhelming agreement that creationism and its more modern variants are not legitimate science.

In its traditional form, creationism is a literal reading of the Book of Genesis repackaged as science. It makes several claims that clash with modern scientific understanding. For example, supporters of this viewpoint contend that the Earth is only a few thousand years old and that humans lived alongside dinosaurs.

Other advocates of creationism concede that the Earth is ancient and admit that evolution may operate in a limited capacity or on lower forms of life. Yet they reject the idea that humans evolved because, they say, people are the products of a special creation by God.

Tellingly, when trying to reconcile disputes over issues such as the age of Earth and the evolution of lower life forms, advocates of creationism turn to the Bible to buttress their arguments, not the scientific laboratory. In fact, virtually all of the groups in America promoting creationism are incorporated as religious ministries. Leaders of these organizations are often fundamentalist clergy who speak openly of their desire to cast doubt on evolution and win new converts to their faith. This is not in any way a true scientific movement.

On the surface, intelligent design appears to be something different. ID advocates claim that they have uncovered scientific evidence that an intelligent force, i.e. God, created humankind and the universe. The concept sidesteps some of the more far-fetched claims of traditional creationists and does not address issues such as the age of the Earth.

But just below ID's surface lurk many of the same discredited anti-evolution arguments that have been promoted by creationists for years. It seems obvious that ID is a form of "creationism lite," deliberately created by fundamentalists to get a foot in the door of the public school science classroom.

A Long-Running Battle

Fundamentalists have opposed the theory of evolution since Charles Darwin conceived it. This issue has been prominent in many states lately because Religious Right activists are gaining political power. They are pressuring state and local school boards to water down or remove evolution from the curriculum.

This fight has deep roots in America. At the turn of the 20th century, some states had religiously motivated laws banning the teaching of evolution in public schools. In 1925, Tennessee teacher John Scopes was convicted of violating a state statute barring instruction about evolution. (His conviction was later overturned on a technicality.)

Many people believe that the creationists were humiliated by the Scopes trial and went into a period of withdrawal after it was over. In fact, fundamentalists simply shifted tactics and assumed a lower profile but continued their crusade. They began pressuring textbook publishers to water down material about evolution in science textbooks, and many did so.

The launch of the Sputnik satellite by the Soviet Union in October of 1957 seriously rattled the American scientific community. There were numerous calls for better science education in public schools. In response, science instruction was beefed up in many schools, and biology classes were improved. Evolution was reintroduced in many areas, but a problem remained: Many states still had anti-evolution statutes on the books.

In 1968, the U.S. Supreme Court invalidated an Arkansas law that banned public school instruction about evolution (*Epperson v. Arkansas*). Undaunted, creationists began pressing legislatures to pass laws mandating "balanced treatment" between evolution and "creation-science." The Supreme Court struck down a Louisiana law like this in 1987 (*Edwards v. Aguillard*), holding that it was obviously religiously motivated.

Creationists continued to regroup. Throughout the 1980s and '90s they repackaged their ideas under several different names, among them "evidence against evolution" and "the theory of abrupt appearance."

But these efforts were also non-starters. Contemporary anti-evolutionists did not really begin to gain traction until the formation of the Discovery Institute, an outfit based in Washington state that promotes intelligent design.

Creationism In The 21st Century
One of the most visible threats to the teaching of evolution is intelligent design. At first glance, ID appears to have some key differences from standard creationism. It strips away some of the more implausible claims of traditional creationism and professes a secular approach.

Yet a closer look shows that ID remains a religious concept. The "designer" whom Religious Right proponents herald could only be God. They have offered no other plausible candidates. (Some ID boosters have actually suggested that a space alien could be the designer – an assertion that can hardly be taken seriously by science. It also begs the question: Who "designed" the space creature?)

ID proponents have conducted a slick public relations campaign aimed at local schools. They often bypass state officials and apply strong-arm tactics directly to local school boards. Board members, who in most parts of the country are democratically elected, can be subject to considerable community pressure. Thus, ID proponents are primarily waging a political, not scientific, battle.

In fact, ID backers' attempts to publish peer-reviewed research have failed. While they have published many books, these works have been subjected to great criticism in the scientific community.

Some ID advocates are forthright about their religious agenda when speaking to sympathetic audiences. Phillip Johnson, considered a founding guru of the movement, told a religious gathering in 1999 that he uses ID to convince people of the truth of the Bible and talk to them about "the question of sin." From there, Johnson said, people are "introduced to Jesus." Jonathan Wells, another prominent ID proponent, says he was persuaded to criticize evolution after becoming a member of the Rev. Sun Myung Moon's Unification Church.

In December 2005, a federal district court in Pennsylvania ruled against ID promotion in Dover public schools. The *Kitzmiller v. Dover Area School District* decision sends a clear message that intelligent design is constitutionally unacceptable in science classes.

Proposing ID as an "alternative" to evolution is not the only tactic being used to push evolution out of schools. Opponents also use disclaimers, either printed inside a textbook or read aloud by a teacher or school administrator, as another way to undermine the scientific validity of evolution. This kind of effort has the same goal as the ID movement – to cast doubt on the theory of evolution – but doesn't usually put forth any specific alternative, scientific or otherwise.

It's worth pointing out that ID and other forms of creationism are grounded only in *certain varieties* of religion. Most major denominations made their peace with evolution long ago because the scientific evidence for it is so compelling. Today, only militantly fundamentalist groups tend to oppose evolution.

Thus, efforts to claim that evolution is somehow hostile to religion are easily disproved, as are claims that evolution promotes a "godless" universe. In fact, evolution says nothing about the origin of the universe or the meaning of life. It merely addresses the non-controversial idea that living things have the ability to change over time.

Nor is evolution incompatible with conservative theology. Pope John Paul II was hardly considered a theological liberal. Yet on at least two occasions John Paul stated that there need be no conflict between religion and science on this matter. The Bible, the pope said, "does not wish to teach how heaven was made but how one goes to heaven." In October of 1997, John Paul issued a statement asserting that "fresh knowledge leads to recognition of the theory of evolution as more than just a hypothesis."

What Is At Stake

Why is this issue important? At its core, creationism undermines the wall of separation between church and state. Parents are free to teach their children religious concepts at home and in houses of worship. That is not enough for the creationists. They want to expose *all* children to those concepts in public school science classes. They want to use a captive audience to spread their theology. This they cannot legally do. Public schools, the Supreme Court has repeatedly said, are not allowed to promote religion.

Furthermore, creationism and ID threaten good science education in America. The core findings of evolutionary theory are no longer questioned by the scientific community. Evolution is taught without controversy in secular universities all over the nation. Failing to teach it in high school does a disservice to our students and leaves them ill-prepared for higher education.

Resistance to standard science instruction could cause our country to fall behind other nations. Religious opposition to evolution is practically non-existent in Western Europe, Japan, Canada and Australia. As a result, the United States' position as the leader in cutting-edge biotechnology is now in jeopardy. Our country will not continue to lead in this area if our students are not adequately educated about modern science.

In light of this, claims that schools should teach both evolution and some form of creationism and let young people decide are unpersuasive. There is no longer a controversy in the scientific community about the validity of evolution. Pretending that there is only does a disservice to our students. We cannot substitute theology for science in our classrooms and expect to remain the world leader in increasingly important scientific fields.

Because so many different religions and cultures have different beliefs about origins, public schools must take care not to elevate any one understanding over others. For this reason, intelligent design and other forms of creationism must be kept out of our science classrooms.

For more information on this or other church-state issues, contact Americans United for Separation of Church and State at our national headquarters in Washington, D.C., (518 C Street NE, Washington, DC 20002) or online at www. au.org. *Americans United has a wide range of books, fact sheets and other literature about church-state separation. We welcome your comments and support.*

2006

Council of Europe

The dangers of creationism in education

Resolution 1580 (2007)[1]

1. The aim of this report is not to question or to fight a belief – the right to freedom of belief does not permit that. The aim is to warn against certain tendencies to pass off a belief as science. It is necessary to separate belief from science. It is not a matter of antagonism. Science and belief must be able to coexist. It is not a matter of opposing belief and science, but it is necessary to prevent belief from opposing science.

2. For some people the Creation, as a matter of religious belief, gives a meaning to life. Nevertheless, the Parliamentary Assembly is worried about the possible ill-effects of the spread of creationist ideas within our education systems and about the consequences for our democracies. If we are not careful, creationism could become a threat to human rights which are a key concern of the Council of Europe.

3. Creationism, born of the denial of the evolution of species through natural selection, was for a long time an almost exclusively American phenomenon. Today creationist ideas are tending to find their way into Europe and their spread is affecting quite a few Council of Europe member states.

4. The prime target of present-day creationists, most of whom are Christian or Muslim, is education. Creationists are bent on ensuring that their ideas are included in the school science syllabus. Creationism cannot, however, lay claim to being a scientific discipline.

5. Creationists question the scientific character of certain items of knowledge and argue that the theory of evolution is only one interpretation among others. They accuse scientists of not providing enough evidence to establish the theory of evolution as scientifically valid. On the contrary, they defend their own statements as scientific. None of this stands up to objective analysis.

6. We are witnessing a growth of modes of thought which challenge established knowledge about nature, evolution, our origins and our place in the universe.

7. There is a real risk of a serious confusion being introduced into our children's minds between what has to do with convictions, beliefs, ideals of all sorts and what has to do with science. An "all things are equal" attitude may seem appealing and tolerant, but is in fact dangerous.

8. Creationism has many contradictory aspects. The "intelligent design" idea, which is the latest, more refined version of creationism, does not deny a certain degree of evolution. However, intelligent design, presented in a more subtle way, seeks to portray its approach as scientific, and therein lies the danger.

Voices for Evolution

9. The Assembly has constantly insisted that science is of fundamental importance. Science has made possible considerable improvements in living and working conditions and is a not insignificant factor in economic, technological and social development. The theory of evolution has nothing to do with divine revelation but is built on facts.

10. Creationism claims to be based on scientific rigour. In actual fact the methods employed by creationists are of three types: purely dogmatic assertions; distorted use of scientific quotations, sometimes illustrated with magnificent photographs; and backing from more or less well-known scientists, most of whom are not specialists in these matters. By these means creationists seek to appeal to non-specialists and sow doubt and confusion in their minds.

11. Evolution is not simply a matter of the evolution of humans and of populations. Denying it could have serious consequences for the development of our societies. Advances in medical research with the aim of effectively combating infectious diseases such as AIDS are impossible if every principle of evolution is denied. One cannot be fully aware of the risks involved in the significant decline in biodiversity and climate change if the mechanisms of evolution are not understood.

12. Our modern world is based on a long history, of which the development of science and technology forms an important part. However, the scientific approach is still not well understood and this is liable to encourage the development of all manner of fundamentalism and extremism. The total rejection of science is definitely one of the most serious threats to human rights and civic rights.

13. The war on the theory of evolution and on its proponents most often originates in forms of religious extremism which are closely allied to extreme right-wing political movements. The creationist movements possess real political power. The fact of the matter, and this has been exposed on several occasions, is that some advocates of strict creationism are out to replace democracy by theocracy.

14. All leading representatives of the main monotheistic religions have adopted a much more moderate attitude. Pope Benedict XVI, for example, as his predecessor Pope John-Paul II, today praises the role of the sciences in the evolution of humanity and recognises that the theory of evolution is "more than a hypothesis".

15. The teaching of all phenomena concerning evolution as a fundamental scientific theory is therefore crucial to the future of our societies and our democracies. For that reason it must occupy a central position in the curriculum, and especially in the science syllabus, as long as, like any other theory, it is able to stand up to thorough scientific scrutiny. Evolution is present everywhere, from medical overprescription of antibiotics that encourages the emergence of resistant bacteria to agricultural overuse of pesticides that causes insect mutations on which pesticides no longer have any effect.

16. The Council of Europe has highlighted the importance of teaching about culture and religion. In the name of freedom of expression and individual belief, creationist ideas, as any other theological position, could possibly be presented as an addition to cultural and religious education, but they cannot claim scientific respectability.

17. Science provides irreplaceable training in intellectual rigour. It seeks not to explain "why things are" but to understand how they work.

18. Investigation of the creationists' growing influence shows that the arguments between creationism and evolution go well beyond intellectual debate. If we are not careful, the values that are the very essence of the Council of Europe will be under direct threat from creationist fundamentalists. It is part of the role of the Council's parliamentarians to react before it is too late.

19. The Parliamentary Assembly therefore urges the member states, and especially their education authorities to:

19.1. defend and promote scientific knowledge;

19.2. strengthen the teaching of the foundations of science, its history, its epistemology and its methods alongside the teaching of objective scientific knowledge;

19.3. make science more comprehensible, more attractive and closer to the realities of the contemporary world;

19.4. firmly oppose the teaching of creationism as a scientific discipline on an equal footing with the theory of evolution and in general resist presentation of creationist ideas in any discipline other than religion;

19.5. promote the teaching of evolution as a fundamental scientific theory in the school curriculum.

20. The Assembly welcomes the fact that 27 Academies of Science of Council of Europe member states signed, in June 2006, a declaration on the teaching of evolution and calls on academies of science that have not yet done so to sign the declaration.

1 *Assembly debate* on 4 October 2007 (35th Sitting) (see Doc. 11375, report of the Committee on Culture, Science and Education, rapporteur: Mrs Brasseur). *Text adopted by the Assembly* on 4 October 2007 (35th Sitting).

Freedom from Religion Foundation

Evolution is a fact, and schools should teach facts.

The phrase "theory of evolution" does not suggest uncertainty about the fact of evolution any more than the phrase "music theory" questions the existence of music. A theory is a framework by which a known process is understood.

The prevailing theory of biological evolution is Darwin's idea of the hereditary transmission of slight variations through successive generations. Some variations are naturally "selected" due to adaptiveness. Biology makes no sense without recognizing the fact that all species of plants and animals (including humans) have developed from earlier forms. Natural selection has withstood more than a century of rigorous scientific testing.

Creationism, a religious belief, has withstood no testing. Whereas scientists will tell you exactly what would falsify evolution (for example, routinely discovering horse skeletons mixed in with trilobite fossils in the Cambrian strata), creationists never volunteer what set of circumstances, if true, would count against their idea that all species emerged at one time. Since creationism is not assailable, not vulnerable to experiment, it is not science.

The bulk of creationist literature consists of attacks against evolution, pretending that the eradication of the idea of evolution would cause creationism to win by default. The only "evidence" creationists present is the story in Genesis, or other religious

Voices for Evolution

texts, that must be accepted by faith, not by rational principles of verification.

Creationism can be discussed in the context of comparative religion, philosophy, politics, or culture. It should not be taught in the science classroom.

Many religious people welcome the fact of evolution, just as they accept the theory of relativity with no threat to their faith. They see evolution as one of the tools their God used in creation.

All human beings, religious or not, should feel enriched by discovering our place in nature and the interconnectedness of all living things. The understanding of evolution by natural selection is wonderfully enlightening to science. It should be loudly and proudly taught.

Institute for First Amendment Studies

The Case for Evolution

A popular bumper sticker reads: "God says it, I believe it, that settles it." For most Christian fundamentalists, that statement neatly sums up their belief in Biblical inerrancy. They believe in creationism because the Bible says that God created everything in six days at some point less than 10,000 years ago.

"Creation scientists" take that viewpoint a step further. By faith they begin with belief in creationism – then they search for evidence to back that belief.

True scientists study the evidence, drawing their conclusions from that evidence. Science does not deal in "truths," but in models which have predictive values. Evolution is a truly scientific model; it is open to examination and challenge. Over the years scientists have modified their evolutionary viewpoints to fit the latest evidence. Because it is Bible-based, creationists never modify their hypothesis, or even admit it could be in error.

Creationism is clearly based upon religion. As such, teaching it in church, Sunday school, parochial school (or even in comparative religion classes in public school) is fine. However, because it is faith-based, teaching creationism as science in tax-supported public schools violates the separation between church and state.

1994

The National Committee for Public Education and Religious Liberty

The National Committee for Public Education and Religious Liberty (National PEARL) is a coalition of over fifty* grassroots, civic, educational and religious groups committed to maintaining the First Amendment's guarantee of separation of church and state in our nation's public schools. National PEARL believes that maintenance of the wall of separation helps to assure a strong public education system and safeguards religious liberty. National PEARL is committed to keeping the nation's public schools a safe haven for the nation's children, free of religious indoctrination and discrimination.

National PEARL opposes teaching creationism, in lieu of or as a "companion" theory to, theories of scientific evolution in public schools. There are several versions of creationism; all share the common view that life, matter, and the universe were designed and created by a divine creator/supreme spiritual being. According to many creationists, all life developed relatively recently. Creationism cannot be taught without reference to the religious ideology from which it springs, namely the account of Genesis in the Bible. Consequently, National PEARL holds that creationism is a form of religious belief.

The teaching of creationism in a public school amounts to use of state-financed, state-run schools to indoctrinate children in a particular set of religious beliefs. This is best demonstrated by the fact that when creationists demand creationism be taught, they insist on the exclusion or denigration of legitimate science. For example, the Louisiana state legislature's consideration of legislation in 1981 that prohibited "discrimination" against teaching creationism but did not prohibit "discrimination" against teaching evolution.

As A Matter of Education Policy

A host of thorny educational issues arise from teaching creationism. These problems generate strife among teachers, between teachers and administrators, students and teachers, parents and the school, parents and students, and among students. If creationism were taught in the schools, it would foment religious strife over the following issues:

Who writes the curriculum? How could a religious curriculum be monitored objectively? Could an administrator require a teacher to teach creationism? If students attempted to opt out of the lesson, how would they be graded, much less treated? What if a teacher refuses to teach creationism?

Teaching creationism would mean that a teacher could answer a student's questions by reference to the book of Genesis or materials that are designed to support a theory of creation that is consistent with Genesis. Teaching creationism in lieu of science could also open a Pandora's box by requiring teachers to teach other religious or less-than-scientific views of other topics, on the theory that if the Biblical treatment of an issue is permitted, all other religious treatment of other scientific issues must have "equal access" to student's minds to avoid inter-religious strife. Conceivably, a Wicca theory of fire, or the Aryan Nation's or the Church of the Creator's theories that God did not create all people equal because some, by virtue of their race, are inferior, or other views like these would have to be permitted in science classes if creationism were permitted.

As a result, students would be presented with a dizzying array of religious doctrines but would not have the scientific training necessary to evaluate them or compete with other students. Preparing students to be well-informed and well educated is the cornerstone of the public school system, and concomitantly, of a functioning democracy.

This is not a case of abrogation of teachers' academic freedom. Proponents of creationism incorrectly appropriate the notion of academic freedom to argue for the right to teach their religious views. Proponents of creationism cannot equate academic freedom with their intent to indoctrinate students in a public school. The fact is, teachers' academic and religious freedom is undermined when they are forced to teach religious doctrines in science class.

Notably, no major union of teachers, including the National Education Association and the American Federation of Teachers, have ever characterized it in this manner. Most teachers are perfectly capable of simultaneously holding private, religious beliefs and teaching scientific evolution. In fact, teachers throughout the United States espouse the sentiment of the Louisiana Science Teachers Association, which stated in 1981 it considered creationism "to be outside the boundaries of bona fide science."

As a Matter of Law

Teaching creationism is impermissible as a matter of law, either in lieu of scientific evolution or as a "companion theory." In both contexts, it has continuously been found to violate the Establishment Clause of the First Amendment of the U.S. Constitution because it puts government-run schools in the position of establishing religion by using their power to teach children compelled to attend school.

Precisely because the state would use its power, in the form of publicly financed schools, to further a particular religious doctrine, teaching creationism violates the major precept of the Establishment Clause, namely that "neither [a state nor a federal government] can pass laws which aid one religion, aid all religions, or prefer one religion over another.' *Everson v. Board of Education*, 330 U.S. 1, 15 (1947). This kind of governmental support for private, religious belief and indoctrination goes against the philosophy of the Founding Fathers when they wrote the First Amendment. That such teachings are promulgated by legislative authorities, not educational experts, testifies to the reality that the real motivation and purpose is the advancement of a particular religious ideology.

Application of the most widely used legal test, known as *Lemon v. Kurtzman,* 403 U.S. 602 (1971), to the practice of teaching creationism in public schools has found it unconstitutional. See *Edwards v. Aguillard,* 482 U.S. 578 (1987). Under *Lemon,* if a practice has a) a religious purpose, b) the effect of advancing religion, or c) it causes or necessitates entanglement of church and state officials to administer it, the practice violates the Establishment Clause.

Under the "endorsement" test, which courts often use in lieu of or in conjunction with the Lemon test, a practice is judged according to how much the state is perceived as endorsing religion. Teaching creationism obviously violates this test because the power of the state is used to endorse a particular religious belief. Furthermore, there is no way to "mitigate" the state's endorsement of the religious message. As PEARL founder and noted constitutional scholar Leo Pfeffer reflected, "In respect to those pupils who do understand what the teachers are saying, teaching creationism as being only a theory would violate the First Amendment's ban on inhibiting religion. To teach pupils that the account of Moses splitting the sea or Jesus walking on it is only a theory could hardly be reconciled with the Amendment's ban on the inhibition of religion. The last thing in the world fundamentalist Christians want is for public schools to teach that God's creation of the world or His relationship to Jesus, or Moses' receipt of the Ten Commandments from Him, are only theories."

Under the "coercion" test, which courts often use in lieu of or in conjunction with the Lemon test, the teaching of creationism in public schools also violates the Establishment Clause. First, children are compelled to attend public school; they cannot "opt out" of science class and assume they will pass statewide, year-end tests. Consequently, forcing students to listen to creationist lectures would use students' captive status coercively. By the very nature of creationist theory, and student questioning or challenging the theory would be put in the position of questioning the religious belief system behind it, and risking the chance of invoking the disapproval of a teacher who espouses the creationist perspective.

For all the foregoing reasons – educational and constitutional – creationism should not be taught in the public schools.

March 1995

*American Association of School Administrators
American Association of University Women
American Civil Liberties Union
American Ethical Union
American Federation of Teachers
American Humanist Association
American Jewish Congress

Americans for Democratic Action
Americans for Religious Liberty
Americans United for Separation of Church & State (and Rochester Chapter)
Anti Defamation League
A. Philip Randolph Institute
Arizona Citizens Project
Association of Reform Rabbis of New York City & Vicinity
Baptist Joint Committee
Central Conference of American Rabbis
City Club of New York
Community Church of New York, Social Action Committee
Council of Churches of the City of New York
Council for Democratic and Secular Humanism
Council of Supervisors and Administrators
Episcopal Diocese of Long Island, Committee on Social Concerns & Peace
Episcopal Diocese of New York
Federation of Reconstructionist Congregations & Havurot
Freedom to Learn Network
Freethought Society of Greater Philadelphia
Humanist Society of Metropolitan New York, Inc.
Institute for First Amendment Studies
League for Industrial Democracy, NYC Chapter
Michigan Council About Parochiaid
Minnesota Civil Liberties Union
Monroe County PEARL
National Council of Jewish Women (& New York Section)
National Center for Science Education
National Education Association
National Emergency Civil Liberties Committee
National PTA
New York Jewish Labor Committee
New York Society for Ethical Culture
New York State Congress of Parents and Teachers
New York State Council of Churches
New York State United Teachers
Ohio PEARL
Public Education Association
Union of American Hebrew Congregations
   (& New York Federation of Reform Synagogues)
Unitarian-Universalist Association
United Community Centers, Inc.
United Federation of Teachers
United Synagogues of America, New York Metropolitan Region
Washington Area Secular Humanists
Women's American O.R.T.
Women's City Club of NY, Inc.
Workmen's Circle, NY Division

People For the American Way Foundation Supports Quality Science Education

People For the American Way Foundation is a staunch defender of public education. We believe that public education – like an independent judiciary and fair elections–is an essential component of our American democracy. We support comprehensive science education including the best scientific knowledge about evolution and Darwin's theory of natural selection.

Science education has long been under attack from right-wing religious activists who have attempted to remove evolution from the classroom. The campaign against evolution is not a scientific movement or an educational movement. It is a political campaign being waged by people who think their religious beliefs should be taught as science in our public school classrooms. Holding science curriculum hostage to religious ideologies is not only educationally unsound, but also violates the constitutional separation of church and state.

Teaching genuine science, including evolution and natural selection, is the only acceptable choice for public schools. "Creationism" and "Intelligent Design" (more accurately called Intelligent Design Creationism) are not science; they are religious beliefs, as federal courts have recognized. As such, they cannot and should not be taught in a science classroom.

The deceptive call to "teach the debate" is just another way to attack science. There is no real scientific debate about evolution. Pretending otherwise for political or religious reasons doesn't change the reality; it only undermines the quality of science our students are taught.

When science education is controlled by religious rather than scientific belief, our children will be unprepared for higher education, citizenship, and life. Americans need critical skills to function in the twenty-first century, and that requires a quality science education.

This does not mean that public school students cannot be taught about religion and religious beliefs. To the contrary, in appropriate courses (such as World Religions), students can and should learn about the beliefs of different faith groups, including beliefs about the origin of the universe and development of humankind. This teaching simply does not belong in science classes.

People For the American Way Foundation strongly defends the teaching of evolution as an essential component of a quality science education. PFAWF works with students, parents, teachers, and community leaders to defend public schools and the integrity of science education when they come under attack from the Religious Right and its political allies.

2006

CPSIA information can be obtained at www.ICGtesting.com
232080LV00002B/2/P